THE SOLAR DECISION BOOK

DESIGN AND ILLUSTRATIONS BY WILLIAM BRINKER
Bradford-LaRiviere, Inc.

THE SOLAR DECISION BOOK

Your Guide to Making a Sound Investment

by
Richard H. Montgomery

with
Jim Budnick

Dow Corning Corporation, Midland, Michigan 48640

Graphics Preparation by: Bradford-LaRiviere, Inc.
709 Lapeer Avenue
Saginaw, Michigan 48607

Printed by: The Segerdahl Corporation
1351 S. Wheeling Road
Wheeling, Illinois 60090

Published by: Dow Corning Corporation
Midland, Michigan 48640

Distributed by: Dow Corning Corporation
Department 2268
Midland, Michigan 48640

Library of Congress Catalog Number 78-66403
ISBN: 0-9601876-1-8
Printed in the United States of America
First Printing, June 1978

NOTE:

The information and data contained herein are believed to be accurate and reliable at the time of printing. Neither the authors nor Dow Corning Corporation can know all of the conditions to which designs and/or products might be exposed. As such, the authors and Dow Corning Corporation cannot be held accountable for the suitability or performance of a system design or product in particular applications. The reader should thoroughly investigate any proposed design or product, and independently conclude suitability or satisfactory performance before use. Recommendations made in this book should not be taken as inducements to infringe on any patents.

FOREWORD

The author's interest in the solar energy market began with a phone conversation in the spring of 1975 with Dr. Douglas Taft, director of Gardenway Laboratories in Burlington, Vermont. Dr. Taft called to ask if Dow Corning had considered the use of silicone fluid as a heat-transfer medium for solar energy collectors in freezing climates. Almost simultaneously, one of Dow Corning's top salespeople, Jerry Plante, submitted the same idea through the company's New Market Opportunities Program.

Attendance at the first annual SEIA meeting that summer revealed problems with the then-available heat-transfer fluids. Those problems indicated that a market need for silicone heat-transfer fluids might be developing. As a result, some market research work was informally undertaken to determine what the extent of Dow Corning's possible involvement should be. The results of that research work were not encouraging.

The second SEIA meeting in the summer of 1976, attended by Robert Krasa of Dow Corning's Technical Service and Development group, revealed a much more encouraging picture. In one year, the industry had grown by leaps and bounds. One major company, State Industries, had introduced a solar water-heating package that used a silicone heat-transfer liquid.

Thus in July of 1976, the decision to enter a test marketing program with silicone heat-transfer fluids was made at Dow Corning. The product was unveiled at the ISES meeting in Winnepeg, Manitoba, in the fall of 1976. The product introduction included a test advertising program in *Solar Engineering* magazine from November of that year through the following spring.

Since that time, more than 50,000 people have requested and received information on silicones for solar systems. And in the fall of 1977, Dow Corning made the decision to terminate its test marketing program and to enter the solar energy business on a commercial basis.

Where is the solar energy market going? ... And how is it going to get there? These two questions are not fully answered as yet, but there are several ways the market growth and direction can be influenced. First, a group of trained solar system installers purchasing from a group of knowledgeable wholesalers must be created to build the systems. To do this within a reasonable period of time, an existing group of mechanical contractors must be utilized. In all likelihood, this group will be the Heating/Ventilating/Air Conditioning (HVAC) contractors. Second, reasonable incentives must be available to help purchasers defray the cost of the solar system investment. Such incentives will most likely be in the form of tax credits and exemptions. Third, and most important, a bridge must be built from the solar scientist to the building owner who will make the investment.

The Solar Decision Book is an attempt to build that bridge between the scientist and the building owner. The main foundations of the bridge will be the wholesaler and the contractor. The goal of The Solar Decision Book is to translate the higher mathematics for determining system performance into the numbers for on-site design and sizing.

Many bright, earnest people have staked their personal fortunes on a successful solar industry. Some have already left the picture for one reason or another. Others will fall by the wayside over the next few years.

With deep respect, this book is dedicated to those who have had to leave the race toward solar energy. Without their attempts, the race never would have been undertaken.

AUTHOR'S NOTES

This book has been three years in the making. During that time, I have studied the Solar Energy Industry in depth. I have spoken with most of the industry's pioneers and technology leaders. I have read and reviewed most of the popular articles and books, trade publications, and technical presentations. And I have served as the Dow Corning spokesman at many industry conferences.

I found a newborn industry that was growing at a remarkable rate. But I also found many conflicting opinions, design differences, and a variety of other problems inherent in building a new industry. Much of the information was extremely valuable. Some was confusing, inadequate, and at best questionable. Some was of no practical use.

In The Solar Decision Book, I have attempted to present a logical and practical approach to good solar system design. I have religiously used information which has been proven in the field.

The book is opinionated. The opinions are mine. Some may not agree with them, while others will recognize a restatement of their own work.

I would like to give the reader the same challenge which I give my colleagues at Dow Corning: "The proven performance of certain components and systems has led me to the conclusions in the book. If you can present facts which I have ignored or overlooked that might require changing those conclusions, I will be happy to consider them. Until you do, this is where we start."

As a new industry, the solar energy industry is having its share of growing pains. Many systems are failing. Many companies are questioning further involvement.

But, energy shortages and spiralling prices demand the continued development of Solar technology and other "soft" energy systems. They are essential for our future. We must press ahead.

Write to me if you feel that I am wrong. And, especially write if you have a suggestion for a better approach, component, or system. Also, write if you have facts which I have seemingly ignored or overlooked. The solar business needs all of us working together.

We have a good start. Now, let's make sure the sun becomes an even-more-attractive energy source.

ACKNOWLEDGEMENTS

More than 150 individuals from some 50 different corporations have played varying roles in the development of The Solar Decision Book. Each shared ideas and experiences that in one way or another influenced the book's editorial approach or technical content. Without such help, the book might never have become reality. Yet, a fair acknowledgement of each and every contribution would be a near-impossible task.

Special mention however, must be given to several individuals. They include some who spent considerable time and effort helping the author to understand the more complex design aspects of solar energy systems. They include some who turned the first draft, rough notes, and even idle thoughts into a book. And they also include some who provided counsel and encouragement when it was needed most.

The detailed comparison of heat-transfer fluids was the result of work by Robert Krasa, Dow Corning Technical Service and Development. The discussion of metal corrosion was drawn with permission from technical papers prepared by Dr. James Popplewell and Dr. Edward Smith of Olin Brass. Valuable data and recommendations for solar system pumps were provided by Jerry Cook and David Rhindal of Grundfos Pumps Corporation and Fred Zimmerman of March Manufacturing. The guidelines for selecting effective heat exchangers came from data developed by Dr. Edward Doucette of Doucette, Inc., and Otto Nussebaum of Halstead and Mitchell. Solar system controls were discussed from the work of Rho Sigma's Robert Schlesinger. The discussion of solar collectors was written based on conversations with many people including Peter Michaels of Revere Copper and Brass; Ronald Goodman, Libby-Owens-Ford; Fred Deans, PPG Industries; William Rapp, Halstead and Mitchell; and Matt Rupp of Olin Brass.

An understanding of the practical aspects of operating a solar energy business was achieved through conversations with Mark Whitesides, president of Groundstar Energy Systems; Ron Davis, chief engineer of General Energy Devices; and Don Bowden, president of Solar Unlimited.

The decisions on system design, sizing, pricing, and installation were developed with the expert help of Gordon Preiss. A leading solar consultant from Connecticut, Gordon is well known in the industry for his solar schools and design work.

Turning the manuscript into a book called for a hectic pace in editing, graphics preparation, and printing. Editing services and creative counsel were provided by Jim Budnick, vice-president of Bradford-LaRiviere, Inc., in Saginaw, Michigan. Jim's firm also provided all graphic services including illustration, typesetting, and keyline preparation. Then, with a seemingly unrealistic deadline, the book was printed and bound by The Segerdahl Corporation of Wheeling, Illinois.

The publisher is also the author's employer. A special thanks must go to Dow Corning Corporation and to Gerald Ziarno, marketing manager for the fluids and lubricants business. Not only for financing the publication, but more so for allowing the author to devote so much time and effort to it.

And last, to my wife and colleagues who suffered through the last year: you deserve the biggest thanks for putting up with my irascibility and single-mindedness.

THE SOLAR DECISION BOOK

CONTENTS

PAGE

We are faced with an energy problem that demands a decision to take action. Our future needs are far above projections of available energy. The higher costs of that energy may become a financial hardship. With the right facts, you can start planning to protect your lifestyle.

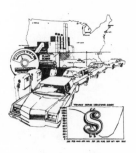

Each person has different energy needs. Each has different energy costs. Understanding your energy needs and costs is the first step toward effective energy planning.

DECISION 3 Conserve Energy

Massive energy conservation is needed to help solve the energy problem. Each person, each business must conserve energy. You should develop a plan.

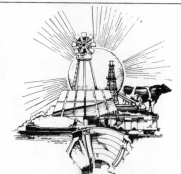

DECISION 4 Consider An Alternate Energy Source

Even with massive energy conservation, a huge shortage will still exist. Alternate energy sources must be considered in light of your energy needs, your environment, and your economic health.

DECISION 5 The Sun: Today's Best Source Of Alternate Energy

The solar energy system is fast-becoming commonplace for water heating, space heating, and space cooling. The reasons include advantages over other energy sources, readily available equipment, and excellent performance in most any area.

DECISION 6 Solar Energy Systems Are Sound Investments

Fossil fuels are costing you more each year. Solar energy is now an attractively priced alternative. The investment is large, but the results are well worth it on both new structures and existing structures.

DECISION 7 Negotiate An Intelligent Loan

If financing the solar investment is required, you should know how to make an intelligent loan. You should understand the effects of the system on cash flow and taxes. A premium-quality system will have the right combination of cost, life, and performance.

DECISION 8 Start Planning The System

You have most likely decided that solar energy deserves a closer examination. Some system planning must be done to see what impact a solar system will have on your energy costs.

DECISION 9 Site The Collectors

The sun's energy strikes the earth at different angles, depending on the area, hour, and season. The collectors must be oriented in the proper direction and tilted at the proper angle. Architectural tastes and landscaping restrictions may enter into the decision.

DECISION 10 Catch The Sun With Flat-Plate Collectors

The flat-plate collector is the workhorse of the solar industry because it can effectively collect all types of solar radiation. The thermal performance of various designs can be accurately compared using standardized test methods.

DECISION 11 Charge The System With Its Life Blood

A liquid heat-transfer medium offers excellent performance. Several fluids are used, but the harsh environment of the solar system makes the fluid choice critical. The various fluids must be compared to find the one that offers maximum corrosion protection and minimum maintenance.

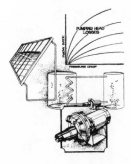

DECISION 12 Pump The Energy Indoors

The pumps are the heart of the solar system. The correct types must be selected. They can be sized for proper flow rate, friction losses, and performance in the system. Fluid requirements can then be easily calculated.

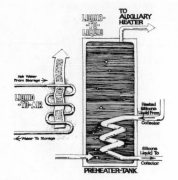

DECISION 13 Select Efficient Heat Exchangers

Two heat exchangers in the solar energy system make heat storage and heat delivery possible. For maximum system efficiency, the heat exchangers must be carefully matched to the system's collectors, storage capabilities, and heat load.

DECISION 14 Bank The Collected Energy

The collectors in a solar energy system normally do not collect usable energy for more than six hours a day. With storage capabilities, the system can provide heat and hot water as needed, day or night, regardless of the weather.

DECISION 15 Include An Auxiliary Heater

Few solar systems provide 100-percent of a building's energy needs. An economical and dependable backup energy source is needed to help insure a good return on your solar investment.

DECISION 16 Deliver The Heat

The heat-delivery system takes the collected energy from storage and puts it to work heating the structure. With proper design, this system will draw energy at very low temperatures and enhance collector efficiency.

DECISION 17 Control The System

The controls for a solar energy system direct the system's activities and make maximum use of its capabilities. Without the correct controls, the system will not produce any useful energy. With the proper knowledge, the correct controls can be easily specified.

DECISION 1

The Energy Shortage Is Here To Stay

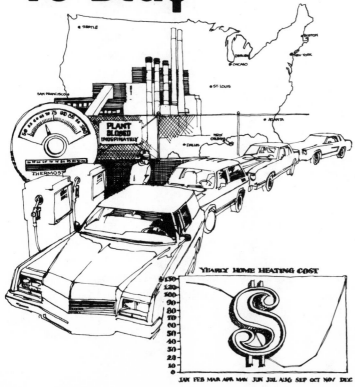

Energy crises have been making headlines for some time now. The oil embargo of 1973 ... the natural gas shortages in the winter of 1976-1977 ... the coal strike in late 1977, early 1978. These crucial situations were indeed crises. They demand a decision to take action. This action might involve formulating a unified national energy policy. Yet, such action has not been taken.

One possible reason for inaction is that many doubt an energy problem even exists. There are exceptions, of course. Some have chosen to modify their energy needs and practice energy conservation. A few have chosen to terminate their use of traditional fuels and live with alternate sources of energy. Most, however, have chosen to continue as in the past.

But, like it or not, an energy problem does exist. Before making any decisions to solve this problem, one very basic decision is needed. You should accept the idea that the energy shortage is here to stay. This section of The Solar Decision Book will help you to make that decision. You will learn that:

- An energy-dependent society consumes huge amounts of energy.

- Future energy needs are far above projections of available energy.

- The costs of available energy are spiraling upward and may become a financial hardship for many.

- Energy planning is needed right now to prevent a catastrophic energy shortage.

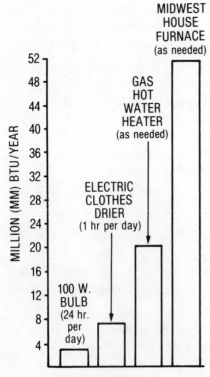

1 HOUR OF CLEAR DAY SOLAR RADIATION
ON 500 SQ. FT. OF SURFACE AT SOLAR NOON

100 CUBIC FEET OF NATURAL GAS

1 GALLON OF FUEL OIL

10 LBS OF COAL

25 LBS OF RED OAK

Figure 1.1 The energy value of certain types of fuel.

Figure 1.2 Typical energy requirements.

WHAT IS ENERGY?

Energy can neither be seen nor tasted. And energy has no sound, feel, or smell. It is not a material substance. Yet, without energy, life would cease to exist.

There are many forms of energy, and many ways to produce energy. Heat is one of the most useful forms of energy. It can cook food, warm a house to a comfortable temperature, and heat water for bathing and other uses. Such heat energy can be produced by burning a fuel such as oil, gas, coal, or wood. It can be produced by electricity, chemical reactions, or nuclear fission. Or, it can be produced by the sun's rays.

While energy cannot be held in one's hand, energy can be measured. The basic unit of measurement in the heating and air conditioning business is the *British thermal unit*, or *Btu*. A Btu is the amount of heat required to raise the temperature of one pound (one pint) of water, one degree Fahrenheit. Thus, to heat a pound of water from 60° F to its boiling point, 212° F, requires 152 Btu (212 - 60 = 152).

A Btu is a small amount of energy. Figure 1.1 shows the energy value of certain types of fuel. Twenty-five pounds of dried red oak will produce about 137,000 Btu of heat energy when it is burned. A gallon of fuel oil will produce about 130,000 Btu. One-hundred cubic feet of natural gas about 100,000 Btu. And 10 pounds of coal about 130,000 Btu.

These amounts aren't much, considering some typical energy requirements. A 100-watt lightbulb, burning continuously for one year, would use three-million Btu. An electric clothes drier, running one hour a day for a year, would use seven-million Btu. A typical gas hot water heater, 20-million Btu per year. And a typical furnace in a midwestern house, over 50-million Btu in a year. These energy requirements are shown in Figure 1.2.

Some energy requirements are very small, however. A simple two-minute shave with an electric razor uses only about one Btu. And the average adult requires only about 10 Btu per day of food energy (1 Btu = 252 calories).

ENERGY AVAILABILITY ... TODAY AND TOMORROW

The United States uses huge amounts of energy. In fact, even though the U.S. has only six-percent of the world's population, that population consumes about 35-percent of the world's energy. Until the recent energy crisis, the use of energy in the U.S. has been virtually unlimited. Whatever energy was needed was available. Today, however, there is a very real possibility that the available energy resources will not be able to meet tomorrow's energy demands.

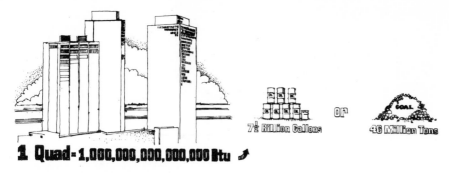

Figure 1.3 A quadrillion Btu is called a quad.

An Energy-Dependent Society

In 1970, the U.S. energy consumption reached 70 quadrillion Btu, or 70,000,000,000,000,000 Btu! For convenience in making energy statements, a quadrillion Btu is called a *quad*. Figure 1.3 helps illustrate the amount of energy that a quad represents. To produce one quad of energy, about 7½-billion gallons of gasoline or about 46-million tons of coal are needed. A city of three million people uses about one quad of energy each year.

Figure 1.4 shows how the U.S. energy consumption has grown since 1900. The use of energy was relatively low for many years. Then, somewhere in the mid-1950s energy consumption in the U.S. took off. Much of the growth that set the stage for the recent energy crisis took place in the 1960s. These were the years of massive expansion in the use of natural gas for home and industrial heating. They were also the years of huge increases in the use of electricity produced from oil, coal, and gas. While the use of oil increased only about 50-percent, the use of natural gas almost doubled and the use of electricity more than doubled.

Of the 70 quad of energy that the U.S. consumed in 1970, about 25-percent was used for transportation. The remaining 75-percent was split about evenly between industrial uses and residential-commerial uses. Generating heat for space heating, water heating and industrial processing amounted to about 27 quad.

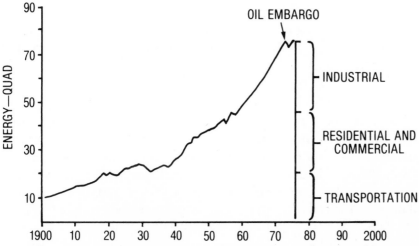

Figure 1.4 U.S. energy consumption since 1900. (U.S. Department of Interior statistics).

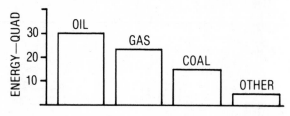

Figure 1.5 The sources for U.S. energy in 1977.

The U.S. energy consumption rose to more than 73 quad in 1977. The sources for this energy were as shown in Figure 1.5. Approximately 41-percent of the total energy was produced from oil. About 32-percent was produced from natural gas. About 19-percent from coal. And about eight-percent was produced from other sources such as nuclear and hydroelectric generating plants.

Of the total amount of oil used in 1977, almost one-half of it was imported. The cost amounted to about 32 billion dollars. This is money that has left the country. It is money that cannot be used for developing a more energy-efficient transportation system. It is money that cannot be spent for developing new energy sources. Had this money been applied toward such developments, the U.S. could become less dependent on the world energy supply. That 32 billion dollars also poses a serious drain on the country's balance of payments. More dollars are going out, than are being returned.

What About The Future?

The need for energy is increasing, not only in the U.S. but worldwide as well. This increased demand for energy is not being matched with new discoveries of *fossil fuels*. These are the energy sources such as oil, gas, and coal on which the world has depended thus far. Huge quantities of these fuels were formed millions of years ago by decayed vegetation under tons of soil and rock. But they are being used up at an alarming rate. And new sources are getting harder to find.

When the next 20 years or so are considered, the need for supplemental heating or a new heating method for the American home is apparent. Already, the days of relatively cheap and seemingly unlimited energy are gone. Those days ended with the energy crises of the 1970s. The crises have drawn attention to an energy shortage that is very real.

So, what about the future? How much energy will be needed? And, more important, what energy sources can be available to match the demand? There are many projections on tomorrow's energy needs. Also, there are just as many educated guesses on tomorrow's energy sources. Some are pure fantasy. They show projected needs that are unrealistically high or low, and they show proposed energy sources that are not possible with current technology.

Suppose, for instance, energy consumption in the U.S. continues to grow at the same rate that it has for the past 30 years. And suppose

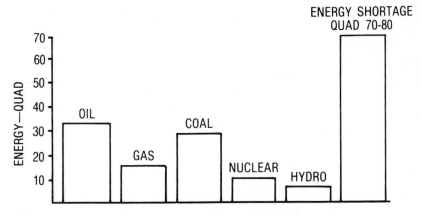

Figure 1.6 A 170-quad future demand cannot be met despite a projected need.

that this demand will be met with fossil fuels as in the past. Many would like to believe that this is possible. It isn't. With the same rate of growth, the U.S. energy needs would triple by the year 2000. Enough fuel would be needed to produce 200 quad of energy.

Such growth is not likely to happen. A more realistic projection is found in data prepared by the Federal Government and the Edison Electric Institute. Assuming that the gross national product grows as expected, the U.S. will need somewhere in the area of 165 to 175 quad of energy by the turn of the century. That's about 2-1/3 times the current usage.

The sources for this energy demand are shown in Figure 1.6. Note that a block of energy as large as today's demand has no known source at this time. The other blocks are optimistic projections. The best that can be expected in the year 2000 is: about 32 quad from oil, 15 quad from natural gas, perhaps as much as 30 quad from coal, about 10 or 11 quad from nuclear power plants, and about five quad from hydroelectric power plants. That adds up to about 93 quad of energy, short of the estimated demand by about 77 quad.

Optimism Only Goes So Far

To expect that enough energy sources will become available to cover a projected shortage of 77 quad is unreasonable. Being optimistic will not heat a building.

Think of the effects a 77-quad shortage would have in the United States. The oil embargo of 1973 created a one-quad shortage. It resulted in the most serious economic recession that this country had experienced in 40 years. The gas shortage in the winter of 1976 was less than one quad. It closed plants across the country and put more than one million workers off the job. There is no doubt: a 77-quad shortage would cause a catastrophic disruption in the American way of life.

Obviously, something must be done to prevent such a shortage. A good share of the problem can be solved with energy conservation. The conservation of energy must become an important part of everyone's life. It is a necessity because there is no known technology which can be ready in time to produce any more than a fraction of that 77-quad shortage.

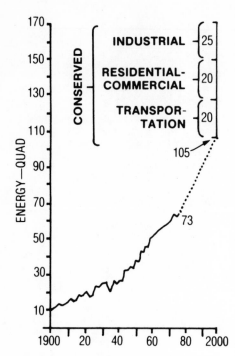

Figure 1.7 The effects of an optimistic conservation estimate. (General Electric projection in Industrial Construction Magazine).

The benefits of energy conservation are clear. For every quad of energy conserved, one less quad of energy needs to be produced. There is a limit, however. In Figure 1.7, the effects of the "most optimistic combination" of various conservation measures are shown. After carefully studying energy projections made by reliable sources, the General Electric Company has proposed that the U.S. can reduce its need for energy to only 105 quad in the year 2000. This is based on the most favorable circumstances involving energy conservation and energy usage.

As shown on the graph, about 65 quad of energy could be trimmed from the shortage. However, that would still leave a projected shortage of 12 quad of energy. This shortage would occur even if: 1) coal production was doubled, 2) all the nuclear plants now on order went into operation, 3) hydroelectric power increased by almost 65-percent, and 4) the best hopes for energy conservation came true. Even doing one of these will be extremely tough to say nothing of doing all four.

Somewhere, sources to produce at least 12 quad of energy by the year 2000 must be found. Current technologies can be depended upon only to a certain extent. Many proposed energy sources are in the very first stages of experimental work. They cannot be expected to become commercially available overnight. Others, notably solar energy systems and windpower systems, are commercially available right now. But these alternate energy sources are just getting started.

The U.S. energy supply pattern is not going to be changed significantly for many years. If, for instance, 20 million houses were heated by solar energy in the next 20 years, only 2½ quad of the projected shortage would be taken away. The remaining 9½ quad of energy would have to come from other alternate fuels and still unknown and unproven energy sources.

To produce that 9½ quad of energy would require over 71-billion gallons of gasoline or 437-million tons of coal. It is the annual energy needed by 28½-million people. And it is the energy demand that may very well go unsupplied.

ENERGY COSTS ... PAST, PRESENT, AND FUTURE

As with the projections of energy demand and supply, predictions of future energy costs abound. Many sources are extremely suspect, as they have a proprietary interest in how the results read.

The reports issued by the United States Bureau of Labor appear to be both meaningful and unbiased. Actual polling of the marketplace is done, and the results are modified based on the potential effects of future market influences. The Bureau of Labor has established an excellent reputation for accurate reporting of the *Wholesale Price Index (WPI)* and the *Consumer Price Index (CPI)*. The WPI is used to predict the selling prices of various energy sources to utilities and fuel outlets, while the CPI is used to predict the cost of all consumer goods. The CPI measures the rate of inflation. These indices will be used in The Solar Decision Book to help predict what tomorrow's energy will cost.

Today's Pricing Situation

Any attempt at predicting tomorrow's energy costs has its problems. Such predictions are complicated by the factors shown in Figure 1.8. First of all, no energy pricing is done in a free market. Federal, state, and local governments exercise regulatory control over energy prices. *OPEC,* an international cartel called the Organization of Petroleum Exporting Countries, regulates the base prices of the energy sources which are imported. This amounts to more than one-half of the U.S. oil supply. Also, although there are many reports of known reserves of domestic oil, these reports often do not agree.

Another complication is that the energy shortage is placing upward price pressures on all fuel and energy sources. There is no way to avoid substantial price increases if some of the newer fossil fuel technologies are ever to produce on a commercial scale. These technologies include coal gasification and liquefaction, shale oil extraction, tertiary oil recovery, oil-tar sand recovery, and liquid natural gas importation. Such potential energy sources are badly needed, but they will be expensive to develop.

Consideration must also be given to the environmental aspects of energy development and use. Various problems exist regarding the use of nuclear energy, oil exploration in wilderness areas, strip or open-pit mining of coal, and the damming of scenic rivers. Other restrictions are being placed on the use of solid fuels, such as coal, without adequate air-pollution controls. If the use of coal is to double by the year 2000, it will require huge investments in mining and transportation equipment. It will also require proven air-pollution control devices which do not currently exist. The *EPA,* or Environmental Protection Agency, will have to issue clear-cut guidelines on the use of such coal.

Needless to say, these restrictions and the other complications are definitely going to have their effects. Energy pricing is uncertain in many respects. And, the timing of when new energy will be available is also uncertain.

A Historical Perspective is Helpful

A look into the past to around 1960 is helpful for predicting future energy costs. The decade from 1960 to 1970 laid the foundation for the problems now occurring. And such a perspective can help explain why energy costs are spiraling upward.

Figure 1.9 shows that energy prices were held artificially low in the 1960s, even though the consumer price index rose 31-percent and the energy demand rose by 50-percent. Fuel oil, coal, and natural gas did not change in price. There were only minor changes in price in 1970 and 1971.

Figure 1.8 Factors that complicate energy cost prediction.

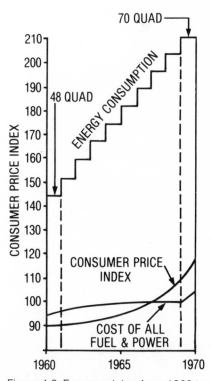

Figure 1.9 Energy pricing from 1960 to 1970. Fuel prices remained unchanged while consumption and the CPI increased substantially.

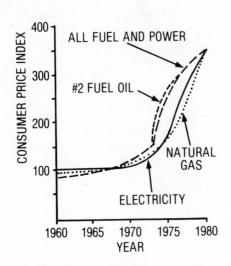

Figure 1.10 The projected growth of fuel costs. The graph shows the rate of increase, not the actual prices. Electricity is priced much higher than either fuel oil or natural gas.

This lack of price inflation was the direct result of coal and oil attempting to compete with natural gas. Gas was under strict government control and suppressed in price. World fuel prices were much higher during the same period.

The increased demand for energy and the shortage of crude oil led to the formation of OPEC. Subsequently, fuel oil prices were adjusted dramatically in 1973, 1974, and 1975. Demand had become high enough that fuel oil no longer had to compete with natural gas. As a result, natural gas producers are holding production to the bare minimum. They will continue to do so, until government regulations allow pricing competitive with fuel oil. This is predicted to occur by 1980.

Tomorrow's Energy Will Be Expensive

From 1980 through the year 2000, the prices for fuel oil, coal, and gas are expected to be competitive. But, because oil represents the largest source of energy in the U.S., future fuel costs will follow oil costs. And with the projected growth of energy demand in the next 20 years, fuel costs will undoubtedly rise faster than the rest of the economy. Figure 1.10 shows how the costs of various energy sources are projected by the author to vary until 1980.

Projecting energy costs beyond 1980 with any degree of certainty is impossible. However, using a wide range of parameters, estimates of the "most likely" prices can be made. The "best" estimates then become a matter of informed opinion.

YEAR	ENERGY WPI	% CHANGE	% ANNUAL CHANGE
58	95.3		
69	100.9	5.9	LESS THAN 1 PERCENT
70	105.9	5.0	
71	114.2	7.8	
72	118.6	3.9	
73	134.3	15.7	13.5 PERCENT AVERAGE
74	208.3	55.1	
75	245.1	17.7	
76	265.5	8.3	
77	290	10.0	
78	325	12.0	
79	364	12.0	
80	407	12.0	
85	686	11.0	
90	1156	11.0	9-13 PERCENT AVERAGE
95	1947	11.0	
2000	3137	10.0	
			BEST ESTIMATE 10-12 PERCENT
			MOST LIKELY 9-13 PERCENT
			WIDEST RANGE 8-14 PERCENT

Figure 1.11 Index of projected wholesale fuel costs until the year 2000, assuming a seven-percent CPI annual inflation.

ENERGY SOURCE	1976 PRICE ($)	1977	1979	1980	1980 $/MM BTU
#2 FUEL OIL $/GAL.	$0.393	$0.44	$0.552	$0.618	$4.754
NATURAL GAS $/CCF	0.186	0.227	0.297	0.475	4.75
ELECTRICITY $/KWH	0.03475	0.03824	0.0446	0.04995	14.64

Figure 1.12 Estimated fuel costs per one million BTU ($/MM Btu) in 1980.

What is the minimum that fuel prices can inflate? Today's consumer price index is moving at a rate of five- to seven-percent. This rate will not slow, and may very well move higher to about six- to eight-percent. At the same time, fuel costs will tend to inflate at a rate higher than the CPI. Past experience and the projected demand indicates that the rate will slow down. By 1980, fuel costs should stabilize and possibly inflate at not less than two-percent faster than the CPI. So, the minimum that fuel costs will inflate might be around eight- or nine-percent annually.

These costs may inflate much faster. So, what is the maximum that fuel prices can inflate? Worldwide inflation is expected to be higher than that in the U.S. This will tend to force the fuel prices upward at a faster rate, depending on the strength of the dollar. The dollar was weak between 1970 and 1977. But it should not become weaker. During that period, fuel costs increased about 13.5-percent annually. This can be used as the maximum that fuel prices might inflate. A figure of 14-percent may be safer.

Using the minimum and the maximum limits, the energy costs beyond 1980 should inflate annually somewhere between eight-percent and 14-percent. The projected index of fuel costs in Figure 1.11 is made assuming that the center of this range will be the average increase from 1978 until 2000. From a projected rate of increase of 12-percent in the late 1970s to 10-percent in the year 2000, a "most likely" and a "best" estimate can be made. The fuel costs will most likely inflate at about nine-percent to 13-percent and the best estimate might be 10-percent to 12-percent.

The costs of fuel oil, natural gas, and electricity in 1980 will "most likely" be at the levels shown in Figure 1.12. The calculations were made based on Bureau of Labor and FEA (Federal Energy Administration) data from 1976. The prices were projected to a competitive pricing level in 1980. These are the anticipated costs for one million Btu of energy. That is the amount of energy produced from about 7½-gallons of oil, about 77-pounds of coal, about 1000 cubic feet of natural gas, or about 293 kilowatt-hours of electricity. But that is if 100-percent of the energy produced could be utilized.

ENERGY SOURCE	1979 $/MM BTU	PERCENT EFFICIENCY	ADJUSTED $/MM BTU 1979 BASE PRICE
#2 FUEL OIL	4.25	60 (50-70)	7.08 (5.07-8.50)
NATURAL GAS	4.25*	60 (50-70)	7.08 (5.07-8.50)
ELECTRICITY	13.18	100	13.18

*Assumes deregulation and competitive pricing.

Figure 1.13 The fuel efficiency must be considered in any comparison.

Most fuels, however, are not converted to useful energy at 100-percent efficiency. Fuel oil and natural gas are converted at about 50- to 70-percent efficiency. Electricity can be converted at 100-percent efficiency for space-heating uses. These efficiencies were used in Figure 1.13 to place the fuel costs on an equal basis for comparison purposes.

The projected base prices in 1979, along with an 11-percent fuel cost inflation rate, are used throughout The Solar Decision Book for economic calculations. These base prices and the fuel costs inflation rate are only an informed opinion. There are other opinions, of course. Regardless, this opinion as well as others readily forecasts much higher fuel costs in the years to come. Today's utility bills are already squeezing the typical family budget. But tomorrow's fuel costs may become an unbearable financial burden in many households and businesses.

Unfortunately, not much can be done to delay, much less prevent, the cost of energy from increasing substantially. OPEC is controlling worldwide oil prices for a huge and still growing market. Coal production and the use of coal are both becoming more expensive. Natural gas prices will be deregulated. And environmental pressures are restricting the use and increasing the cost of hydroelectric and nuclear power.

Somehow, ways to ease the burden of increased energy costs must be found.

ENERGY PLANNING ...
TODAY, FOR TOMORROW

Some forecasts of severe energy shortages and higher fuel costs were made as long ago as the early 1960s. Yet, most of America was totally unprepared for the energy crises of the 1970s. Many studies, projections, and frightening predictions have been made because of the crises. Still, however, a unified national energy policy is not in use. There is an understandable reason for this apparent lack of planning and action. No single approach appears capable of solving the energy shortage and easing the financial burden all by itself.

There are many partial solutions that have been discussed and investigated. Some require simple lifestyle changes that will reduce energy needs. Some involve more efficient use of the available energy. Some, such as energy conservation, are already being widely used. A few, such as solar energy systems, are just starting to gain acceptance. Many others won't become available for many years.

Some of these partial solutions may help solve the energy problem until sufficient quantities of alternate energy sources become available. To accomplish this, proper energy planning is needed right now, today. Tomorrow will be too late. Though many might disagree, such planning has not taken place. There is little evidence of coordinated action. And, for any planning to do much good, the plans must be put into action.

A Matter Of Personal Comfort

The U.S. has enjoyed an era of cheap and available energy. During that era, the American lifestyle became one of maintaining maximum personal comfort without much regard to its cost in energy consumption. With the passing of that era, decisions regarding personal comfort must be reconsidered.

Four comfort considerations are shown in Figure 1.14. These are: 1) the comfortable temperature range, 2) the comfortable humidity range, 3) comfort without drafts, and 4) sensible, comfortable clothing. Comfort is possible with less use of energy.

Most people are comfortable in temperatures of 70° to 75° F and relative humidities of 40- to 60-percent. Is 65° to 85° F an acceptable range? It was before 1960. Is year-round humidity control possible? It can broaden the acceptable temperature range, and the investment and energy requirements can be minimal. Are drafts causing discomfort? Drafts seriously affect comfort, and they must be eliminated to insure proper temperature and humidity control. Is sensible clothing being worn? The human body radiates heat energy. But a sweater in the winter traps the heat. Comfort is possible at lower temperatures. Light, airy clothing in the summer lets air flow across the skin and take heat away. Comfort is possible at higher temperatures.

Figure 1.14 Four comfort considerations.

Wise Use Of Available Energy

One very startling aspect about the U.S. energy consumption is that more than one-half of the energy is lost. As shown in Figure 1.15, the least efficient use of energy is in transportation uses. Of the total energy supplied, only 25-percent was actually converted to useful work in moving cars, trucks, and other modes of transportation. Steam-powered electric-generating plants are only about 40-percent efficient. Almost 60-percent of the heat produced by burning coal, oil, or gas is lost in making electricity. In contrast, industrial uses of heat energy from all sources, including electricity, are about 70-percent efficient. And the same 70-percent efficiency is seen for residential-commercial uses.

A more efficient use of the available energy would help considerably in solving the energy problem. Mass transportation is needed. Efficient production of electricity, such as from nuclear or hydroelectric plants, is needed. Less energy waste is needed in industry as well as the home.

On a personal level, car pools are one way to make better use of the transportation energy. The elimination of nonfunctional or unneeded lighting is one way to make better use of the electrical energy. Heat drawn from waste water is one way to make better use of industrial energy.

And there are many ways to make better use of energy around the home. With minimal service, the home furnace can be kept in top working condition. Dialing down can save heat for when it's needed most. Closing the drapes at night, closing off unused rooms, and closing the fireplace damper are simple steps to better energy use. Other important steps might be more efficient use of hot water and an energy-conscious approach to buying and caring for appliances. The hot water heater is second only to the furnace in using energy, while appliances generally account for about 20-percent of the energy needs in a typical home.

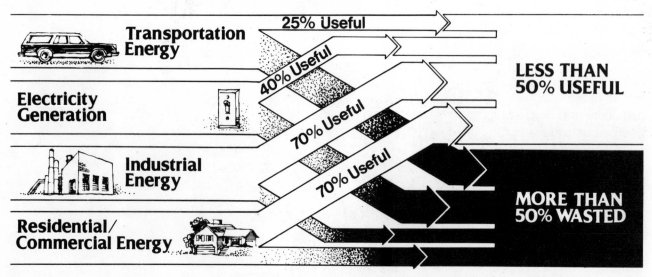

Figure 1.15 The efficiencies of various energy uses.

Energy Conservation

Much has been written about energy conservation and its obvious benefits in the upcoming years. There is no way energy conservation can be avoided. Incentives for conserving energy are likely, and penalties for wasting energy are a distinct possibility.

Some of the savings that can be realized through energy conservation have been distorted. Yet, in most cases, even a minimal saving may be worth the investment in time and money. When considering any conservation measure, the cost and anticipated results of that measure must be weighed. High costs for questionable results should be avoided. Remember, energy is needed to produce the materials that may be needed for the conservation method.

The various conservation steps that can be taken around the home are detailed later in The Solar Decision Book. These include installing adequate insulation on the house as well as the hot water heater. Sealing doors and windows, caulking cracks, controlling heat loss and gain through windows, and using the proper types of doors and windows are other steps. Such energy conservation is shown in Figure 1.16.

Figure 1.16 Some energy conservation measures.

Alternate Energy Sources

This subject is also detailed later in The Solar Decision Book. Right now, the best way to minimize the effects of the energy shortage is to conserve the existing fuel sources. But new energy sources must become available to replace those being used up. Solar energy systems are quickly becoming a factor in new housing designs. And, there is little doubt that some energy sources now in the experimental stages will become part of the American energy supply before long.

As shown in Figure 1.17, today's alternate energy sources include manufactured propane gas, solar energy, windpower, wood-burning stoves and furnaces, nuclear and hydroelectric power plants. All should gain increasing acceptance in the years to come. Other sources require further development before they can be commercialized.

MAKING A DECISION

In this section of The Solar Decision Book, you have learned that the U.S. is faced with a potentially disastrous energy shortage. This is a possiblity that many would prefer to ignore. You have learned that energy costs are sure to rise faster than the rest of the economy, and quite possibly faster than personal incomes can support. No matter what data is used, higher costs are inevitable. Only the rate of those increases is open to question. You have also learned that proper planning and immediate action is needed to avoid major changes in the American lifestyle. This is something that has not happened thus far. And, again, it is something that many have preferred to ignore.

The decision is up to you. The energy shortage is here to stay. If you can accept that, you can start planning to protect your lifestyle.

Figure 1.17 Today's alternate energy sources.

DECISION 2

Study Your Energy Needs And Costs

There are many misconceptions about the energy shortage and rising energy costs. Much of the confusion has been caused by an inadequate understanding of how energy is put to work. Why is so much energy needed? Can less energy be used? Why are energy costs so high? Can the fuel bill be held to a reasonable level? Where will energy planning do the most good?

The answers to such questions are not the same for everyone. Each person has different energy needs. Each has different energy costs. And each requires planning that is unique to the individual energy needs and costs.

So, understanding your energy needs and costs is the first step toward effective energy planning. Your need for energy will continue. But you must decide whether your energy needs will remain the same, or if those needs can be decreased or must be increased. It is an important decision because your ability to pay for tomorrow's energy will depend on how much or how little energy is used.

This section of The Solar Decision Book will help you to make that decision. You will learn that:

- Heat losses occur according to certain basic principles.
- Heat can be lost in many areas of a building.
- Energy needs can be determined.
- Costs for space heating, hot water, appliances, and cooling can be estimated.

Figure 2.1 Heat escapes from a poorly insulated house. As heat energy leaves, the inside temperature drops.

HEAT AND TEMPERATURE

Heat and temperature are not one and the same. Heat is a form of energy, while temperature is a measure of hot and cold. If there is little heat energy in a given space, the temperature of the space will be low. In a smaller space however, the same heat energy would cause a higher temperature. Thus, the same amount of heat energy can be stored in a small tank of hot water or in a large tank of cool water.

Temperature changes are caused by the gain or loss of heat energy. A space or object that gains heat energy will become hotter. A space or object that loses heat energy will become colder. While heat energy can be produced, it is never destroyed nor used up. Instead, the heat energy may be dispersed over a greater area. Its amount does not change, but the temperature of the area decreases.

A hot object may cool off by warming the surrounding air. A warm room may become cooler as heat escapes into other rooms or out of the house. A poorly insulated house, as shown in Figure 2.1, is literally an attempt to heat the outdoors.

HEAT LOSS PRINCIPLES

Space heating and hot-water heating are the two largest uses of energy in most houses and buildings. For that reason, an understanding of how heat losses may occur is essential for effective energy planning. There are certain *heat loss principles* that describe how heat energy moves from a space or an object to another space or object. These principles apply to heat losses in buildings as well as to heat losses from hot-water heaters.

When a space or an object is heated or cooled, a temperature difference is created. The space or object becomes hotter or colder than the air around it. This temperature difference acts as an energy source to drive heat out of or into the space or object. Just as water seeks its own level, a heated or cooled object will seek a temperature equilibrium with its surroundings.

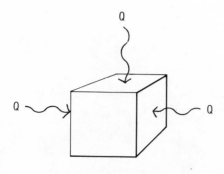

Figure 2.2 Heat energy will always move from hot to cool.

As shown in Figure 2.2, the heat energy will always move from hot to cold. A hot plate placed in a refrigerator will always cool off. A cold plate placed on the kitchen counter will always warm up to the room temperature. When the outside temperature is in the nineties, a building will try to warm to that temperature. When the outside temperature is below freezing, a building will try to cool to that temperature. The greater the temperature difference, the faster the heat will move into or out of a building.

The energy needed to keep a space or an object at a certain temperature is easily calculated. If the desired temperature is higher than the surrounding air, energy needs to be put into the space or object. This energy is labeled Q in Figure 2.3. With a temperature difference, however, some of this energy will gradually move from the space or object to the surrounding air. This energy loss is labeled Q_L in Figure 2.4. The heat energy retained is labeled Q_R.

Figure 2.3 Energy (Q) is put into a space or an object to raise its temperature.

More energy has to be put into the space or object to keep it at the desired temperature. But that energy will not be the same as originally needed. Some energy will always be retained, no matter what the temperature difference. Only the energy lost, or Q_L, must be replaced. So, the total heat energy, or Q_T, needed to maintain a certain temperature follows a simple formula:

$$Q_T = Q_R + Q_L$$

Energy conservation is very basic. It is simply a matter of reducing energy losses, or making Q_L smaller. Such losses can be reduced by reducing the movement of energy. Energy moves by three methods: *radiation, convection,* and *conduction.*

Radiation is heat energy given off as rays from a warm body, as shown in Figure 2.5. Since the surfaces of the object are warmer than the surrounding air, they radiate energy to the air. In an enclosed space, these heat losses can be small. The object's surface and the enclosed surrounding air quickly reach temperature equilibrium.

However, such heat losses can also be large. In an open space, as the surrounding air is heated, it becomes lighter and rises away from the warm object. The warmed air is then replaced with cooled air. This type of energy movement is called convection. Heat losses by convection are shown in Figure 2.6.

The third way energy moves is by conduction. It is heat movement through a solid mass, as shown in Figure 2.7. In contrast, radiation is heat movement from a surface and convection is heat movement in a moving body of air or liquid. The heat in an object will move from the inside to the surface by conduction, move from the surface by radiation, and move from the object by convection.

Two other commonly used terms involving energy movement are *heat transmission* and *infiltration.* As shown in Figure 2.8, heat transmission is the rate at which heat is conducted through a solid. It is measured in Btu/sq ft/°F/hr, and is expressed as the *U factor* of a material. "U" equals the number of Btu which will pass through one square foot of solid if there is a one degree (F) difference between the two sides.

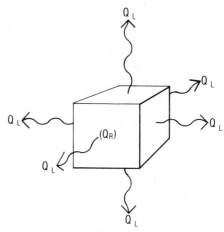

Figure 2.4 Energy losses (Q_L) occur when a temperature difference exists between a space or an object and the surrounding air. Some heat energy is retained (Q_R).

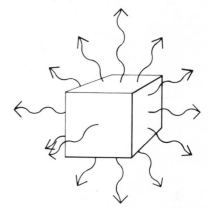

Figure 2.5 Heat movement by radiation.

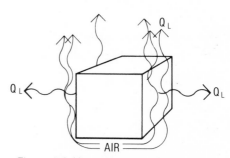

Figure 2.6 Heat movement by convection.

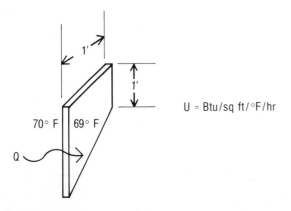

$$U = Btu/sq\ ft/°F/hr$$

Figure 2.8 Heat transmission is the rate at which heat is conducted through a solid.

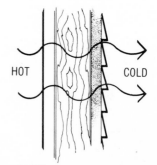

Figure 2.7 Heat movement by conduction.

Figure 2.9 Infiltration is the rate at which air moves into a space from outside.

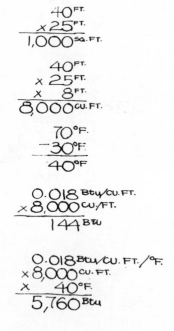

As shown in Figure 2.9, infiltration is the rate at which air moves into a space from outside. The air will infiltrate to equalize the pressure on both sides of a wall. It is measured in cubic feet per hour. To heat one cubic foot of air one degree Fahrenheit, 0.018 Btu is needed.

HEAT LOSS IN BUILDINGS

Understanding heat losses (Q_L) in buildings is not difficult. In the following sections, a simple building structure is discussed. You will learn, step by step, where heat is lost.

Basic Considerations

To keep things simple, build yourself a 1000-square-foot building. Use a simple plan as shown in Figure 2.10. The building is 40-feet long by 25-feet wide. It rests on a concrete slab foundation, and it is covered by a flat roof. The ceilings are eight-feet high. The walls are standard two-by-four drywall construction with standard two-by-eight ceiling joists. There are neither windows nor doors. These will be added later.

This building has 1000 square feet, and it contains 8000 cubic feet of air.

Suppose the outside temperature is 30° F, and that an inside temperature of 70° F is needed. This is a temperature difference of 40-degrees.

Since 0.018 Btu is needed to raise the temperature of one cubic foot of air one degree, 144 Btu will be needed to raise the building temperature one degree. And, 5760 Btu are needed to make up the 40 degree temperature difference.

This is the amount of heat energy needed to keep the building at 70° F. So it is the amount of energy that must be retained (Q_R). On a 30° F day, Q_R is 5760 Btu. And, because of the building size, Q_R on any day is 144 Btu/°F. The amount of heat energy needed for any inside temperature can thus be calculated by multiplying 144 by the difference between the outside temperature and the desired temperature.

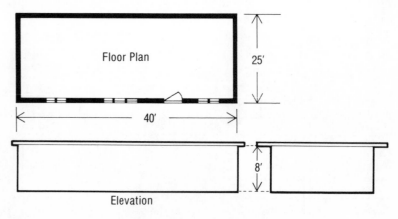

Figure 2.10 Basic plan for use in discussing building heat loss.

Air Changes

People living or working in any building use up oxygen by breathing. The oxygen is replaced with carbon dioxide. The building can quickly become stuffy and uncomfortable.

To keep the air inside the building fresh and comfortable, new air must be introduced. This air change must be a minimum of 15 cubic feet of fresh air per minute for each person as shown in Figure 2.11. If there are four people, 3600 cubic feet of fresh air is needed each hour.

Heating this amount of fresh air will take 64.8 Btu per hour for each degree of temperature difference. Or, 2592 Btu per hour when the outside temperature is 30° F and 70° F is needed inside.

Such air changes are essential, and the new air must be heated. In some buildings where activity is greater or where odors and smoke collect, 25 cubic feet of fresh air per minute for each person may be required.

Heat Transmission Through Walls, Ceiling

A second source of heat loss is through the walls of this simple building. As shown in Figure 2.12, there are 1040 square feet of wall area. The rate of heat transmission depends on the U factor as discussed previously. U is measured in Btu/sq ft/°F/hr.

There are many types of wall construction, but for the sake of discussion use these:

No insulation (air)	U = 0.22
Partial insulation (1 inch fiberglass)	U = 0.12
Full insulation (4 inches fiberglass)	U = 0.07

If no insulation is used, the heat loss through the walls would be 229 Btu per hour for each degree difference. With partial insulation, the loss would be cut to 125 Btu per hour per degree F. And, with full insulation the heat loss would be only 73 Btu per hour per degree F.

Other heat losses occur through the ceiling and the floor. Each type of ceiling and floor has a different U factor. The heat loss calculations are made in the same way as wall calculations. For the ceiling, 640 Btu per hour per degree F is lost with no insulation, 190 Btu per hour per degree F with partial insulation, and only 80 Btu per hour per degree F with full insulation. For the cement-slab floor,* 1250 Btu per hour per degree F is lost with no insulation, 210 Btu per hour per degree F with partial insulation, and only 80 Btu per hour per degree F with full insulation.

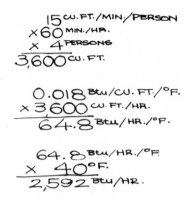

$$
\begin{array}{r}
15 \text{ cu. ft./min./person} \\
\times 60 \text{ min./hr.} \\
\times 4 \text{ persons} \\
\hline
3,600 \text{ cu. ft.}
\end{array}
$$

$$
\begin{array}{r}
0.018 \text{ Btu/cu. ft./°F.} \\
\times 3600 \text{ cu. ft./hr.} \\
\hline
64.8 \text{ Btu/hr./°F.}
\end{array}
$$

$$
\begin{array}{r}
64.8 \text{ Btu/hr./°F.} \\
\times 40 \text{°F.} \\
\hline
2,592 \text{ Btu/hr.}
\end{array}
$$

Figure 2.11 Air changes are essential for comfort.

$$
\begin{array}{r}
130 \text{ ft.} \\
\times 8 \text{ ft.} \\
\hline
1,040 \text{ sq. ft.}
\end{array}
$$

$$
\begin{array}{r}
1040 \text{ sq. ft.} \\
\times 0.22 \text{ Btu/sq. ft./hr./°F.} \\
\hline
229 \text{ Btu/hr./°F.}
\end{array}
$$

$$
\begin{array}{r}
1040 \text{ sq. ft.} \\
\times 0.12 \text{ Btu/sq. ft./hr./°F.} \\
\hline
125 \text{ Btu/hr./°F.}
\end{array}
$$

$$
\begin{array}{r}
1040 \text{ sq. ft.} \\
\times 0.07 \text{ Btu/sq. ft./hr./°F.} \\
\hline
73 \text{ Btu/hr./°F.}
\end{array}
$$

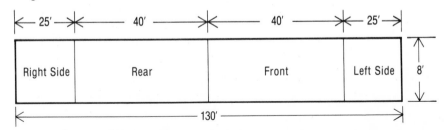

Figure 2.12 Wall area in simple building used for heat loss calculations.

*This concept is presented for simplicity. Actually, the floor's edge losses must be calculated. These calculations are shown in Appendix A, "Heat Loss Calculations."

$$\frac{1}{0.08} = 12.5$$

These heat losses by air changes and transmission through the walls, ceiling, and floor are tabulated in Figure 2.13. As shown, partial insulation cuts the energy loss by 73-percent, while full insulation cuts it by 86-percent.

About Insulation

If you've read about energy conservation, you've read about insulation *R values*. "R" is the resistance to heat flow. It is the tested insulation value which is used to calculate the U factor:

$$U = \frac{1}{R}$$

So, when the U factor of a certain wall construction is 0.08, R is 12.5.

Many energy conservationists are specifying wall R values of R = 20, and ceiling R values of R = 30. These translate to a wall U factor of 0.05, and a ceiling U factor of 0.03. Knowing this relationship will help you calculate the Btu savings from adding more insulation to achieve these greater R values.

HEAT LOSS SOURCE	Btu/hr/°F LOST		
	NO INSULATION	PARTIAL INSULATION	FULL INSULATION
Air Changes	65	65	65
Wall Transmission	229	125	73
Ceiling Transmission	640	190	80
FLoor Transmission	1250	210	80
Total Loss	2184	590	298
Q_L - Percent Energy Saved		73%	86%

Figure 2.13 Heat losses and the effects of insulation in a simple building.

Window and Door Heat Losses

Suppose you add windows and doors to the simple building as in Figure 2.14. Heat losses occur through these windows and doors at a different rate than through the walls. Also, the heat losses through the walls must be recalculated. There are 42 square feet of door area and 96 square feet of window area, so the walls now take up only 902 square feet.

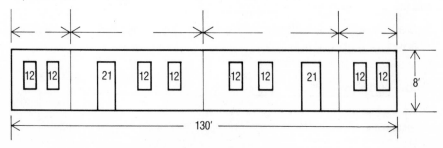

Figure 2.14 Window and door plan for a simple building.

The window and doors have different rates of heat transmission depending on their type. These different U factors are used in the calculations:

- The windows ...

Single glass	(96) (1.31) = 126	Btu/hr/°F
Thermopane	(96) (0.61) = 59	Btu/hr/°F
Storm Windows	(96) (0.45) = 43	Btu/hr/°F

- The doors ...

3/4" Solid core door	(42) (0.69) = 29	Btu/hr/°F
1 5/8" Solid core door	(42) (0.46) = 19	Btu/hr/°F
1 5/8" Solid & storm door	(42) (0.32) = 13	Btu/hr/°F

These figures, plus the new heat loss figures for the smaller wall area, are tabulated in Figure 2.15. The effects of insulation are again obvious. Partial insulation cuts the energy loss by 72-percent, while full insulation cuts it by 85-percent.

HEAT LOSS SOURCE	Btu/hr/°F LOST		
	SINGLE GLASS WINDOWS 3/4" DOORS NO INSULATION	THERMOPANE WINDOWS 1⅝" DOORS PARTIAL INSULATION	SINGLE GLASS & STORMS 1⅝" DOOR & STORMS FULL INSULATION
Air Changes	65	65	65
Wall Transmission	198	108	63
Ceiling Transmission	640	190	80
Floor Transmission	1250	210	80
Window Transmission	126	59	43
Door Transmission	29	19	13
Total Loss	2308	651	344
Q_L - Percent Energy Saved		72%	85%

Figure 2.15 Heat losses and the effects of insulation and different types of doors and windows in a simple building.

Infiltration*

Any wall opening has air infiltrating through it. The heat loss by infiltration through the door, window, and other cracks must be calculated.

As shown in Figure 2.16, a door has a total crack equal to twice its height and twice its width. For the two doors shown earlier, this amounts to 40 feet of crack. A double-hung window has a total crack equal to twice its height and three times its width. For the eight windows shown earlier, this amounts to 136 feet of crack. The total crack for the doors and windows is 176 feet.

Depending on the type of construction and the wind velocity, the amount of air passing through the crack varies. At 10-mph wind velocity, the amount of air infiltrating per foot of crack each hour is:

Door/Window Description

Poor fitting, no weatherstripping ....69 cu ft/hr/ft
Average fitting, no weatherstripping or
    Poor fitting, weather-stripped ....20 cu ft/hr/ft
Average window, weather-stripped...............13 cu ft/hr/ft

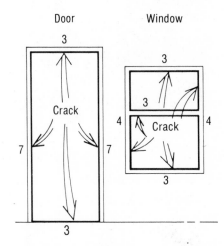

Figure 2.16 Calculating window and door cracks.

*The "crack" method of measuring infiltration is presented for discussion purposes. In Appendix A — "A Method For Calculating Building Heat Loss" — a newer, simplified calculation method is utilized.

$$176^{FT.}$$
$$\times 69 \text{ cu. ft./hr./ft.}$$
$$\times 0.018 \text{ Btu/cu. ft./}°F.$$
$$219 \text{ Btu/hr./}°F.$$

$$176^{FT.}$$
$$\times 20 \text{ cu. ft./hr./ft.}$$
$$\times 0.018 \text{ Btu/cu. ft./}°F.$$
$$63 \text{ Btu/hr./}°F.$$

$$176^{FT.}$$
$$\times 13 \text{ cu. ft./hr./ft.}$$
$$\times 0.018 \text{ Btu/cu. ft./}°F.$$
$$41 \text{ Btu/hr./}°F.$$

The heat losses would be: 219 Btu per hour per degree F for poor fitting; 63 Btu per hour per degree F for average; and, 41 Btu per hour per degree F for good fitting.

These figures have been added to our previous calculations, and the final heat loss totals for the simple building are shown in Figure 2.17.

HEAT LOSS SOURCE	Btu/hr/°F LOST		
	NON-WEATHERSTRIPPED POOR FITTING DOORS & WINDOWS — NO INSULATION	NON-WEATHERSTRIPPED AVERAGE FITTING DOORS & THERMOPANE WINDOWS — PARTIAL INSULATION	WEATHERSTRIPPED STORM DOORS & WINDOWS — FULL INSULATION
Air Changes	65	65	65
Wall Transmission	198	108	63
Ceiling Transmission	640	190	80
Floor Transmission	1250	210	80
Window Transmission	126	59	43
Door Transmission	29	19	13
Infiltration	219	63	41
Total	2527	714	385
Q_L - Percent Energy Saved		72%	85%

Figure 2.17 Total heat losses in simple building.

Financial Considerations

Even with the heat losses in this simple building, you can readily see how heating costs can become a financial hardship.

Suppose the building is located in Omaha, Nebraska, a city with a typical midwestern climate. In an average winter, Omaha has 6612 *degree days*. A degree day is a day in which the average temperature for the day is one degree below 65° F. In other words, if the average outdoor temperature is 45° F on a certain day, that day would have 20 degree days. If the temperature is 60° F, it would be five degree days. All the degree days are added to give an annual degree-day load.*

The heating cost is calculated by multiplying the daily heat loss per degree F, times the degree days times the fuel costs per million Btu. In 1978, fuel oil cost about $6.92 per million Btu. Figure 2.18 shows the fuel costs for the three possible levels of heat loss in the simple building. It also shows that an 11-percent fuel inflation rate will more than double the fuel costs by 1985.

Figure 2.19 The three primary energy sources for space heating.

HOUSE TYPE	HEAT LOSS		DEGREE DAYS	1978 $ COST	11% INFLATION 1985 COST
	HOUR	DAY			
Poor	2,527	60,648	6,612	$2775.00	$5761.00
Good	714	17,136	6,612	784.00	1628.00
Best	385	9,240	6,612	423.00	878.00

Figure 2.18 Fuel oil costs for three levels of heat loss in a simple building in Omaha, Nebraska.

*Degree days are usually calculated using 65° F as the desired temperature. A building's occupants and equipment will raise the inside temperature to a comfortable level. The degree days for a given area is an average figure for several years. This minimizes the effects of a severe or mild winter on the figure.

Calculating Heat Losses

The procedures for calculating heat losses in any building are detailed in Appendix A of The Solar Decision Book. These calculations are necessary for sizing furnaces, and they are necessary for sizing a solar energy system. An added benefit: by knowing your building's heat losses, you can better understand where your heating dollar is going. And the calculations can help show you the impact of various conservation measures.

FUEL	ESTIMATED 1979 FUEL COSTS
	$/MM Btu
Natural Gas	$5.32
Fuel Oil	$7.08
Electricity	$13.18

Figure 2.20 Estimated 1979 fuel costs per million Btu.

ESTIMATING YOUR ENERGY NEEDS AND COSTS

Space Heating

The three primary energy sources used for space heating are fuel oil, natural gas, and electricity. These are shown in Figure 2.19.

Fuel oil as delivered to the user has a minimum heating value of about 125,000 Btu per gallon. But a typical furnace will burn the fuel at only about 60-percent efficiency. So the actual heating value of a gallon of fuel oil is 75,000 Btu (60-percent of 125,000). Or, for one million Btu of heat energy, a maximum of 13.3 gallons of oil is needed at average efficiency.

$$\frac{1,000,000 \text{ Btu}}{\div \ 75,000 \text{ Btu/GAL.}} = 13.3 \text{ GAL.}$$

The cost per million Btu is calculated by multiplying the per-gallon cost time 13.3 gallons. If the oil costs $0.532 per gallon, the cost per million Btu is $7.08.

$$\begin{array}{r} \$ \ 0.532 \text{ GAL.} \\ \times \ 13.3 \text{ GAL./MM. Btu} \\ \hline \$ \ 7.08 \text{ MM. Btu} \end{array}$$

Natural gas is sold in units of 100 cubic feet (ccf). Such units contain about 100,000 Btu of energy. But, the net fuel value assuming some losses is about 93,000 Btu per ccf. And, with the furnace operating at 60-percent efficiency, the fuel value drops to about 55,800 Btu. One million Btu of heat energy requires 17.92 ccf of gas.

The cost per million Btu is calculated by multiplying the per-ccf price by 17.92 ccf. If the unit price is $0.297, then the cost per million Btu is $5.32.

$$\begin{array}{r} \$ 0.297 \text{ ccf.} \\ \times 17.92 \text{ ccf./MM. Btu} \\ \hline \$ 5.32 \text{ MM. Btu} \end{array}$$

Electricity is sold in kilowatt-hours (kwh). A kwh is 1000 watt-hours. This is the amount of electricity used by a 100-watt lightbulb burning for ten hours. One kilowatt-hour is worth 3414 Btu, and electrical resistance heating is considered 100-percent efficient. So, for one million Btu of heat energy, 293 kwh are needed.

$$\frac{1,000,000 \text{ Btu}}{\div \ 3414 \text{ Btu/Kwh}} = 293 \text{ Kwh}$$

If the electrical rate is $0.045 per kilowatt-hour, then the cost for one million Btu is $13.18.

$$\begin{array}{r} \$ 0.045 \text{ Kwh} \\ \times \ 293 \text{ Kwh/MM. Btu} \\ \hline \$ 13.18 \text{ MM. Btu} \end{array}$$

These are the average fuel costs projected for the 1978-1979 heating year. They are placed on a "cost per million Btu" basis because this figure is easiest to work with when estimating heating costs. Estimated 1979 prices are summarized in Figure 2.20. As noted previously, prices for natural gas and fuel oil should equalize around 1980.

Using these fuel costs, you can estimate your heating costs. The following steps outline a typical procedure:

1. Determine the building heat loss in Btu per hour. (See Appendix A.)

2. Calculate the daily heat loss (Btu/hr x 24 hr).

3. Determine the average number of degree days for your area. This information may be available from your local weather bureau or utility. Appendix C contains a listing of degree days for 96 major cities. You may wish to use the figure for a city close to yours.

4. Determine the fuel cost you are paying. This cost per gallon, 100 cubic feet, or kilowatt-hour is usually listed on your utility bill. If there are any questions, call your utility for the latest information.

5. Calculate your fuel cost per million Btu. Use the effective energy values shown for fuel oil, natural gas, and electricity.

6. Calculate your estimated heating costs by multiplying the daily heat loss times the degree days times the "cost per million Btu".

As an example, suppose the heat loss in your building is 300 Btu/hr/°F. Your area has 6646 degree days. And your fuel oil cost is $6.38 per million Btu. You would need 47,851,200 Btu per year to heat the building. This amount of heat energy would cost you $305.29 for a year.

Such a calculation, of course, would estimate only your cost of fuel. It would not estimate the cost of energy for running furnace fans, boiler pumps, or other such aids to move the heat throughout the building. By making the calculations, however, you can easily estimate the effects of energy conservation or higher prices on your fuel bill.

Most degree day averages for a given area are based on a temperature of 65° F. So, if the thermostat is set lower than 70° F, your estimate may be slightly high. If the thermostat is set higher, the estimate may be low.

Water Heating

The average person uses about 20 gallons of hot water each day. Water heater efficiency can be measured by looking at the number of gallons that can be heated 100° F in one hour and comparing it to the Btu of energy required to obtain this temperature rise.

One gallon of water weighs 8.3 pounds. One Btu of energy is needed to heat one pound of water one degree Fahrenheit. Thus, 830 Btu is needed to heat a gallon of water 100° F.

Electric elements are rated in watts, and your electrical bill is figured in $/kwh. One kwh = 3414 Btu.

Gas burners are rated in Btu output. Your gas bill is submitted in 100 cubic feet (ccf). One ccf contains 100,000 Btu.

Water heater efficiency can be calculated by:

$$\frac{\text{Btu Output}}{\text{Btu Input}} = \text{Efficiency}$$

For electric water heaters, this is:

Input = 5,500 watts (5.5 kwh)

At 4½¢/kwh cost of operation - $.045 x 5.5 = $0.25/hr

$$
\begin{array}{r}
300 \text{ Btu/HR./°F.} \\
\times\ 24 \text{ HR/DAY} \\
\times\ 6646 \text{ DEGREE DAYS} \\
\hline
47,851,200 \text{ Btu/YEAR}
\end{array}
$$

$$
\begin{array}{r}
47.8512 \text{ MM Btu/YEAR} \\
\times\ \$\ \ 6.38 \text{ MM Btu} \\
\hline
\$305.29 \text{ YEAR}
\end{array}
$$

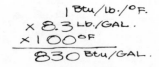

$$
\begin{array}{r}
1 \text{ Btu/Lb./°F.} \\
\times\ 8.3 \text{ Lb./GAL.} \\
\times\ 100 \text{ °F} \\
\hline
830 \text{ Btu/GAL.}
\end{array}
$$

Btu input = 18,777 Btu (5.5 x 3414)
Output = Temperature rise of 100° F for 22.5 gallons

Btu Output = (22.5) (8.3) (100) = 18,675 (Btu)

Efficiency = $\frac{18,675}{18,777}$ = 99.4%

Cost = 18,675 Btu for 25¢ or $13.39/MM Btu

Checking a number of electric water heaters indicates that these figures are typical. Electric water heater recovery costs about $13.25/MM Btu at $0.045 kwh. Tank efficiency is about 99.5%.

For natural-gas water heaters:

Input = 50,000 Btu/hour

At 2.70/MM Btu = 13.5¢/hour

Output = temperature rise of 100° F for 42 gallons

Btu output = (42) (8.3) (100) = 34,860 Btu

Efficiency = $\frac{34,860}{50,000}$ = 69.7%

Cost = 34,860 Btu for 13.5¢ or $3.87/MM Btu

With these calculations, the cost of heating water with electricity appears to be about three-and-a-half times higher than that of heating water with natural gas.

What does this mean in 1977 annual costs? Assuming a family of four uses 80 gallons of 140° F hot water which enters the house at 55° F:

180) (8.3) (365) = 242,360 lbs of water/year
(242,360) (140-55) = 20.6 MM Btu/year

Electric = 20.6 x 13.25 = 272.95/yr = $22.75/month
Gas   = 20.6 x 3.70 = 76.22/yr = $ 6.35/month

Natural gas prices are expected to rise by 50-percent shortly. So the future cost ratio might be about 1 to 2.4, gas to electricity. This gives the following estimate:

Gas   = $114/year = $ 9.50/month
Electricity = $273/year = $22.75/month

Gas water heating would remain much more economical. However, electricity is available at lower rates during off-peak hours such as during the night. This tends to make electricity somewhat more competitive.

Increasing Water Heater Efficiency

In a gas-fired water heater, combustion efficiency is important. A periodic maintenance check by a competent serviceman is recommended. Also, most gas water heaters contain a continuously burning pilot light. There is some waste — about 30-percent of the pilot gas burned. An alternate ignition device for an automatic pilot flame is available.

In both gas and electric water heaters, the major losses are through the tank insulation jacket. The surface areas of three common sizes of water heaters are shown in Figure 2.21. Assuming

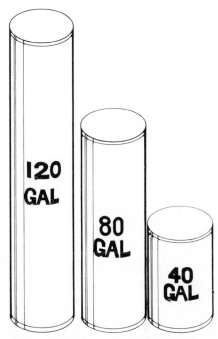

Figure 2.21 The surface areas of three common-size water heaters.

$$\begin{array}{r} 413 \text{ Btu/HR.} \\ \times\ 24 \text{ HR./DAY} \\ \times 365 \text{ DAYS} \\ \hline 3.6 \text{ MM. Btu} \end{array}$$

$$\begin{array}{r} 104 \\ \times\ 24 \\ \times\ 365 \\ \hline 0.91 \text{ MM. Btu} \end{array}$$

the tank is at 140° F in a building at 70° F, the temperature difference between the tank and its surroundings is 70° F. Heat is constantly being radiated away from the tank.

The table in Figure 2.22 shows the effect of three insulations on the tanks. Using these heat loss figures, you can calculate how better insulation might reduce the water heating costs. For instance, an 80-gallon tank with U = 0.2 insulation loses about 3.6 MM Btu per year. The same tank with U = 0.05 insulation would lose only about 0.91 MM Btu per year. At a cost of $9.30 per MM Btu (an average figure between gas and electricity), the losses from the first tank would be $33.48 a year or $2.79 a month. The losses from the second tank would be only $8.46 a year or $0.71 a month. Upgrading the insulation would save $25.02 a year or $2.08 a month.

By comparison, an uninsulated 80-gallon tank would lose 18.1 MM Btu per year. The cost would be $168.33 or $14.02 a month.

INSULATION VALUE	Btu LOSS/HR		
	40 GAL	80 GAL	120 GAL
U = .2 (R-5)	273	413	542
U = .1 (R-10)	137	207	271
U = .5 (R-20)	68	104	136
No Insulation	1365	2065	2709

Figure 2.22 Insulation has an effect on the heat loss from water heaters.

Electric Appliances

Every building structure contains electrical appliances of some type. Energy conservation should include an estimate of how much electricity is used by each appliance. It should also include an estimate of the costs for operating each appliance.

To determine this, you must know how many watts of energy the applicance consumes. Many appliances have this wattage stamped on the name plate. Operational cost is determined as follows:

$$\frac{\text{Watts}}{1000} \text{ X (Hours operated) X (\$/kwh)} = \text{Cost of operating}$$

If wattage is not indicated but amperage is, the wattage may be calculated by multiplying the voltage by the amperage.

(volts) x (amps) = watts

As an example:

An appliance which operates on 110 volts uses eight amps at a rate of $0.05/kwh. Determine the cost to operate the appliance for 100 hours.

(volts)   (amps)   (hours)   (rate) = cost

(110) X (8) X (100) X (0.05) = $4.40

Many appliances such as pumps and refrigerators contain motors. By knowing the horsepower and, thus, the watts used by the motor, the cost of operation can quickly be determined.

The costs of running various appliances for 100 hours at different electrical rates is shown in Figure 2.23.

Appliances using the most energy are clothes dryers, stoves, and water heaters. Their use should be kept to a minimum.

Electric heaters, fry pans, french friers, irons, tabletop ovens and roasters, toasters, and room air conditioners also add quickly to the electric bill. Light bulbs are cheap individually, but in groups they quickly add up. Microwave ovens are extremely cheap to run, compared with regular stoves.

APPLIANCE TYPE	WATTS, TYPICAL	KWH REQ., TYPICAL	COST TO RUN 100 HRS. $ AT STATED KWH COST					
			3¢/KWH	3½¢/KWH	4¢/KWH	5¢/KWH	6¢/KWH	8¢/KWH
Coffee Percolater	650	.65	1.95	2.28	2.60	3.25	3.90	5.20
Dehumidifier	540	.54	1.62	1.89	2.16	2.70	3.24	4.32
Dishwasher, residential	750	.75	2.25	2.63	3.00	3.75	4.50	6.00
Disposal	390	.39	1.17	1.37	1.56	1.95	2.34	3.12
Clothes Dryer	5600	5.6	16.80	19.60	22.40	28.00	33.60	44.80
Electric Air Cleaner	11	.01	nil	nil	nil	nil	nil	nil
Electric Heater, Portable	1250	1.25	3.75	4.38	5.00	6.25	7.50	10.00
Fry Pan	1250	1.25	3.75	4.38	5.00	6.25	7.50	10.00
French Frier	1150	1.15	3.45	4.03	4.60	5.75	6.90	9.20
Iron	1150	1.15	3.45	4.03	4.60	5.75	6.90	9.20
Light Bulbs	150	.15	.45	.53	.60	.75	.90	1.20
Light Bulbs	100	.10	.30	.35	.40	.50	.60	.80
Light Bulbs	60	.06	.18	.21	.24	.30	.36	.48
Microwave Oven	650	.65	1.95	2.28	2.60	3.25	3.90	5.20
Motor 1/3 hp	470	.47	1.41	1.65	1.88	2.35	2.82	3.76
Motor 1/2 hp	660	.66	1.98	2.31	2.64	3.30	3.96	5.28
Motor 3/4 hp	930	.93	2.79	3.26	3.72	4.65	5.58	7.44
Motor 1 hp	1200	1.20	3.60	4.20	4.80	6.00	7.20	9.60
Motor 2 hp	2300	2.30	6.90	8.05	9.20	11.50	13.80	10.40
Motor 5 hp	5500	5.50	16.50	19.25	22.00	27.50	33.00	44.00
Oven, Tabletop	1150	1.15	3.45	4.03	4.60	5.75	6.90	9.20
4 Burner Stove Top	6400	6.4	19.20	22.40	25.60	32.00	38.40	51.20
Oven, Stove	7900	7.9	23.70	27.65	31.60	39.50	47.40	63.20
Roaster Table Top	1500	1.5	4.50	5.25	6.00	7.50	9.00	12.00
Range Hood	175	.175	.53	.61	.70	.88	1.05	1.40
Toaster	1200	1.2	3.60	4.20	4.80	6.00	7.20	9.60
Room Air Conditioner	1100	1.1	3.30	3.85	4.40	5.50	6.60	8.80
TV, Color Solid State	140	.14	.42	.49	.56	.70	.84	1.12
TV, Color Tube	750	.75	2.25	2.63	3.00	3.75	4.50	6.00
Washer	720	.720	2.16	2.52	2.88	3.60	4.32	5.76
Water Heater	6700	6.7	20.10	23.45	26.80	33.50	40.20	53.60

Figure 2.23 Typical electric appliance operating costs.

Frost-free refrigerators work by adding electric resistance heating elements to defrost the freezer section. The energy to run these heating elements is additional to the energy required to run the refrigerator cycle. Consequently, these units are more energy consuming. The energy use of typical combination refrigerator-freezers is shown in Figure 2.24.

TOTAL REFRIGERATED VOLUME IN CUBIC FEET	COST OF ENERGY IN DOLLARS PER MONTH AT A RATE OF 4 CENTS PR KILOWATT-HOUR FOR MODELS WITH			
	Partial Automatic Defrost		Automatic Defrost	
	Minimum	Maximum	Minimum	Maximum
Less than 11.5	$2.40/mo	$2.40/mo	—	—
9.5 to & including 12.5	1.90	4.20	4.60	4.60
10.5 to & including 13.5	1.90	4.40	4.60	5.30
11.5 to & including 14.5	1.90	4.40	3.50	5.80
12.5 to & including 15.5	2.00	4.40	3.50	6.30
13.5 to & including 16.5	2.00	4.10	3.40	6.30
14.5 to & including 17.5	2.00	3.80	3.40	6.80
15.5 to & including 18.5	2.00	3.20	3.40	6.80
16.5 to & including 19.5	3.20	3.20	3.60	8.20
17.5 to & including 20.5			3.60	8.20
18.5 to & including 21.5			4.00	8.20
19.5 to & including 22.5			4.60	7.60
20.5 to & including 23.5			4.60	7.60
21.5 to & including 24.5			4.90	7.20
22.5 to & including 25.5			4.90	8.50
23.5 to & including 26.5			5.50	8.50
24.5 to & including 27.5			6.20	8.50
25.5 to & including 28.5			6.80	7.70
26.5 to & including 29.5			7.40	7.40
27.5 to & including 30.5			7.40	7.40
28.5 and over			—	—

(Data reprinted with permission of The Association of Home Appliance Manufacturers.)

Figure 2.24 Energy consumption of various combination refrigerator-freezers.

Cooling Costs — Central Air Conditioning

In the summer months, outdoor temperatures rise to 80° F and higher. Structure heat loss becomes heat gain because the heat flow is into the structure.

Air conditioning removes the heat by providing cooling energy (or colder air). Through a refrigeration cycle, heat energy is removed from the interior air and exhausted outdoors.

To examine what this costs, you have to know the efficiency of Btu output (cold air) versus Btu input (energy to run the compressor). If output is divided by input, an efficiency is established.

Figure 2.25 shows four commercial room air conditioners examined in this manner. What this table indicates is that electricity is working at about 200- to 260-percent efficiency. Taking 2.3 (230-percent) as an average and costs at $0.045/kwh or $13.18/MM Btu, air conditioning costs average about $5.73/MM Btu.

UNIT	COLD AIR OUTPUT	÷	ENERGY INPUT	=	EFFICIENCY
1	24,500 Btu		9,389 Btu		2.6
2	56,000 Btu		23,557 Btu		2.4
3	22,000 Btu		9,559 Btu		2.3
4	23,000 Btu		11,266 Btu		2.0

Figure 2.25 Four commercial room air conditioners checked for efficiency.

MAKING A DECISION

In this section of The Solar Decision Book, you have learned that heat and temperature are two different concepts. Heat moves and creates temperature differences. You have learned that such heat movement occurs according to several basic principles. You have used these principles to understand and calculate heat losses in buildings. You have also learned that a knowledge of heat loss and energy consumption by various devices can help you estimate your energy needs. By estimating costs, you can see the effect that simple conservation methods can have on your utility bill.

Your decision at this point may be to continue your present energy use patterns. Or, you may see areas in which you can reduce your energy needs. Using the cost data projected for the future, see what those needs will be costing you in the 1980s and beyond. The costs may tell you that energy conservation and alternate fuels must be included in your future.

DECISION 3

Conserve Energy

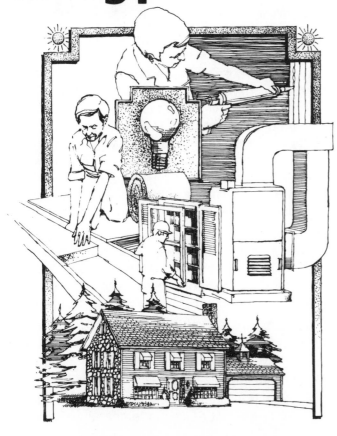

The United States is faced with a continuing need for energy, rapidly rising energy costs, and a substantial energy shortage. That much is certain, and the need for massive energy conservation is just as certain.

Such conservation is needed — by each person, by each business — because the Federal Government alone cannot solve the energy problem. It can create an awareness of the problem. It can investigate possible solutions. And it can provide the leadership needed to channel the efforts of public as well as private interests into productive solutions. But the action required to solve the problem rests with the American people.

You and your family, or you and your employees play the most important role in energy conservation. Any decision to conserve energy must be based on the individual situation. This section of The Solar Decision Book will help you to make that decision. You will learn that:

- The building structure can be designed to enhance energy conservation.
- Furnace maintenance pays off in efficient and economical heating.
- Your choice of fuel is critical when you consider the future costs.
- Every building owner can undertake a number of simple energy conservation steps at very little cost.

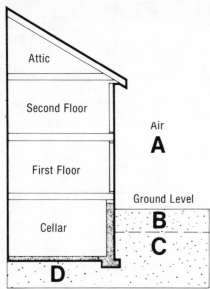

Figure 3.1 A cross-sectional view of a simple two-story house.

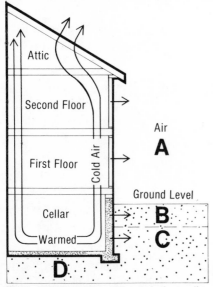

Figure 3.3 Heat flows through the walls and roof depending on their U factor.

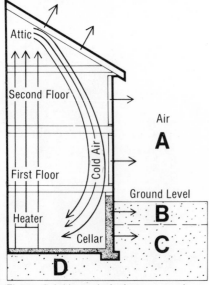

Figure 3.4 Heated air rises upward.

THE BUILDING STRUCTURE

Your energy needs and costs can be reduced simply through proper design of the building itself. The building structure should be engineered for proper air flow in the interior. It should be engineered to take maximum advantage of materials with a high *thermal mass* ... those with an ability to soak up and retain heat energy. It should be engineered for proper treatment of the walls that face the sun. In addition, significant energy savings are also possible with the correct choice of architecture and heating fuel.

Interior Air Flow

Figure 3.1 shows a cross-sectional view of a simple two-story house. Surrounding the structure are four basic temperature conditions which change each season: the outside air (A), the ground down to the frost line (B), the ground below the frost line (C), and the ground below the building (D). Figure 3.2 shows a set of typical temperature conditions for each season.

AREA	TEMPERATURE CONDITIONS			
	WINTER	SPRING	SUMMER	FALL
Outside Air	20° F	60° F	90° F	50° F
Ground to Frost Line	30° F	50° F	60° F	50° F
Ground Below Frost Line	50° F	50° F	50° F	50° F
Ground Below Building	60° F	60° F	60° F	60° F

Figure 3.2 Typical temperature conditions in four areas around a house.

Heat flows from hot to cold. During the winter, heat energy will attempt to escape from a structure to the cooler air outside. This heat flows through the walls and roof at a rate determined by the U factor. For an unheated structure in which air can move freely from floor to floor, warm air from the cellar will rise to the attic. This is shown in Figure 3.3. The cellar becomes the coldest part of the house, while the attic becomes the warmest part. However, very little temperature difference exists between floors. The maximum heat flow to the outside occurs from the attic. This is where the driving force (temperature difference) is the greatest. The minimum heat flow to the outside occurs from the cellar. This is where the temperature difference (cellar to ground) is the least.

If a heater is added to the structure as shown in Figure 3.4, the warm air would again circulate to the attic. Cooler air would circulate to the cellar. The cellar could be kept cool, and the floors could be heated as needed by increasing or decreasing the air flow to each.

If no air could flow from floor to floor, the cellar would be the warmest area of the house. Heat for the upper stories could be transmitted only through the solid floors. The temperature difference between floors would be substantial. This is shown in Figure 3.5.

In Figure 3.6, each floor is isolated and each has an outlet from the heater. Each floor can be kept at a desired temperature.

Generally, the first rule of effective winter heating is to isolate the building levels from each other and to supply each level only with the required energy. The second rule is to heat the levels only to the temperature required for their function. Bedrooms do not usually require as much heat as living areas. Nor do these areas require heat at the same time. Bathrooms usually require more heat than either bedrooms or living areas.

Conditions in the summertime are different. Figure 3.7 shows that large quantities of heat are now flowing into the house from the surrounding air. Some heat may or may not be flowing from the ground level (B). But the areas (C and D) around the cellar are colder than the house interior air. Heat can flow from the house to those areas. If air can move freely from the cellar to the attic, then the cellar will be the coolest and the attic the hottest. By venting the roof, the hot air is encouraged to escape from the structure after the sun goes down and the outside air cools off. If the air could not move freely between floors, the entire structure would trap heat. The first rule of summer cooling is to interconnect the building levels. Heat can then escape from the structure, particularly at night.

Fall and spring are usually combinations of the summer and winter problems. Proper design of the house interior will insure proper air flow for the needs of the occupants during the different seasons of the year. Sometimes air circulation is desired; other times, it is not. In existing houses, minor interior modifications will quite often accomplish this. In new home construction, air flow should be carefully studied during the design stages.

Interior Thermal Mass

Thermal mass plays an important role in conserving building heat. This fact is usually forgotten or ignored in today's buildings. How thermal mass works is easily demonstrated with a mental exercise. Suppose you purchase ten 55-gallon drums, bring them into the house, roll them in front of a south-facing window, fill them with water, and let the sun play on them all day. If the water starts at 60° F and by night has warmed to 75° F, the total heat stored will be 68,722 Btu.

$$\begin{array}{r} 10 \text{ DRUMS} \\ \times\ 55 \text{ GALLONS/DRUM} \\ \times\ 8.33 \\ 15 \text{ °F.} \\ \hline 68,722 \text{ Btu} \end{array}$$

As the room cools down, this stored heat is released to the air in the room. At $7.10 per million (MM) Btu, that's 49¢ a day in heat savings or an annual savings of $178.85. Actually, such thermal mass will work whether it is in the sunlight or not. It will be warmed from the air in the house.

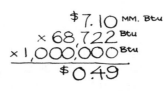

$$\begin{array}{r} \$7.10 \text{ MM. Btu} \\ \times\ 68,722 \text{ Btu} \\ \times\ 1,000,000 \text{ Btu} \\ \hline \$0.49 \end{array}$$

Drums of water are not the most convenient means of saving energy by thermal mass. Many materials used in construction have high thermal mass. Concrete, bricks, stone, masonry, and similar materials are examples.

$$\begin{array}{r} \$0.49 \text{ DAY} \\ \times\ 365 \text{ DAYS/YEAR} \\ \hline \$178.85 \text{ YEAR} \end{array}$$

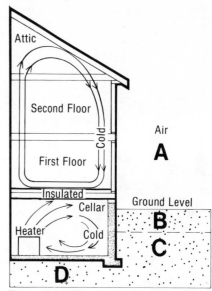

Figure 3.5 Without air circulation from floor-to-floor, the cellar would be the warmest part of the house.

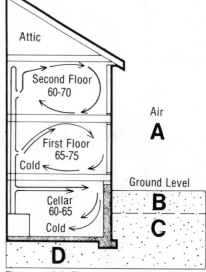

Figure 3.6 Temperature conditions when each floor is isolated and each has a heater outlet.

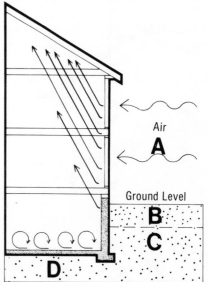

Figure 3.7 In the summer, heat flows into the house.

Figure 3.8 Building orientation toward the sun is important.

Figure 3.9 Possible treatments for a north-facing wall.

Figure 3.10 Possible treatments for an east or west wall.

Thermal mass also works in reverse. It can absorb heat from a room on a hot day and radiate it into cooler air at night. A building with a high amount of thermal mass is easier to heat and cool. Thermal mass serves to reduce or slow temperature cycling. A more even temperature can be maintained.

Exterior Orientation

As shown in Figure 3.8, the orientation of a building toward the sun also plays an important role in energy conservation. The sun rises in the east, travels across the southern sky, and sets in the west. The south side of a structure receives solar radiation most of the day; the east side, only in the morning; and the west side, only in the evening. The north side does not receive any radiation. The direction in which each wall faces will affect your decisions on how to treat the walls for maximum energy conservation.

The North-Facing Exterior Wall. This is always the coldest wall. To reduce heat losses in winter, the north-facing exterior wall should have a high resistance to heat transmission. It should be protected from winds to lower convection losses. It should be a dark color to absorb the maximum amount of reflected solar radiation. It should also have a high thermal mass to slow down temperature cycling.

To enhance cooling in summer, the north-facing exterior wall should have some means for drawing in cool air. For cooling efficiency, air conditioning evaporators should be mounted in the shade of this wall. And heat from inside the structure should not be exhausted along this wall.

These requirements for the north-facing exterior wall are shown in Figure 3.9. The windows should be small and well insulated. Doors should be eliminated when practical. Masonry, or other high-thermal-mass materials, should be used. Power vents should be installed to draw in cool summer air. Evergreen plantings should be made to intercept winter winds. Insulation should be maximized.

The East- and West-Facing Exterior Walls. The treatment of these walls should be similar to that of the north-facing wall. However, provision should be made to either shade or expose the walls to solar radiation, depending on the geographic location and season of the year. Such radiation is available only during a small part of the day, so devices to control the sun's penetration should be installed.

The possible treatments for east- and west-facing walls are shown in Figure 3.10. Windows should be employed to a greater extent. But, deciduous plantings should be used to provide summer shade. Awnings should be placed on windows. Doors should be protected and insulated. The east wall can be used for air conditioning evaporators, if the north wall is not available. Heat exhaustion should take place on the west wall, unless local conditions dictate otherwise. And, as with the north wall, the east and west walls should have a high thermal mass and maximum insulation.

The South-Facing Exterior Wall. The treatment of the south-facing exterior wall is highly critical. This is the wall which receives maximum heat energy from the sun's rays. It is always the hottest wall of the structure. The possible treatment of this wall is dependent on its function. Its function is determined by geography and climate. The south wall must be an efficient solar collector when the structure requires heat. It must reflect solar energy when the structure requires cooling.

Figure 3.11 Possible treatments for a south wall.

The possible treatments for a south wall are shown in Figure 3.11. Control of solar radiation is important year-round. Large window walls are required to collect solar heat in the winter. As such, exterior plantings should not interfere with winter solar radiation. Yet, shade is desirable in the hot summer months. Usually, these requirements can be met with awnings, overhangs, and other controllable devices. Deciduous trees can also be used. The winter sun can penetrate when the leaves are off the tree, but the summer sun cannot penetrate when the leaves are on the tree.

Such control of solar radiation on the south wall can reduce your energy costs. A 40-foot-long, 8-foot-high south wall can receive more than 200,000 Btu on a sunny day (five hours of direct sun on the wall). For a 120-day heating season with 50-percent sunshine, that's more than 14 million Btu. At $7.10 per million Btu, more than one-hundred dollars in fuel costs can be saved. These savings are important during the heating season, but they can be lost if the solar radiation is not controlled during the air conditioning season.

Passive Solar Architecture

Building structure treatments which help the structure become a heat trap and a solar collector are known as *passive solar architecture*. Passive solar devices built into the structure are the least expensive way of utilizing the sun's energy. The Solar Decision Book discusses some options for passive solar architecture. You can also consult one of several books on the subject. An excellent professional textbook is *Solar Energy: Fundamentals in building design* from McGraw Hill Book Company. A more popular book is *The Solar Home Book* from Cheshire Books. Both are written by Bruce Anderson of Total Environmental Action, a well-known architectural firm specializing in solar design.

$$40^{\text{FT.}} \times 8^{\text{FT.}} \times 5^{\text{HR}}$$
$$\underline{\times 150^{\text{Btu/Sq.FT.}}}$$
$$240,000^{\text{Btu/DAY}}$$

$$240,000^{\text{Btu/DAY}}$$
$$\underline{\times 120^{\text{DAYS}} \times 0.50}$$
$$14,400,000^{\text{Btu}}$$

$$14.4^{\text{MM.Btu}}$$
$$\underline{\times \$7.10^{\text{MM.Btu}}}$$
$$\$102.24$$

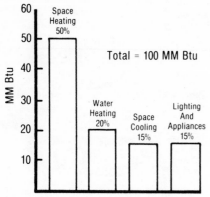

Figure 3.12 The annual energy requirements for a typical residential building. The total energy demand of 100 million Btu is divided among various uses as shown.

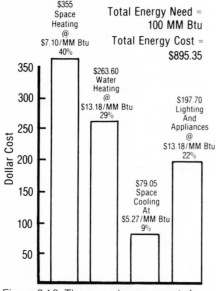

Figure 3.13 The annual energy costs for a residence using fossil-fuel heating and electric water heating.

Your Choice Of Fuel Is Critical

The annual energy requirements for a typical residential building are shown in Figure 3.12. In this example, 100-million Btu of energy is required. Of this demand, 50-percent goes for space heating, 20-percent for water heating, 15-percent for cooling, and 15-percent for lighting and appliances. These percentages will vary from one residence to another.

The costs for these various energy uses do not follow the same percentages. An example of annual energy costs is shown in Figure 3.13. In the example, space heating is done with a fossil fuel (oil, gas, or coal), water heating with electricity, cooling with air-to-air air conditioners, and lighting and appliances with electricity. The total energy cost is $895.35 for the 100-million Btu.

Figure 3.14 shows the energy costs for an all-electric structure. The cost for space heating increases dramatically. And the total fuel bill jumps to $1199.35.

Figure 3.15 shows the energy costs for a structure using fossil fuel whenever possible. The costs for space heating and water heating are reduced, and the total fuel bill drops to $773.75. This represents a savings of more than 35-percent compared to the costs of all-electric energy useage.

Figure 3.16 shows what energy conservation and the use of solar energy can do to reduce fuel costs even more. In the example, total energy requirements are reduced by 10-percent through energy conservation. Sixty-percent of the energy demand for heating comes from passive and active solar systems. A liquid-to-air heat pump is used for cooling. The total energy bill is now reduced to $409.50. This is a savings of 66-percent over the all-electric costs and 47-percent over the building making the maximum use of fossil fuel. The largest energy cost left is that for lighting and appliances, an excellent area to practice further energy conservation. With a 10- to 12-percent annual fuel cost inflation almost certain, energy savings must become a major consideration. Otherwise, the costs will become an unbearable financial burden.

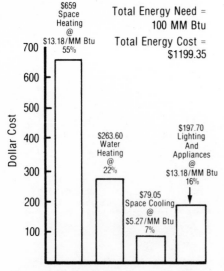

Figure 3.14 Typical energy costs for an all-electric structure.

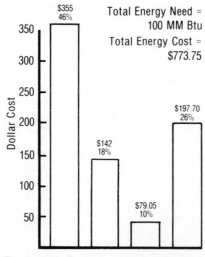

Figure 3.15 Typical energy costs for a structure using fossil fuel for both space heating and water heating.

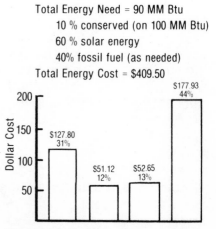

Figure 3.16 Typical energy costs for a structure using fossil fuels, some conservation, and some solar energy.

FURNACE MAINTENANCE

A poorly maintained furnace can have a fuel efficiency of as little as 45- to 50-percent. A well maintained furnace can have a fuel efficiency as high as 70- to 75- percent. How is this possible? During the combustion process, the rapid combination of burning fuel and oxygen results in the release of heat. Two chemical reactions take place:

Carbon plus oxygen $\longrightarrow$ carbon dioxide plus heat

Hydrogen plus oxygen $\longrightarrow$ water vapor plus heat

Carbon and hydrogen come from the fuel, while the oxygen comes from the air. If too little oxygen is present, not all of the fuel will be burned. If too much oxygen is present, heat will be wasted heating the air from which the oxygen is obtained. Good combustion efficiency demands that exactly the right proportions of fuel and oxygen are combined. This is why a poorly maintained furnace can have a very low efficiency.

The fuel-and-oxygen mixture is ignited (started burning) by an external source of heat. The lowest temperature at which the fuel will ignite is called the *fuel ignition temperature.* The oil-burner spark or the gas pilot must produce this ignition temperature. However, these sources of ignition use energy. They may waste fuel, if not properly set.

Most common fuels produce flame temperatures in the range of 3360° to 3800° F. The improper fuel-and-air ratio can reduce this temperature and the furnace efficiency.

The heat released from the combustion process does four things: it heats the combustion products; it heats the incoming air and fuel; it supplies heat to break down the fuel; and, it radiates heat to the surroundings. Only the heat which is radiated to the surroundings is useful. The radiation of this heat to the surrounding firebox shell heats either air or water. This heated air or water is then transported throughout the house to heat the various rooms. The heat which is not needed in the combustion process or for heating the house is lost to the outside air through a chimney or furnace stack.

The control of oxygen and fuel at the firebox is both complicated and critical. The adjustments should be performed by an experienced serviceman with the proper tools. For maximum efficiency, a furnace should be checked and adjusted at the beginning of each winter heating season.

Recently, residential stack control devices have been in the news. These devices automatically close the stack when the furnace is not operating. They prevent the furnace interior from cooling down, and they stop heat losses up the stack to the outside air. These devices should be installed only by experienced servicemen. Also, only those devices approved for the furnace and only those with demonstrated safe performance should be installed. An improperly installed stack damper can be very dangerous. So can one that is not designed for a particular furnace type.

Excessive draft, dirty heating surfaces, undersizing, defective combustion chambers, and overfiring with too much fuel are typical furnace problems. Such problems can result in high stack temperatures and decreased furnace efficiency. Stack temperatures should be less than 750° F. Improper air delivery, insufficient draft, oil pump malfunction, defective fuel nozzles, improper fuel-and-air ratios, and excessive air leaks will result in smoky combustion and clogged stack and furnace surfaces. Soot, ash, and other deposits are poor heat conductors. Such conditions can cause more heat to go up the stack and less into the building structure. A 10-percent increase in furnace efficiency can mean a 10-percent reduction in your space-heating fuel bill. So, change furnace filters on a regular schedule. And have the furnace professionally serviced once a year.

ENERGY CONSERVATION

Several low-cost, simple energy conservation steps have been detailed here in Decision 3 of The Solar Decision Book. These include: increasing air flow efficiency, raising thermal mass, trapping solar energy, choosing the least expensive fuel, and burning fuel efficiently. For buildings under construction, these steps can be easily accomplished. For existing structures, some of these steps may be impractical. The remodeling costs may outweight the energy savings.

There are, however, a number of practical measures for energy conservation in existing structures. Such measures are detailed in many free or low-cost publications available from the government or the local newstand. A complete discussion of these measures will not be given in The Solar Decision Book. Instead, the measures will be outlined as a basic checklist to use in your energy planning. A form is given in Appendix B for costing an energy conservation investment.

Lowering Heat Transmission

One way to conserve energy is to lower the heat transmission through walls, floors, and ceilings. As you learned in Decision 2 of The Solar Decision Book, this can be accomplished by increasing the R value of the exterior walls, floors, and ceilings. Some of the ways to do this are shown in Figure 3.17. These include:

- Installing storm windows and doors.
- Insulating the attic ceiling and/or floor depending on functional need.
- Insulating walls, if they were not properly insulated during construction.
- Insulating the edges of cement slab floors.
- Insulating floors over unheated crawl spaces, garages, and porches.
- Insulating basement walls exposed to the outside air.

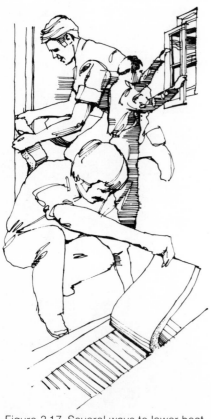

Figure 3.17 Several ways to lower heat transmission losses.

A note of caution: The quality of insulation is extremely important. Some insulations are a fire hazard or they emit noxious fumes or gases on burning. Other types of insulation will not withstand high humidity. They will slump and compact, ruining their insulation value. Other insulations will pick up moisture and may mildew and rot. Fiberglass and rock wool insulations are proven by years of service. Vermiculite, perlite, polystyrene, urethane, urea formaldehyde, and cellulose are more limited in their applications. Insulation must be used with caution.

Lowering Air Infiltration

Another way to conserve energy is to lower the air infiltration into a structure. A certain amount of air infiltration is needed to maintain comfort. But many existing structures have so much air infiltration that heat is wasted. Some of the ways to lower air infiltration are shown in Figure 3.18. These include:

- Installing storm windows and doors.
- Caulking and/or weatherstripping doors and windows.
- Caulking cracks and seams on foundation sills, door frames and windows, joints between garages, porches, steps, chimneys, and siding corners.
- Caulking and/or insulating around exhaust vents, plumbing pipes, heat pipes and ducts, and air conditioners.
- Repairing or replacing chimney dampers that are warped or damaged so that they do not properly close.

Again, a note of caution. There are many sealants and caulking compounds available in the marketplace. Some are designed for specific tasks only. Some are short lived and require regular upkeep. Others cannot be painted. Polysulfides and latex caulks generally perform well. Silicone, polyurethane, and Neoprene® sealants are the high performers. Dow Corning® silicone rubber sealers are excellent for residential and commercial applications.

The same type of caution goes for gasketing and weather-stripping. These materials should be carefully matched to the application. Also, storm doors and windows come in all ranges of quality. Avoid inexpensive designs if you expect good, longterm performance.

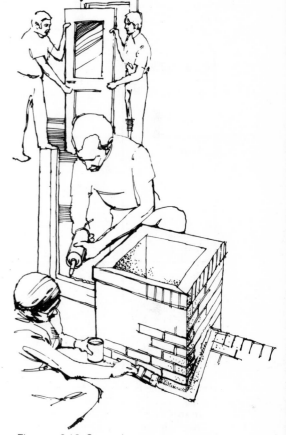

Figure 3.18 Several ways to save energy by lowering air infiltration.

Planning To Conserve

All the best intentions in the world won't conserve energy. Effective energy conservation calls for a well-thought-out plan of the steps you will take. These steps can be spread out over a period of time. And you need to take the necessary action to make your plan work. It helps to sit down, plan your energy conservation goals and objectives, determine the financial cost of meeting those objectives, and lay out an action plan to follow. At today's fuel prices, energy conservation pays for itself in reduced monthly fuel costs. You may want to use those savings to borrow money for meeting your goals and

"Neoprene" is a registered trademark of E. I. duPont de Nemours.
"Dow Corning" is a registered trademark of Dow Corning Corporation.

objectives sooner than you could otherwise. Figure 3.19 shows a sample form which you can use for planning energy conservation.

Planning to conserve energy also means planning to use energy wisely. Your plan should include the structural changes you will be making. And it should also include an energy conservation plan for each member of the household or each employee of the company. Heat, hot water, cooling, lighting, and appliances can all be used more efficiently without major lifestyle changes. Have each person draw up a schedule of the daily energy he or she uses. Then, have each person carefully review this schedule to see where savings can be made. You will most likely be amazed at how much energy is wasted. You will undoubtedly find many opportunities to conserve. And today, that can mean savings of many dollars.

OBJECTIVE	COST	ACTION PLAN	BY WHEN?
Circulate Air Efficiently			
Trap More Solar Energy			
Increase Thermal Mass			
Choose Least Expensive Fuel			
Burn Fuel Efficiently			
Reduce Heat Transmission			
Reduce Air Infiltration			
Reduce Personal Energy Use			

Figure 3.19 A sample form for planning energy conservation.

MAKING A DECISION

In this section of The Solar Decision Book, you have learned that energy conservation is needed to help solve this country's energy problem. This is a decision that each person, each business must make. You have learned that both the interior and the exterior of the building can be designed to conserve energy as well as to take maximum advantage of the sun's energy. You have learned that your choice of fuel is becoming critical in terms of cost. You have learned that furnace maintenance is essential for burning fuel efficiently. And, you have learned that every building owner can take a number of low-cost, simple steps to conserve building energy. You have also learned that just talking about energy conservation isn't enough. You need to start developing a well-thought-out plan.

DECISION 4

Consider An Alternate Energy Source

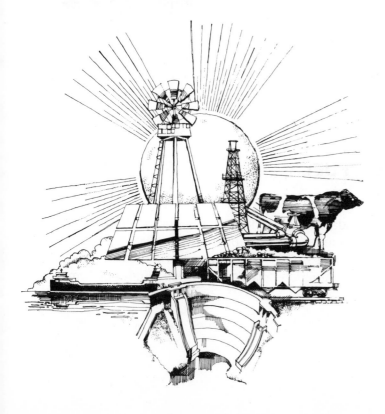

The Hon. Mike McCormack, U.S. Representative from the State of Washington, commented in his introduction to the 1976 Energy Fact Book that the American people are faced with a three-cornered problem: a massive need for energy, environmental protection with resource conservation, and the maintenance of a stable and responsive economic system.

He said: "The unfortunate fact is that this nation has no energy policy at all, and that we, the general public and the government, have acted as if all sources of energy were cheap, inexhaustible, and until recently, nonpolluting ... that is as if there were no dynamic relationship between energy, the environment, and the economy." And he called for: "A national energy policy (which) must itself be a set of dynamic guidelines and criteria which can change and evolve as new knowledge becomes available."

Energy conservation must be a part of any such policy. But, with a projected 12-quad shortage, alternate energy sources must also be considered. What are these sources? Which ones are available today? This section of The Solar Decision Book will answer those questions. It will also help you to make a decision regarding alternate sources of energy. You will learn that:

- Domestic sources of fossil fuels are numerous. But sufficient development and production of these energy sources will take decades, cost tens of billions of dollars, and result in very high energy costs.

- Some nonfossil fuels can be used to generate electricity. Two of these fuels are ready now, and others will become available in the future. However, electricity is not economical for heating.

- Several natural energy sources are available today and they can provide economical heating.

- Any alternate energy source must be considered in light of your energy needs, your environment, and your economic health.

OVERVIEW

The energy crises of the 1970s have underscored the need for new or alternate energy sources. This country has depended upon fossil fuels — oil, natural gas, and coal — for the bulk of its energy needs. Until recently, the supply of such fuels was unquestioned. And, in fact, the American people were given incentives to use more and more of these fuels. Such incentives included cost savings for increased use and for the use of certain fuels.

The sales program succeeded. The idea of cheap and inexhaustible supplies of fossil-fuel energy became part of the American dream. But, to use a popular expression: "we went to the well once too often." The fuel marketers created a bigger demand than the supply could support. While domestic sources of oil and natural gas are plentiful, advanced production technologies are needed before the flow of imported oil and gas can be turned off. While domestic sources of coal far outstrip those worldwide, the coal industry is saddled with labor problems as well as with environmental restrictions and outdated production methods.

The current situation with fossil fuels is frustrating at best. Energy from such fuels is no longer readily available nor is it considered cheap. There are a number of new technologies however, which are being developed to make greater supplies of fossil-fuel energy available.

Certain nonfossil fuels may help ease the energy shortage somewhat. These are fuels for generating electrical energy. They include nuclear, hydroelectric, and thermal energies. Here too, new technologies may increase the energy supply. If enough electricity could be generated with such fuels, the oil, gas, and coal now used in power generating plants could be switched to meeting other energy needs.

The new technologies for fossil as well as nonfossil fuels will solve only part of the energy problem. A good share of the solution will lie with a third category of energy sources. These are the so-called natural fuels. They include the sun, wind, waste recycling, and wood. If properly harnessed, these energy sources can meet a variety of energy needs.

THE FOSSIL FUELS

Petroleum

The American standard of living demands huge amounts of petroleum. Petroleum is needed not only for energy but also to manufacture plastics, food, textiles, shoes, medicines and many other essentials in your lifestyle. America survives on a petroleum economy.

The shortage of petroleum products has now become very apparent. The cost of imported oil was more than 32 billion dollars in 1977. And this will continue to grow each year. These huge imports of oil are rapidly draining the financial resources of our nation and transferring it to the oil-exporting countries. A serious balance-of-payments deficit is being built up, and the American dollar is growing weaker and weaker.

What, if anything, can be done about it? Are petroleum imports so necessary? Are there domestic resources that can be developed to reduce the need for imports? Are there other fossil fuels which can help?

The United States does have domestic fossil-fuel resources that can be developed, with time and money, to ease petroleum imports. Unfortunately, the time is decades and the money is tens of billions of dollars. Ultimately, the price of energy from these sources will be more than two or three times today's prices.

Figure 4.1 shows the sources and uses of crude oil. Imported oil currently amounts to more than three-billion barrels a year. Production from domestic wells amounts to slightly more than another three-billion barrels. The domestic reserves, or that oil "known to be recoverable", currently amount to 35.3-billion barrels. About a 5.8-year supply, if the imports are stopped.

These domestic reserves are recoverable by primary and secondary methods. With primary oil recovery methods, the oil flows to the wellhead under its own pressure or by pumping. With secondary oil recovery methods, the oil field is flooded with water or gas to push the oil to the wellhead.

The "ultimate reserves", that oil thought to be recoverable by present and new technologies, lie between 200- and 400-billion barrels. A 33- to 66-year supply.

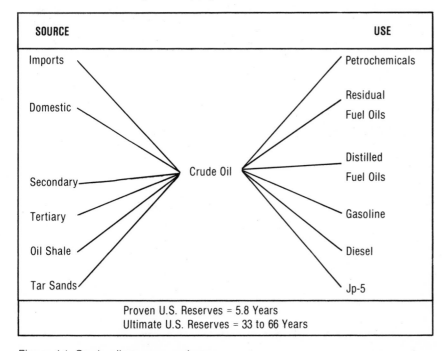

Figure 4.1 Crude oil sources and uses.

Tertiary oil recovery is one of the technologies needed to recover some of these ultimate reserves. This method involves techniques such as injecting a slug of solvent into the oil field from side injection wells. It recovers the oil remaining after primary and secondary methods have been used. The solvent carries the oil remaining in the field to a central recovery well for pumping. About 50- to 60-billion barrels of oil could be recovered by tertiary methods.

Oil from *oil shale* is another emerging recovery technology. This method has been in the news off and on. Such oil-bearing rock is found in huge quantities in two western states. The rock must be mined and then retorted (cooked) to drive the oil out. About 80-billion barrels of oil could be recovered from oil shale.

A third oil source is *tar sands*. Deposits of these tar sands are found in the U.S., Canada, and South America. Various processes can be used to strip the oil from the sand. Estimates of recoverable oil range up to 16-billion barrels for U.S. deposits and well beyond 300-billion barrels for Canadian deposits. Oil from Canadian deposits is not counted in the estimate of the U.S. ultimate reserves.

Oil from all of these sources is expensive. It starts at about 12 dollars a barrel and escalates to more than twice that figure. Domestic oil is currently priced at an average of approximately seven dollars a barrel. These prices may become acceptable by the time substantial production from the new sources becomes available. Such production won't occur until the late 1980s or early 1990s.

Natural Gas

Figure 4.2 shows the sources for and uses of natural gas. Gas is available from domestic wellheads. *Liquid Natural Gas* (LNG) is being imported from overseas in cryogenic (ultracold) tankers, and *Synthetic Natural Gas* (SNG) can be made by coal gasification. LNG does not solve the economic problem. It increases this country's dependence on imports. SNG plants are not being built and such plants would take many years to build. Also, there are environmental objections to opening the vast coal mines needed for feeding the SNG plants.

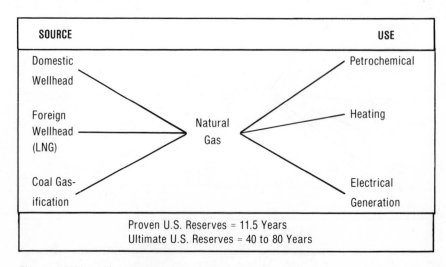

Figure 4.2 Natural gas sources and uses.

The U.S. currently has 250-trillion cubic feet of natural gas. It is being used up rapidly. Only about 11.5 years of proven reserves remain. The ultimate reserves are estimated high enough to sustain 40 to 80 years of continued use.

Coal

Coal is the most plentiful fossil fuel. Figure 4.3 shows how coal can be processed for various end uses. Traditionally, coal has been mined and burned. Burning coal produces heat and also produces steam for electrical generation. The newer technologies involve coal gasification and liquefaction.

Coal gasification produces SNG, or synthetic natural gas. It also can be used in production of coke for blast furnaces and in the production of petrochemicals. Coal gasification is a complex process, however. One of the methods being used to produce SNG is shown in Figure 4.4. Coal is reacted with steam and air to form carbon monoxide, hydrogen, methane, nitrogen, carbon dioxide and hydrogen sulphide (low-Btu gas). This is cleaned up to remove the

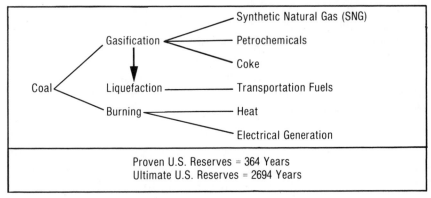

Figure 4.3 How coal can be processed for various end uses.

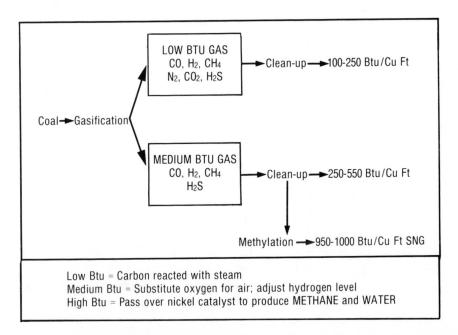

Figure 4.4 Coal gasification to produce SNG.

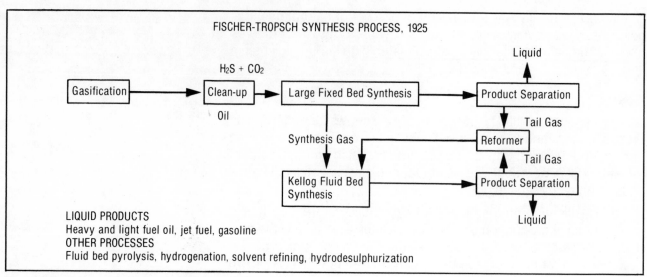

Figure 4.5 Coal liquefaction to produce syncrude.

hydrogen sulphide. The result is a low-Btu gas because of the presence of noncombustibles — nitrogen and carbon dioxide. If oxygen is used instead of air, no nitrogen or carbon dioxide is formed. A medium-Btu gas is manufactured. This medium-Btu gas can be passed over a nickel catalyst which produces methane and water, or SNG (high-Btu, pipeline-quality gas).

The process for coal liquefaction is also complex, as shown in Figure 4.5. The coal gas is converted to a variety of liquid petroleum end products. These products are the equal of those refined from natural crude oil. The process for making this synthetic crude, or *syncrude*, requires many more years and dollars for full development. A syncrude plant will cost from 250-million to one-billion dollars to build. And the syncrude is expected to cost about 28 to 29 dollars a barrel.

Regardless of the costs, syncrude is expected to become a major source of fuel by the year 2000. The availability of raw material (coal) is too great to be ignored. Also, the needed technology is available and understood.

The Outlook For Fossil Fuels

What can be concluded from these projections and estimates? First, if the price is right, energy can be obtained from new fossil-fuel sources. Second, the price appears extremely high by today's standards. Third, tens of billions of dollars must be invested and several decades of time are needed before enough production is available to eliminate a need for imported petroleum. Legal problems, and regulatory problems will impede the progress. In short, this new energy from fossil fuels will not contribute significantly toward reducing the energy shortage until near the end of the century.

NONFOSSIL FUELS

Nuclear Energy

Twenty-five years ago, nuclear generating plants for electricity were expected to change the face of the power industry. This new fuel source was clean, safe and economical. Nuclear fission would become a common energy source for new electrical power plants. More than 400 nuclear plants would be in operation by the year 2000.

At the beginning of 1975, only 53 nuclear generating plants were licensed to operate. An additional 180 plants had been announced or were under construction. However, some serious questions have been raised about nuclear power's environmental imposition. Also, the costs of nuclear fuel have skyrocketed. Consumer and environmental advocates are fighting new construction in the courts with stunning success. How fast the 180 plants already announced can be constructed and put into service is very hard to project. Long delays have become commonplace because of environmental restrictions, complex licensing procedures, and construction and supply constraints.

The installation of a nuclear power plant requires the integration of a large number of complex and highly varied activities. With no delays from legal actions or environmental problems, the average nuclear plant takes ten years to construct from the date of licensing. Any major benefits from nuclear power lie beyond the year 2000.

Hydroelectric Power

The United States generated about 491-billion kw of electricity at 1,176 hydroelectric plants in 1971. That is about 1.7 quad of energy. During the period from 1950 through 1971, capacity grew at six-percent compounded annually.

The Federal Power Commission *(FPC)* estimated in 1967 that only one-quarter of the hydroelectric potential of the United States was being utilized. Of that potential, about 25-percent lies in Alaska — too distant from the states which need the power. As such, the total potential for hydroelectric power in the "lower 48" part of the U.S. is about 5.5 quad of energy.

The Pacific Northwest contains 57-percent of this potential and any additional generating capacity will have to share the water with the need for irrigation, fisheries, and flood control. Experience of the last few years indicates that any additional dam sites will be heavily opposed by environmentalists. Also, many of the best sites are gone. A typical example is the Columbia River. The river descends 1290-feet in its 754-mile length, yet all but 80-feet of this drop is already being utilized.

Similar problems exist with the Tennessee Valley Authority *(TVA)*. The TVA controls 48 fully developed dam sites in the Tennessee river basin. It is the world's largest single producer of electrical power. And, Niagara Falls is also fully developed with the power being shared between Canada and the United States.

Like nuclear power, further growth of hydroelectric power faces legal problems in construction from environmentalists and irrigationists. Delays will often be long and costly.

Ocean Tidal and Ocean Thermal Energies

Harnessing the ocean's tide to produce electric power has been talked about since the early 1900s. And, the ability to run an engine by the difference in temperature between the upper warm water layer of the ocean and the cold lower layers was demonstrated by Georges Claude in 1929.

Electric power can be produced by using the rise and fall of ocean tides to turn electric generating turbines. Construction was started on the first *ocean tidal* power plant in 1961 in the Gulf of St. Malo, Brittany, France. Plant start-up took place in 1967 with a capacity of 240,000-kw. The USSR completed a small 1000-kw pilot unit on the White Sea in 1969. Plants have been proposed for the Bristol Channel in the United Kingdom, the San Jose Gulf in Argentina, and at various points on the west coast of Australia. In North America, the two most likely spots appear to be the Passamaquoddy Bay area of Maine and the Bay of Fundy off Nova Scotia, Canada. Around the world there are only about 100 possible ocean tidal sites.

No *ocean thermal* power plants are being utilized at this time, but government-funded studies are underway. With ocean thermal, the difference in water temperature is used to turn the electric generating turbines. Current predictions are that ocean-thermal plants will work best in tropical waters, will be very subject to storm damage, and will be uneconomical to build.

Electrical generation from ocean tidal sources appears to be a very feasible source of a limited amount of energy. But, the use of ocean-thermal energy is too new to evaluate at this time.

Geothermal Energy

Geothermal energy, heat stored in the earth, is of no practical value in most locations. However, highly localized thermally active areas do exist. These areas are widely distributed over the globe.

There are several types of geothermal resources of varying degrees of value. The most attractive type is the *vapor-dominated reservoir.* Only six sites of this type are known to exist in the world, and only one in the United States: The Geysers, California. These sites contain superheated steam which can be fed directly from the wellhead to steam turbines for generating electricity. A plant has been operating at The Geysers quite successfully for some time and a larger facility is planned. Costs are comparable to those for the other steam-generation plants.

A second type of geothermal resource in the *liquid-dominated reservoir.* Most geothermal sites throughout the world are of this type. The reservoir contains a mixture of hot water (or brine) and steam. This can be used in two ways: *direct process* and *binary process.* In the direct process, the steam is separated from the water or brine and is sent to the turbine to produce mechanical work. In the binary process the water or brine is circulated through a heat-exchanger. This heats a second working fluid, which is then sent through the turbine to produce the mechanical work required to manufacture electricity. When the binary process is used, the turbine is not subjected to the scaling, corrosion, and errosion effects from the hot brine. This increases efficiencies and prevents plugging.

The technology to use liquid-dominated reservoirs is expected to be available by the early 1980s. There are many uncertainties in the cost picture and many of them are reservoir dependent. There are potentially harmful environmental impacts which need to be studied. These include gaseous emissions, liquid waste disposal, subsidence, thermal pollution, and surface water contamination. However, the longterm outlook for this type of geothermal energy is favorable. Unfortunately, the major reservoirs exist only in the western states.

Other types of geothermal energy are also being investigated. They are very experimental at this time, and a prediction of their usefulness is impossible. Even so, geothermal energy should become an important, localized energy source in the 21st century.

The Outlook For Nonfossil Fuels

The four nonfossil fuels can be used for generating electrical power. The costs would be equal to or higher than present costs of electrical generation. The cost of using these sources will increase, along with the costs of fossil-fuel generating plants. They are small but important fuel sources which will assume more of the load as time goes on.

These nonfossil fuels do have one major drawback, however. As energy sources, they cannot heat your building structure economically. The cost of electricity will continue to be two to three times more expensive than the direct burning of heating fuel. These sources of fuel cannot be brought to your house in any form other than electricity.

NATURAL FUELS

There are a number of natural energy sources which can be used to heat your building structure directly. Some of these are ready for use today. Others will be ready in the near future. They all deserve close examination.

Solar Energy

To understand the future role of solar energy, you must realize the role solar energy already plays. The vacuum of space is at a temperature of absolute zero, or about minus 459° F. All of the surface energy that the earth receives is from the sun. Since most locations on earth range from 0° F to 100° F, then the current role of solar energy is to increase the temperature of the earth's surface by 459 to 559 degrees. The actual increase depends upon location, time of day, and time of year. The future role of solar energy is to create the narrow temperature band of 65° F to 85° F that humans call the comfort range. The energy to do this is there. The question that requires an answer is: how can the energy best be harnessed?

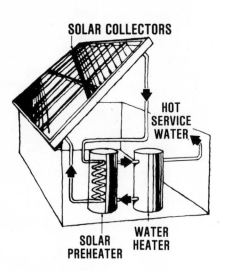

SOLAR COLLECTORS

HOT SERVICE WATER

SOLAR PREHEATER

WATER HEATER

Figure 4.6 A typical solar energy water-heating system.

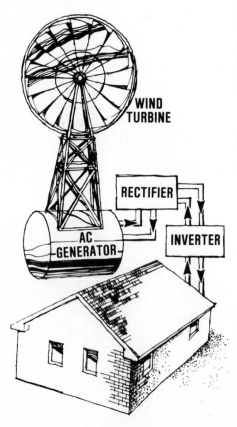

WIND TURBINE

RECTIFIER

AC GENERATOR

INVERTER

Figure 4.7 A typical home-use wind-power system.

For millions of years, the earth has been "banking" the sun's energy by creating the fossil fuels: oil, gas, and coal. In the past 200 years, man has drawn heavily on that bank account and the reserves are running low. Man must now learn to use the energy from today's sun. Not the energy produced by a sun which shone millions of years ago.

Solar energy just got off the ground in 1977 with an estimated 90,000 to 110,000 units installed. Most of these units were water heaters, such as that shown in Figure 4.6. Assuming that these units average about 10-million Btu each, they will supply 100-trillion Btu annually or one tenth of one quad of energy. The use of solar energy is expected to grow dramatically over the next few years and to supply from two to three quad of energy by the end of the century. This will all be heat energy. Additional electric power generation may come from experiments being conducted now, but this is by no means assured.

Solar energy is characterized by one outstanding characteristic. The fuel cost is constant. It is not subject to inflation. This does not hold true, however, for the equipment and labor needed to utilize solar energy. These costs will inflate along with other building materials and labor costs.

Wind Power

Wind power is feasible for generation of electrical energy at the point-of-use. A typical home-use wind-power system is shown in Figure 4.7. The major problem is reasonably priced storage and transmission of the power. Commercial wind-powered generating equipment is now available but only at very high cost. The next few years should see a number of economic and technical problems solved. Also, advanced commercial equipment such as vertical axis wind generators should become available.

In certain areas, wind power may be combined with hydroelectric power. Water pumped by the windmill into storage ponds could be used to generate electric power during peak hours. Many attractive sites exist in the northeast, southeast, and around the Great Lakes.

Like solar energy, the cost of wind power is constant and not subject to inflation. Nor does it have any environmental restrictions.

Biomass Energy

The word *biomass* is much misunderstood. It seems to conjure up visions of large amounts of animal manure standing around converting to odoriferous byproducts. Biomass is defined more broadly, however. It actually refers to a large and varied number of waste products: paper and paperboard, plastics, and other organic solid refuse. It also refers to agricultural residues from crops, waste sludges, and to animal wastes.

Paper, paperboard, plastics and other solid waste can be easily prepared for burning by a home trash compactor. Costs are minimal to install the compactor; and fuel is free. The time to sort out undesirable waste (metal, glass) before compacting is minutes. How many thousands of "free Btu" do you give to the trash man each week?

The large scale use of biomass however, particularly that of a more unstable or less desirable nature, can best be accomplished by local biomass-energy recovery systems. Figure 4.8 shows a typical system. Such systems can either burn the biomass to produce electricity or manufacture SNG to pipe back to your furnace.

Biomass represents a very large source of available energy which can be recycled through the economy again and again. This recycling can help solve two problems: the energy shortage, and the pollution of the environment. Some biomass plants exist now, but many more are needed. The use of biomass for energy should become more significant in future years.

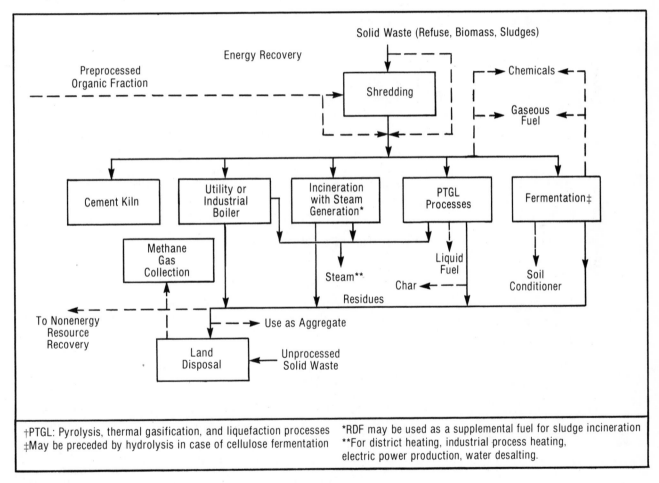

†PTGL: Pyrolysis, thermal gasification, and liquefaction processes
‡May be preceded by hydrolysis in case of cellulose fermentation
*RDF may be used as a supplemental fuel for sludge incineration
**For district heating, industrial process heating, electric power production, water desalting.

Figure 4.8 A typical biomass-energy recovery system.

Wood

Wood is generally available, although its cost depends on location. Wood burns readily, but its efficiency depends on the equipment in which it is burned. Wood is also inconvenient, nonautomatic, and not geared to the demands of a fast-paced society.

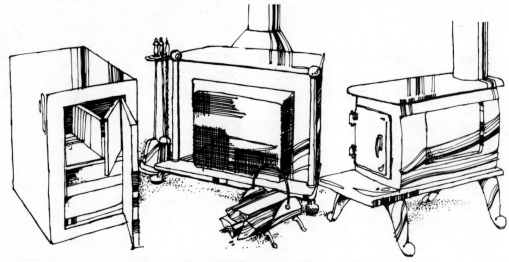

Figure 4.9 Various types of wood-burning equipment are now available.

All of this is changing rapidly, except perhaps for the price in urban and city areas. Figure 4.9 shows various types of wood-burning equipment now available. Combination furnaces which burn both oil and wood have been developed making wood-burning automatic and efficient. More efficient wood-burning stoves have found their way back onto the market. Commercial boilers are being installed to burn wood chips. By-products, dead woods, and scrap trees are being processed to fuel them. This trend will continue and wood will play an important role in our fuel economy in the next 25 years.

The Outlook For Natural Fuels

The four natural fuels are all available to you. All, except for wind, have immediate application. All, except for wood, cost little or nothing. But you must make an initial investment to use them effectively. All are relatively inflation proof, except for the equipment needed to utilize them. And the use of these natural energy sources are generally nonpolluting and will not require costly imports.

MAKING A DECISION

In this section of The Solar Decision Book, you have learned about the various traditional fuels and the alternate fuels. You have learned that there are three categories of energy sources: fossil fuels, nonfossil fuels, and natural fuels. Some of these sources will be expensive and will take time to develop. Some are available now, with a reasonable cost and without environmental problems.

The decision to be made is simple. Just decide to consider an alternate fuel in terms of your energy needs and costs. And consider the impact the energy shortage has already had and will continue to have on your lifestyle. New sources of fossil fuels may not be ready soon enough to ease that shortage. Nonfossil fuels may help only by increasing the supply of electricity. And, for many, tomorrow's energy may very well come from one of the natural fuels.

DECISION 5

The Sun: Today's Best Source Of Alternate Energy

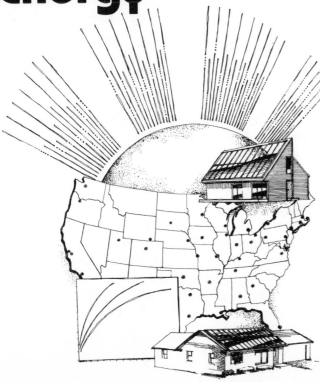

Much has been written about solar energy's rapid development to a commercialized stage. Newspapers report on Sun Days and Solar Seminars and everything in between. Popular magazines as well as trade journals relate new twists in solar technology, the building owner's expectations, the architect's dreams, the contractor's solutions to a variety of problems. And books, by the expert and the not-so-expert, bare truths and untruths alike about tapping the sun's energy for water heating, space heating, and cooling.

A curiosity only a few years ago, the solar energy system is fast-becoming commonplace. One reason is that many have already decided that the sun is today's best source of alternate energy. This section of The Solar Decision Book will help you to arrive at the same decision. You will learn that:

- The sun can be utilized as an alternate energy source without the drawbacks of other energy sources.

- The equipment as well as the necessary system design and installation technology is available now.

- Excellent performance can be predicted for solar energy systems in most any area of the country.

- From a dollars-and-sense viewpoint, the time to make the solar decision is now.

SOLAR ENERGY VS. THE OTHERS

There is increasing acceptance of the solar alternative. This is hardly surprising. The sun does offer today's best source of alternate energy. Such a conclusion becomes obvious when solar energy is considered in light of the other potential energy sources.

Consider, for instance, that solar energy is readily available throughout the country ... that the technology for putting the sun to work is fully developed ... that the sun's energy is free and not subject to inflation ... and that solar energy is clean and nonpolluting.

This is not the case with the fossil fuels. Domestic petroleum and gas supplies are dwindling, and a good share of tomorrow's supplies will need to be imported. Sufficient supplies can be generated by new processes, but such technology will not be ready for many years. Even so, all future supplies of fossil fuels will be priced much higher than today's supplies. Coal offers some hope because plentiful supplies can be made available. Here again, though, some much-needed technology must be developed. This includes the necessary pollution controls to eliminate the environmental problems presented by some types of coal.

A number of drawbacks are also seen with the nonfossil fuels such as nuclear, hydroelectric, and thermal energies. The construction costs for nuclear power installations have skyrocketed in recent years. Also, numerous legal questions have been raised on environmental and safety grounds. Proposed hydroelectric installations are faced with similar legal challenges — principally on environmental grounds. Ocean tidal, ocean thermal, and geothermal energies are excellent in concept, but short on technology as well as general availabilty.

Even such natural fuels as wind, biomass, and wood have their disadvantages when compared to solar energy. Wind power is clean, but much more development work is needed before this energy can be moved into a commercialized state. Biomass energy is readily available, but there are problems of inconvenience, pollution, and inadequate processing technology. Wood energy is also readily available. So is the necessary wood-burning equipment. But, again, there are problems of inconvenience and pollution. Also, the costs of wood are sure to inflate as the demand rises.

THE SOLAR TECHNOLOGY IS READY NOW

Two basic types of solar energy systems are in use ... the passive solar system and the active solar system. Passive solar systems are relatively inexpensive, have no maintenance requirements, and last indefinitely because there are no moving parts to wear out. Such systems, however, are relatively inefficient compared to active systems. They do not provide for long-term heat storage nor for automatic control of the building heat.

Active solar systems are more expensive because they require the installation of special equipment. The cost can range from a few hundred dollars to many thousands, depending on the size of the system. Such systems have some maintenance requirements and the system life depends on the quality of design, equipment, and installation. Active solar systems do provide for heat storage and they do have automatic controls.

Passive Solar Systems

In a passive solar system, the structure is designed to capture heat during daytime hours and gradually release that heat during nighttime hours. It has no means to transfer the heat energy from one room to another except by natural heat flow phenomena: convection, radiation, and conduction.

The Solar Decision Book deals primarily with active solar systems. But passive solar systems for heat gain and controlled heat loss are extremely important. They can provide the building structure with large amounts of "free" energy.

The sun's energy can be collected simply by adequate planning of the structure as shown in Figure 5.1 The structure can be built in many shapes — square, rectangular, L-shaped, T-shaped, or a variation of these. Rectangular structures present the largest roof and wall areas to the sun. The structure can be oriented in any direction. But, for maximum energy collection, the structure should be oriented along the east-west axis and faced between south to 30 degrees east of south. The structure can be built of many materials. But, north, west, and east walls should have minimal window area and maximum resistance to heat flow. The south wall should have maximum window area. The building exterior can have many treatments. And, in passive solar energy collection, the proper landscaping can shield the structure from summer heat and winter cold. Also, movable awnings can be placed on windows to permit entry of the winter sun but block entry of the summer sun.

Once the building is designed as a solar collector, it should be engineered to hold the heat. It can be built of materials having a high thermal mass. Stone, brick, concrete walls and ceilings or floors soak up heat and release it when the outside temperature drops. Window shutters and extra insulation slow down the heat transmission from the building.

Active Solar Systems

An *active solar system* consists of equipment to trap the sun's heat and to utilize that heat for hot water or space heating. Such systems normally have automatic controls. They may or may not have a conventional hot-water or heating system that serves as a backup energy source. The technology is ready for active solar systems used for hot-water, space heating, and cooling. A system can be designed for one, two, or all three of these energy needs.

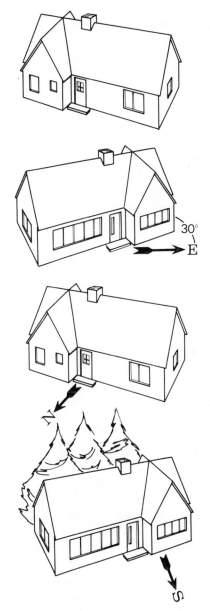

Figure 5.1 The structure as a passive solar collector.

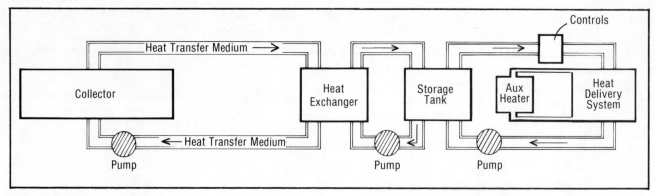

Figure 5.2 The major components of a simple solar energy system for hot water and space heating.

Figure 5.2 shows a block diagram of a simple solar energy system for hot-water and space heating. The diagram is used only to show the major components in an active solar system. The *collector* is the means by which the system traps the sun's energy. It is normally mounted on the building roof or close to the building. In its simplest form, the solar collector is nothing more than a flat box with a piece of clear plastic or glass over its surface. The sun's energy flows through the cover and is trapped inside.

The collector usually has tubes inside which contain a *heat-transfer medium*. This medium may be water or some other liquid. The heat-transfer medium flows through the collector, is heated by the sun's energy, and is circulated through the system by pumps.

The heated liquid is pumped to a heat storage tank, usually a tank of water. When the heat is needed, pumps circulate the hot liquid to a *heat exchanger*. A typical heat exchanger looks like your automobile radiator. Warm water is pumped through the coils and air from the building is blown across the fins on the coils and warmed for heating.

Active solar systems differ from passive solar systems in that they have a forced heat-delivery system. Heat will be mechanically delivered on demand to its area of use. Depending on the system, it may transfer the heat from liquid to air, air to air, or liquid to liquid. Such systems will also have controls for regulating the hot-water or building temperature. They work much the same as the thermostat controls on conventional heating systems. Certain controls are used to regulate the flow of heat-transfer media from the collector to the storage area. Other controls regulate the flow of energy from the storage area to the delivery system.

Because the sun does not shine 100-percent of the time, most solar systems require an auxiliary heater. This could be a gas- or oil-fired heater for hot water. Or, for space heating, it could be a conventional furnace or boiler.

Evolution of Active Solar Systems for Water Heating

Figure 5.3 shows the simplest form of solar water heating. It is called a *drum or pillow rooftop heater.* A vessel is placed in the sun at a point higher than its intended use. The vessel is filled with cold water in the

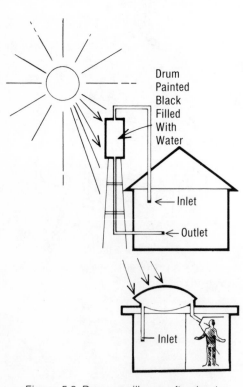

Figure 5.3 Drum or pillow rooftop heater.

morning. By the afternoon, the water has trapped enough heat to be used as domestic warm water. It works. It's simple. And it's cheap. But, such solar collection would be neither useful nor reliable in this country for most of the year.

A solar collector, designed to catch and hold the sun's energy, has been added in Figure 5.4. The system is filled with water and purged of air. As the water in the collector is heated by the sun, it becomes lighter and flows into the drum. This natural convection loop is known as a *thermosyphon loop.* The difference in density between hot and cold water causes the water to flow around the loop. An expansion tank is added to the system because water expands as it heats up. A pressure and temperature relief valve acts as a safety device if the water overheats. When hot water is desired, the hot-water valve is opened and water drawn. Water-main pressure (or a pump) provides the driving force to deliver the hot water.

Obviously, the systems in Figures 5.3 and 5.4 have some drawbacks:

- The water tank must be higher than the collector to allow thermosyphoning.

- Little or no freeze protection is possible or provided.

- No control over temperature is available.

- The heat storage is outdoors and energy is lost as the outside temperature drops.

Figure 5.5 shows the storage tank placed inside the building structure. This is called a pumped loop system. The tank is now below the collector and the water will not thermosyphon. A pump must be added to circulate the water through the system. A set of controls is also needed to turn the pump on only when the collector is hotter than the tank. A check valve is added so that hot water in the storage tank will not thermosyphon into a cold collector. If the outside temperature never went below freezing, and if the water were pure (noncorroding), this would be an effective solar system. However, this is not the case.

A water draindown system is shown in Figure 5.6. Some major system changes have been made.

- A second tank has been installed in the center of the storage tank. The water in the inside tank is the heat-transfer fluid. It is separated from the building's service water. The two do not mix.

- The inside tank is filled only part way with the heat transfer fluid. The remainder serves as an expansion tank.

- The heat-transfer fluid is treated chemically to prevent system corrosion.

Operation of the draindown system is simple. When the controls indicate that the collector fluid is hotter than the service water, the pump turns on. It moves the heat-transfer fluid to the collectors where it is heated and then returned to the tank. Heat is transferred through the tank walls to the service water. When the pump is turned

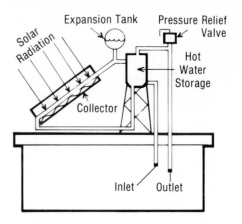

Figure 5.4 Thermosyphon-loop solar collection system.

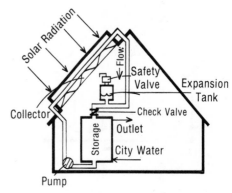

Figure 5.5 A pumped-loop system.

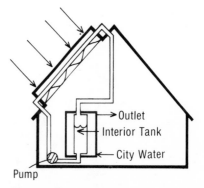

Figure 5.6 An open pumped-loop water draindown system.

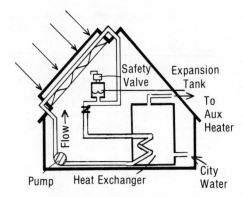

Figure 5.7 A heat-exchanged closed-loop system with corrosion and freeze protection.

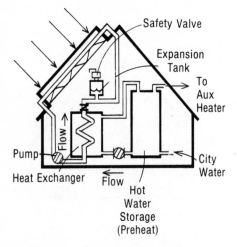

Figure 5.8 A closed-loop system with an external heat exchanger and secondary pumping loop.

off the heat-transfer fluid drains back into the tank by gravity. This provides freeze protection.

If drainback always takes place and the anticorrosion chemicals in the fluid are renewed annually, the draindown system is workable. Thousands of these systems are installed in the southern part of the United States. However, draindown systems are not fail-safe. Installation is critical, the chemical *inhibitors* must be continually renewed to prevent corrosion, and the pumping energy required to overcome gravity is substantial.

Figure 5.7 shows a *heat-exchanged, closed-loop system*. The interior tank has been replaced by a heat-exchanger coil. The expansion tank is now separate and the collector loop is closed to the atmosphere. In this system, inhibited water is replaced with nonfreezing, nonboiling heat-transfer fluid. When the collector fluid becomes hotter than the tank, the pump turns on and drives the heat-transfer fluid around the loop. As the heated fluid passes through the heat exchanger, heat is transferred to the service water. Pump power is only large enough to overcome friction losses. When noncorroding heat-transfer fluids are used, maintenance is minimal.

An external heat exchanger with a secondary pumping loop is shown in Figure 5.8. This has a number of advantages in larger systems. Energy is pumped to the heat exchanger, transferred to the secondary fluid, and pumped into the hot-water tank. An auxiliary heater has also been added, but is kept separate from the solar tank. Solar heat and auxiliary heat should not be combined. Combined systems cut down badly on the amount of solar energy collected.

The heat exchanged closed-loop system completes the evolution of the active solar system. This type of system is a key to successful solar water heating. Each of its components are discussed in detail in later sections of The Solar Decision Book.

In Figure 5.9, the heat-exchanged closed-loop solar system is shown as a schematic. Schematics simplify the drawings by using common symbols or diagrams for the system components. Schematics will be used throughout The Solar Decision Book.

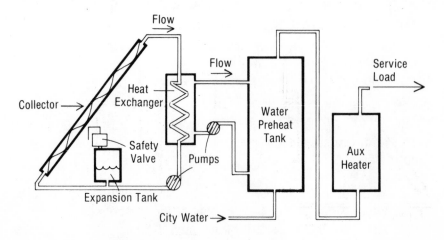

Figure 5.9 A schematic of a heat-exchanged, closed-loop solar system for water heating.

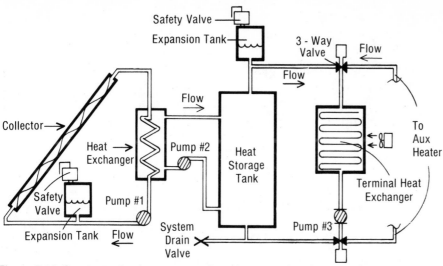

Figure 5.10 One type of solar energy system for space heating.

Solar System for Space Heating

The closed-loop system with an external heat exchanger provides the starting point for a solar space-heating system. The following changes, as shown in Figure 5.10, need to be made:

- The collectors and the hot-water preheat tank need to be resized to carry the heating load. The preheat tank in the hot-water system becomes the storage tank in the space heating system.
- The connection to the water main is eliminated. A closed-loop going to a space-heating delivery system is added. The heat-delivery system is generally a fan coil or a series of fan coils in each room of the structure. A pump, expansion tank with safety valves, and piping is added to circulate the water.
- To provide auxiliary backup heat, a hot-water boiler is also connected to the heat-delivery system. Suitable valving is added to prevent water in the auxiliary boiler from mixing with solar-heated water.

A water heating loop can also be added to the system. Such a system for both hot-water and space-heating uses is shown in Figure 5.11.

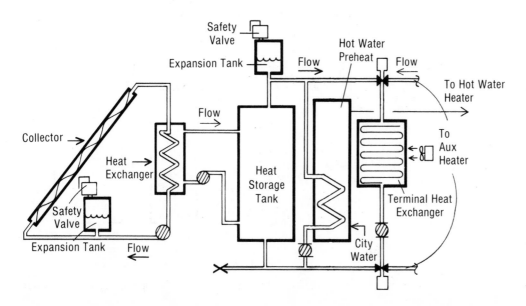

Figure 5.11 One type of solar energy system for water heating and space heating.

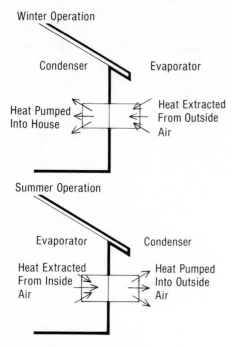

Figure 5.12 Operation of an air-to-air heat pump.

Solar System for Cooling

There are currently two ways to use the sun's energy to provide building space cooling. A heat pump may be used as an auxiliary heater. It can increase the energy collected during the winter heating season and be operated for cooling during the summer months. Absorption chillers are the second choice. They are run directly from the solar heat-storage tank.

HEAT PUMPS. What is a *heat pump*? A heat pump is an air-conditioner mounted backwards. An air-to-air heat pump is shown in Figure 5.12. The heat exhaust (condenser) is mounted on the inside of the building structure. The evaporator is mounted on the outside of the house. It extracts heat from the outside air. In the summer, the condenser and the evaporator positions are reversed. Heat is then extracted from the house and pumped outdoors. The heat pump accomplishes this reversible function by changing the flow of refrigerant within its system. The building owner must select the correct operating mode for the season.

Where winter temperatures are mild, the air-to-air heat pump described provides both heating and cooling. Efficiencies are poor below about 20° F. These heat pumps provide about 2 to 2.5 units of energy for each unit of energy used to run them. They cut electrical bills by at least half when compared to electrical-resistance heating.

Liquid-to-air heat pumps are also available. They work as shown in Figure 5.13. Heat is either extracted from or added to a source of water. Solar storage tanks make an excellent source from which to extract heat, while cooling towers are excellent for building heat removal. Liquid-to-air heat pumps are more efficient. They operate at 300- to 350-percent efficiency and reduce the electrical needs by 67- to 72-percent.

ABSORPTION CHILLERS. These are a different type of air conditioner. They can be run directly from solar storage to obtain cooling. They use a dual refrigerant, but cannot be used for auxiliary heating during the winter months.

The use of absorption chillers is currently limited to very hot climates. Hot water at about 185° F is needed to operate these chillers efficiently. Most solar storage units are designed to operate at temperatures between 100° and 200° F. So, only the top 15 degrees can be effectively used for absorption chilling.

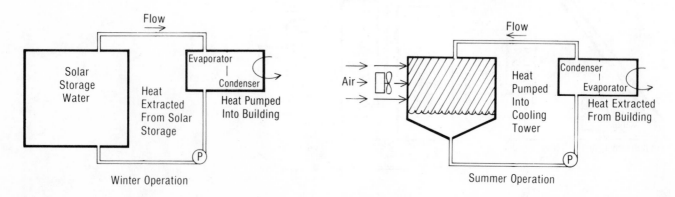

Figure 5.13 The operation of a liquid-to-air heat pump.

SOLAR ENERGY SYSTEMS PERFORM

A solar energy system can provide all of the building's energy needs for hot water and for space heating. However, in most locations, the cost would be extremely high. The savings would be questionable. Rather, for most locations the solar energy system is usually sized to provide about 45- to 65-percent of the building's energy needs for heat and hot water. This requires the use of a conventional heating system as a backup energy source for extended sunless periods. Such systems can easily generate energy cost savings, and pay back the initial investment in a reasonable amount of time. If the structure is well-insulated and designed for maximum passive solar collection, the solar energy system will generate even higher savings and the need for a backup system will be minimized.

System Performance: "Equivalent Energy Value"

The performance of a typical solar energy system can be determined through mathematical calculations. These calculations take into consideration weather data, the system design, the heat required, the collector site and efficiency, the hot water requirements, and the geographic location of the system. Each of these considerations is detailed in later sections of The Solar Decision Book. Recommendations for the best possible combination of design criteria are given to maximize system performance.

Suppose however, that a liquid heat-transfer system is used. It has a high efficiency collector that faces due south and is angled toward the sun. The building heat loss is 300 Btu per hour per degree Fahrenheit. And the hot water requirements are 80 gallons a day at 120° F.

With the proper calculations you can find out how much heat energy is needed for your location. And how much of that energy can be obtained with a medium-sized array of solar collectors. Since the weather is different in different parts of the country, the energy required will be location dependent. To provide the same percentages of that energy will require different-sized collector arrays. Northern areas will require larger systems than those needed for the southern areas.

Doing the calculations by hand is possible, but a tedious and time-consuming job. A special computer program is available to accomplish these calculations. The program contains the weather and sun data needed for different locations. Figure 5.14 shows a set of typical

CODE	VARIABLE DESCRIPTION	VALUE UNITS
1	Air System = 1, Liquid System = 2	2.00
2	Collector Area	200.00 ft²
3	$F_R.\tau\alpha$ Product (Normal Incidence)	0.75
4	$F_R.U_L$ Product	0.67 Btu/hr/°F/ft²
5	Number of Transparent Covers	2.00
6	Collector Slope	57.00 degrees
7	Azimuth Angle (e.g. South = 0, West = 90)	0.00 degrees
8	Storage Capacity	16.70 Btu/°F/ft²

CODE	VARIABLE DESCRIPTION	VALUE UNITS
9	Effective Building UA	300.00 Btu/hr/°F
10	Constant Daily Bldg Heat Generation	0.00 Btu/day
11	$\epsilon \cdot C_{min}$/Bldg UA	2.00
12	Hot Water Usage	80.00 gal/day
13	Water Set Temperature	120.00 °F
14	Water Main Temperature	55.00 °F
15	City Call Number	34.00
16	Thermal Print Out By Month = 1, By Year = 2	1.00

Figure 5.14 Typical computer input data for solar system calculations.

MONTH	PERCENT SOLAR	INCIDENT SOLAR (MM BTU)	HEATING LOAD (MM BTU)	WATER LOAD (MM BTU)	DEGREE DAYS
January	30.5	6.00	7.83	1.35	1088.
February	35.9	6.19	7.00	1.22	972.
March	50.4	8.05	6.09	1.35	846.
April	63.5	7.55	3.69	1.30	513.
May	96.4	8.57	1.50	1.35	208.
June	100.0	8.13	0.26	1.30	36.
July	100.0	8.62	0.0	1.35	0.
August	100.0	8.50	0.06	1.35	9.
September	100.0	8.26	0.43	1.30	60.
October	82.6	7.77	2.28	1.35	316.
November	43.6	5.58	4.34	1.30	603.
December	29.0	5.41	7.08	1.35	983.
YEAR	52.1	88.64	40.56	15.86	5634.

Figure 5.15 Typical computer output data for solar system calculations.

input data to the computer. And Figure 5.15 shows a set of typical output data from the computer.

These same calculations were made for 34 cities across the country. For each city, the collector size was varied to provide about 50- to 60-percent of the heating energy requirements. As shown in Figure 5.16, the solar energy systems collected an average of about 200,000 Btu per square foot of collector. Millions of Btu were collected even in some of the coldest areas of the country. The collector size, of course, was much larger than that for warmer areas.

That average of 200,000 Btu per square foot per year amounts to four million Btu per square foot over a 20-year period.

Assume that fossil fuel costs will be about $7.10 per million Btu in 1980 and that those costs will inflate at a rate of 11-percent a year from 1980 to 1999. If that happens, the average cost of fossil fuels during that period will be a huge $22.71 per million Btu.

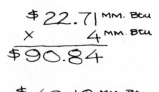

As such, the average "equivalent energy value" of a square foot of solar collector under the conditions discussed will be $90.84.

Measured against electricity, the value is even higher. The cost for electricity will be about $13.18 per million Btu in 1980. With the same 11-percent inflation, the electricity costs will average about $42.18 per million Btu. And the average "equivalent energy value" of a square foot of collector will be $168.72.

This equivalent energy value is an important measure of solar system performance. Depending on the type of solar system, the installed costs for solar energy are currently running about $25 to $40 a square foot of collector. This comparison indicates that solar energy competes extremely well in the energy marketplace.

CITY	STATE	SQ. FT. OF COLLECTOR	% SOLAR HEAT	MM BTU COLLECTED	BTU COLLECTED/ SQ. FT.
Boston	MA	200	52	29.4	147,000
New York	NY	200	52	26.3	131,500
Baltimore	MD	150	54	27.1	180,667
Richmond	VA	125	55	23.7	189,600
Charleston	SC	75	62	18.0	240,000
Jacksonville	FL	50	55	13.2	264,000
Miami	FL	50	85	13.7	274,000
Rochester	NY	200	50	32.1	160,500
Pittsburgh	PA	200	59	31.5	157,500
Charlotte	NC	75	50	18.9	252,000
Atlanta	GA	75	49	18.2	242,133
Pensacola	FL	50	52	13.5	269,800
Sault Ste. Marie	MI	225	51	42.1	187,111
Detroit	MI	225	53	32.6	144,888
Louisville	KY	150	52	25.0	166,533
Chattanooga	TN	100	51	20.5	204,900
Memphis	TN	100	54	20.4	203,700
New Orleans	LA	75	61	14.9	198,800
St. Paul	MN	225	50	37.4	166,222
Des Moines	IA	200	54	34.8	174,200
Kansas City	MO	150	54	28.8	192,266
Tulsa	OK	100	52	21.3	213,000
Dallas	TX	75	57	17.7	236,133
Great Falls	MT	175	55	40.1	229,000
Salt Lake City	UT	150	54	32.2	214,533
Phoenix	AZ	50	67	17.3	346,000
Seattle	WA	225	57	27.4	121,690
San Francisco	CA	75	55	20.7	276,266
Los Angeles	CA	50	56	15.6	312,800
Moncton	NB	300	52	41.9	139,566
Montreal	ONT.	300	51	38.8	129,166
Kapuskasing	ONT.	400	55	56.3	140,850
Winnipeg	MANT.	250	53	50.2	200,680
Vancouver	BC	300	53	30.1	100,300
AVG					200,000

Figure 5.16 Energy collected for various sizes of solar collectors in different locations.

Estimating Thermal Performance

In Figure 5.17, the thermal performance for various collector sizes in various cities across the country was studied by computer. The same 34 cities were used in the analysis, with the same size collectors to give 50- to 60-percent of the annual heat requirements. These calculations show how much heat can be collected using the assumed size of collectors. They also show how many square feet of collector is needed to produce an estimated 50-percent of the required winter heat. The size of the storage system was also calculated.

CITY	STATE	COLLECTOR SIZE SQ. FT.	WINTER HEAT LOAD DAILY BTU	WINTER HEAT COLLECTION BTU/FT.²/DAY	ANNUAL HEAT LOAD DAILY BTU	ANNUAL HEAT COLLECTION DAILY BTU/FT.²	SYSTEM SIZE REQUIRED TO PROVIDE 50% WINTER HEAT	
							COLLECTOR FT²	STORAGE, GAL.
Boston	MA	200	277,000	497.5	154,600	404	278	556
New York	NY	200	253,000	435.8	138,360	359	290	580
Baltimore	MD	150	246,000	626.1	133,400	481	196	392
Richmond	VA	125	217,000	664.0	117,800	520	163	326
Charleston	SC	75	139,000	775.6	80,220	658	90	180
Jacksonville	FL	50	108,000	840.0	66,270	726	64	128
Miami	FL	50	53,000	860.0	44,330	752	31	62
Rochester	NY	200	316,000	517.9	176,000	439	305	610
Pittsburgh	PA	200	268,000	550.0	147,600	432	236	472
Charlotte	NC	100	188,000	766.7	103,600	607	123	246
Atlanta	GA	100	183,000	713.3	101,150	583	129	258
Pensacola	FL	50	120,000	791.7	71,230	739	76	152
Sault Ste. Marie	MI	225	380,000	641.9	225,300	513	296	592
Detroit	MI	225	307,000	473.7	170,000	397	325	650
Louisville	KY	150	243,000	557.8	131,160	456	219	438
Chattanooga	TN	100	197,000	652.5	109,260	562	151	302
Memphis	TN	100	191,000	656.7	103,750	558	146	292
New Orleans	LA	75	108,000	572.2	67,420	545	94	188
Minneapolis	MN	225	378,000	586.7	204,380	456	322	644
Des Moines	IA	225	330,000	604.4	175,800	451	273	556
Kansas City	MO	150	272,000	669.4	145,260	527	203	406
Tulsa	OK	100	212,000	734.2	112,700	584	144	288
Dallas	TX	75	153,000	767.8	85,300	647	100	200
Great Falls	MT	175	331,000	757.1	199,700	628	219	438
Salt Lake City	UT	150	281,000	655.6	164,820	588	212	424
Phoenix	AZ	50	118,000	1,135.0	70,710	950	52	104
Seattle	WA	225	198,000	297.9	130,710	333	332	644
San Francisco	CA	75	134,000	757.6	104,200	757	88	176
Los Angeles	CA	50	109,000	948.0	76,000	857	58	116
Moncton	NB	300	368,000	433.0	218,930	382	425	850
Montreal	QU	300	378,000	455.5	208,600	354	415	830
Ottawa	OT	250	393,000	632.0	219,100	468	312	624
Kapuskasing	OT	400	482,500	538.0	281,700	386	448	896
Winnipeg	MA	250	464,200	766.7	257,450	550	303	606
Vancouver	BC	300	230,000	207.5	155,600	275	554	1,108

Figure 5.17 Thermal performance for various solar systems in 34 cities. Collector and storage tank sizes are calculated for system to provide 50-percent of the winter heat load.

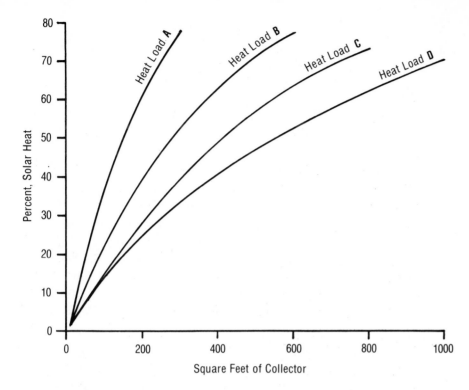

Figure 5.18 A typical solar system thermal performance chart for sizing the system to meet energy and budget requirements.

More on system sizing is given in a later section of The Solar Decision Book, as well as in Appendix C.

Thermal Performance Charts

Attempting to obtain 100-percent of the building's required heat with an active solar system is not economical. Depending on location, weather, and the cost of alternate fuels, a system which provides 45- to 65-percent of the building's heat is most economical.

In sizing the system to meet your budget and energy needs, you can use a chart such as the one shown in Figure 5.18. Complete instructions for building such a chart for your location are included in Appendix C. With such a chart you can basically select the size of collector to fit your budget, or select the amount of energy you would like the solar system to provide. In each case, you will know at a glance how much energy can be generated by a certain size of collector for the area you live in and for your building's heat load requirements.

THE SOLAR DECISION

The solar energy industry is young, but it is growing up at an almost phenomenal pace. Much of the early growth can be classified as experimental. Many mistakes were made. Yet, the successes proved solar energy to be a very attractive alternative to other potential energy sources. The rough edges of the early years are being smoothed. And, new developments as well as refinements in existing technology, have led to substantial growth in the number of solar systems being installed. This growth can only accelerate to an even faster pace. The steadily rising costs of fossil fuels, plus the dim outlook for overnight development of some new energy source, have made solar energy very competitive in the energy marketplace.

Growth of Solar

Excluding solar-heated swimming pools, approximately 100,000 solar systems for hot water and more than 3,000 solar systems for space heating were installed in 1977 alone. This almost quadrupled the number of installations made in the years of 1975 and 1976 combined.

Some of the most important developments also took place in 1977. A matched system for water heating, preassembled and ready for installation, was developed and offered by several manufacturers. Such systems range in price from less than one thousand dollars to about 3,500 dollars. Another development was the entry of major U.S. corporations into both the solar components business and the packaged system business. And a third key development was the setting of standards for collector efficiency.

The first development makes the installer's job exceedingly simple. It also helps those contractors faced with potential projects by matching up the correct components for a workable system. The second development assures that quality systems backed by firms with good financial resources will definitely be available for many years to come. And the third development allows the installer to compare the relative performance of various collectors and to make an intelligent collector choice.

Other key trends that developed included:

- The flat-plate collector will continue as the most popular collector through the 1980s. Some minor performance improvements will be made. However, no major technical breakthroughs or cost reductions are anticipated. Cost savings from volume production will most likely be swallowed up by inflation.

- Heat storage methods are fairly well established. Rock pebble beds are used for air-collector systems, and water tanks are used for liquid-collector systems. Rock pebble beds have a size disadvantage. They take up 2½ to 3 times the volume of water storage tanks.

- Either a silicone or a hydrocarbon oil appears to have the inside track for a good heat-transfer medium. Water and glycol-water systems have serious drawbacks with regards to system corrosion, scale, freezing, boiling, and breakdown. While air beats those problems, it requires bulky storage, large heat exchangers, and much auxiliary energy. In addition, air is much slower for heating water.

The Future

Advanced collector technologies are beginning to appear. But these will not be commercially available for some time, and may not be competitive either in performance or cost with the flat-plate collector. Future developments will continue to increase the collector efficiency somewhat.

Considerable work is also being done on shrinking the storage system for solar energy. Chemical salt systems are being investigated, but the availability appears some years away.

Good progress is being made in defining an adequate heat-transfer medium. More than 1,000 systems with silicone fluid were installed in 1977. Also, many manufacturers are now recognizing the value of noncorrosive, stable, nonfreezing, and nonboiling fluids. They help protect the equipment investment, lower system maintenance costs, and reduce the payback period for the system. Costs saved on maintenance are just as important as those saved on fuel.

Why Buy Solar Now?

The future will not bring radically different, lower cost solar systems to the American public. Tomorrow will only bring higher costs for conventional fuels. And, even if enough of those fuels are available, their cost may create a financial burden in many budgets.

A solar system wisely chosen today will start generating savings on your fuel bill immediately. The system will become an excellent investment that will appreciate as the home or building grows older. A building with low fuel costs will surely be attractive on the real estate market.

New technology will not make today's system obsolete. Today's system is little different from that of the 1930s. And new technologies appear far in the future or far too costly for widespread use.

The cost will not get lower. The energy, after all, is free. No inflation. But the cost of the system is highly dependent on the design and installation labor, and to some extent (30-percent) on the materials and equipment. These costs are sure to rise with inflation in the coming years. Should the demand for labor and materials put pressure on the supply in future years, these costs may jump substantially.

Another argument often heard against solar systems is the one concerning the structure itself. Solar energy systems can be added to existing structures just as well as they can to new structures. You don't have to build a new structure to take advantage of solar energy. In many cases, the collector easily adapts to the existing roof or to the yard area. The only caution would be to make the structure the most effective passive solar collector possible, and to insulate where necessary. With a new structure, the solar system can be integrated with the latest passive techniques as well as with the latest insulation and building techniques.

The cost of fuel can only increase. And, while a good solar system is a wise investment, waiting will only increase the cost of that investment. At the same time, the fuel savings lost will cut into the money available to design and construct a good solar system.

Solar energy is no longer a curiosity. It is here, and developed for widespread use.

MAKING A DECISION

In this section of The Solar Decision Book you have learned that solar energy is a clean, readily available, and competitive energy source. It does not have the disadvantages seen with today's fossil fuels, other energies, or fuels currently in development. You have learned that the solar system technology has evolved to a well-thought-out, effective system. The design calls for correct matching of components and system configurations for the desired uses and energy needs. The installation uses standard construction techniques. And the equipment is generally available now, with refinements being made continually. You have learned that excellent performance can be expected in any part of the country. The solar system is by no means restricted to the sun-belt areas. Colder climates simply call for a larger system. You have also learned about the increasing popularity of solar energy, the latest developments that spell an intelligent approach to the solar business, and the reasons solar energy is a wise investment today. The time will never be better for making the solar decision.

The sun is today's best source of alternate energy. The facts make the decision an easy one.

DECISION 6

Solar Energy Systems Are Sound Investments

Fuel is not getting cheaper. It is costing you more each year. That alone is the biggest reason solar energy systems are going up throughout the country. The technology has been ready for some time now. All that was necessary were the right economic conditions for solar to become an attractively priced alternative to conventional fuels. Could the money pumped into a solar energy system be paid back in energy cost savings in a reasonable amount of time? Could solar energy become an attractive investment?

The answers are both "yes". Without qualification. Solar energy systems are good investments. And more and more people are coming to that very decision. This section of The Solar Decision Book will help you to make the same decision. Thorough computer analysis and experience will ultimately convince you that such a decision is the right one. You will learn that:

- Solar energy systems can be a good investment on existing structures and new structures.

- The investment is large, but the results are well worth it.

- A long system life is necessary to protect the solar investment.

- Operational costs and maintenance costs are low and can be estimated.

- The actual investment value can be accurately calculated.

BASIC CONSIDERATIONS

An investment in solar energy can be as small or as large as you want. Some of the options are shown in Figure 6.1. Certain building treatments such as awnings, drapes, and selective landscaping can cost very little. Steps such as remodeling to increase thermal mass or to make the structure a heat trap may involve a major capital expenditure. But they may not, depending on the particular structure. A solar energy system for hot water alone can cost several hundred dollars or a few thousand. A solar energy system for both hot water and space heating in an existing structure can cost much more. And, of course, designing and building a new structure with maximum use of both passive and active solar energy systems would require the largest capital expenditure.

Although there is a limit, the savings in fuel costs can also be as small or as large as you want. Substantial savings can be realized through wise use and conservation alone. Wasted energy can never be recovered. Added savings can be generated through simple steps toward making the building a heat trap. Such savings can become significant when a solar energy system is integrated into a building's energy supply. The amount of savings depends on the building's location, the area weather, and the size of the system installed.

A 100-percent savings in fuel costs is not possible. The actual savings can be pennies a day or hundreds of dollars a year ... a tiny fraction of your present energy costs or as much as 60- to 70-percent. Even the smallest fraction, though, can become significant in the coming years.

Energy conservation can stand alone and contribute much toward your energy savings. But solar energy should not be used without energy conservation. For the maximum savings and the fastest return on your investment, the solar energy system must be intelligently combined with adequate energy conservation measures. The structure should be properly insulated at the very least. Pouring solar energy — any energy for that matter — into a poorly insulated structure would be like pouring water into a sieve.

Existing Structures

Owners of existing structures should proceed in well-planned steps. The structure's heat losses need to be minimized. The comfort level desired needs to be defined. And, reasonably priced, passive-energy-collection devices need to be used wherever possible.

While taking these steps, the owner of an existing structure should examine the feasibility of installing a solar energy system for hot water only. This type of system does not rely on the structure's ability to collect and trap heat. And the investment is minimal. Solar hot-water systems are readily available, complete with matched components. They range from simple do-it-yourself kits to sizeable, fully installed and warranted systems.

In examining, or possibly using, a solar hot-water system, the owner of an existing structure can then investigate the costs and

Figure 6.1 Some options for a solar energy investment.

potential savings of a completely integrated system of passive and active energy collection devices.

New Structures

Planning a new structure offers much opportunity for cutting your future energy needs and costs. Every aspect of the building's architecture should be examined for its impact on solar heating and cooling. Every means of collecting and trapping solar heat should be incorporated. The desired aesthetics can be achieved in both active and passive energy collection devices.

At the time of construction, the solar system can be completely integrated into the structure. The most pleasing aesthetics and performance can be obtained for the lowest possible cost. There is no other time during the life of the structure that this low cost can be duplicated. And, as the costs of traditional fuels continue to rise, an energy-efficient building will grow in value.

Weighing The Investment

There are several key considerations in making a sound investment in solar energy. You should understand that solar energy systems are more expensive than traditional means of heating water or of heating a building. This larger investment is readily understandable in light of the equipment needed and the savings possible. The solar system must have a long life and it must be properly designed with premium materials. Otherwise, the system may never be capable of giving you a fair return on your investment. The system must also be designed to insure a low operational cost. Dollars spent on excessive power for blowers and pumps will lower the value of the investment. The same holds true for maintenance costs. Some operational and maintenance costs are necessary, but they can be minimized through proper system design.

All of these investment considerations are discussed in the following sections. The equipment and design parameters needed for an efficient, long-lasting system are detailed later in The Solar Decision Book.

WHY A SOLAR ENERGY SYSTEM REQUIRES A LARGE INVESTMENT

Traditional Fuels And Equipment

Standard water heaters and furnaces are far less expensive than solar energy systems. This is the case regardless of whether the equipment is fueled with electricity, oil, gas, or coal.

The average water heater for residential use will cost between 75 and 180 dollars. This is the cost for the heater alone, without piping, auxiliary controls, and installation. Such a heater may be required to heat 80 gallons of water from 55° F to 140° F daily. If the costs of fossil fuels are $7.20 per million Btu, this type of heater costs $148 a year to operate.

$$80 \text{ GAL/DAY}$$
$$\times 8.3 \text{ LB./GAL.}$$
$$\times 85 \text{ Btu/LB.}$$
$$\times 365 \text{ DAYS/YR.}$$
$$\times 11.13 \text{ MM. Btu}$$
$$\div 1,000,000$$
$$\overline{\$230.00 \text{ YR.}}$$

If the heater uses off-peak electricity at 3.8 cents a kilowatt-hour, it costs $230 a year to operate. Actually, the costs are higher because of some heat losses.

These costs show that the annual fuel costs of the water heater are about equal to the cost of the heater itself.

The same types of calculations can be shown for furnaces operated with fossil-fuels or electricity. A basic furnace for fossil fuels will cost between 600 and 1200 dollars. The heat-delivery system, controls, and installation costs will more than double this cost. Generally, the furnace will quickly devour an amount of fuel equal to or greater than the initial equipment cost. While an electric-heating system may cost less, the fuel costs will be much greater than those for the fossil-fuel furnaces.

Solar Energy And Equipment

In contrast, a solar energy system burns no fuel. The costs of operation are a fraction of those seen with traditional fuels and equipment. Some costs are incurred to power the system pumps and blowers. Other costs are incurred to heat water or provide building heat during extended periods of no sun.

A solar energy system needs a large array of collectors to gather the sun's energy. It also needs a large storage area in which to store the collected energy. Thus, a solar energy system is much more expensive than a water heater or furnace fueled with oil, gas, coal, or electricity. Let's take a look at how much more, using the water heater as an example.

A standard water heater costs between $75 and $180, or an average of $130. A solar water heater costs between $1000 and $1600, or an average of $1300.

This is a cost ratio of 10 to 1, solar to standard. When the costs of auxiliaries and installation are added, this ratio remains fairly constant. In the case of the standard water heater, the costs are $200 to $230 installed. In the case of the solar water heater, the costs are $1800 to $2400 installed. What justifies this large cost difference?

Assume an average cost of $190 to operate the standard water heater every nine months. In 100 months, the fuel savings would pay for the extra expense of using solar energy instead of standard fuels. That's only about eight years.

But fuel costs are rising at about 11-percent compounded annually. The payback period will be cut to only five or six years. If necessary, the fuel savings can be applied to a loan for the larger solar investment.

The bottom line is that a solar energy system can be a self-liquidating investment. As soon as the system is paid for out of fuel savings, the only costs of operation are about four to ten dollars annually for running blowers and pumps. And maintenance costs can also be held low.

The same logic can be used for solar space heating systems. However, since heating requirements are seasonal and since solar heating systems are more expensive, the length of time needed to liquidate — or payback — the investment increases to about nine to 12 years. As solar cooling becomes available and can be added to the solar heating system, the payback period will drop back to the five-or-six year period seen for solar hot-water systems.

Durability Costs More

That statement is simple enough. But with solar energy systems, durability is a must for good economics. The system must be durable. Understandably, that costs money.

If a $210 water heater lasts for only five years, the cost of replacing it can be considered as a minor dislocation of your finances. If such a catastrophe occurs, you have lost only $42 a year.

The story is much different if a solar water heater fails prematurely. Failure after only five years would cost you about $420 a year. That can seriously affect most household budgets, and be a most unwelcome expense for many businesses. After only five years, the fuel savings may not have been sufficient as yet to pay for the equipment.

So, with solar energy, the system life becomes extremely important. The equipment should last long enough to be paid for from fuel savings. And, ideally, the equipment should generate savings well beyond the cost of the equipment. That is the goal of using solar energy. A system that lasts 15 to 25 years, will pay for itself many times. But durable equipment carries a premium cost.

Throughout The Solar Decision Book, a 20-year-life design concept is unfolded. Such system life is the key to making a sound investment in solar energy.

ESTIMATING SOLAR SYSTEM LIFE

The right solar energy system is well-designed, made of premium materials, matched to its location, and properly installed and maintained. Such a system can last the life of the building. This would put the system life well in excess of 25 years.

On the other hand, the wrong solar system will be fortunate to run five years. Such a system would be poorly designed, made of average materials, installed improperly, and neglected. It may not even survive the first summer of "cooking" in the hot sun, and thus may fail to provide heat in the second winter.

Most of today's solar energy systems fall into those two classifications. Very poor or very good. A two-to-five-year system or a 20-to-25-year system. Rarely, anything in between.

There are five rules for estimating solar system life as shown in Figure 6.2. If these rules are followed and the system designed to meet the necessary requirements, there's no reason a 20-year-design life is not achieveable.

Quality Materials

Surprisingly — or unfortunately — there is little difference in cost between a poor solar system and a good solar one. The reason is that the cost of any solar energy system is usually tied up in labor. It costs

1. Know the quality of system materials.
2. Understand the effects of heat-transfer fluids on system performance and maintenance.
3. Realize that the price of neglecting fluid maintenance is early failure.
4. Recognize that conditioning storage water is important.
5. Recognize that the system is exposed to extreme environmental conditions.

Figure 6.2 Five rules for estimating solar system life.

just as much to install a poor system as it does a good system. Most systems cost from 25 to 35 dollars a square foot of collector installed. The materials used in the system normally cost about six to ten dollars a square foot of collector. Materials amount to only 25- or 30-percent of the total investment. An increased cost for better materials will have a small effect on the overall system cost.

Thus, the first rule of estimating solar system life is to know the quality of the materials used in the system. Various sections of The Solar Decision Book spell out the preferred materials and equipment for a 20-year-design-life system.

A Suitable Heat-Transfer Medium

The internal passages of the solar system, collector tubes, piping, heat exchangers, pumps, connectors, and valves are in intimate contact with the heat-transfer fluid. In the winter, the temperature of this fluid can drop to -30° F. In the summer, the temperature may rise to over 400° F. Heat and cold tend to break down the fluid to acids and sludge. The acids eat away the metal and shorten the system life. The sludge attaches to and clogs the heat-transfer passages. This drastically reduces the efficiency of the system.

This problem can be handled in one of two ways. One choice is to use cheap fluids that break down easily. These can be regularly changed every year or so, depending on the type of fluid and the service conditions. The system maintenance costs are understandably high, and the risk of system failure is great. The other choice is to use a premium fluid. Such a fluid would be matched to the operating conditions and designed to last the life of the system. The maintenance costs would be minimal, and so would the risk of system failure.

Thus, the second rule of estimating solar system life is to understand the effects of various heat-transfer fluids on the system performance and maintenance. The options available are covered in a later section of The Solar Decision Book.

Maintenance Is Important

The third rule of estimating solar system life is to realize that the price of neglecting maintenance of the heat-transfer fluid is early failure. Corrosion and scale will build up and block the fluid passages in the system. Corrosion, once started, does not stop when the fluid is changed. It continues doing its damage until the system finally fails. Also, any sludge or scale buildup cannot be readily removed when a fluid is changed out. Such deposits normally remain behind to continue hindering efficiency.

The Conditioning Of Storage Water

The storage water, although contained in a separate loop of the solar energy system, must be properly demineralized and inhibited. The temperature of the storage water can range up to 200° F. At these high temperatures untreated water can drastically shorten the system life. It can ruin the efficiency of the heat exchanger, the circulating pump, and the system piping.

As such, the fourth rule of estimating system life is to recognize that the storage water must be conditioned.

Environmental Conditions

The solar system environment is very harsh. The environmental enemies of the collector system as it sits out in the sun are many.

ULTRAVIOLET RADIATION: Ultraviolet radiation has very little effect, if any, on metals. Its damage is limited to plastics, rubbers, and paints. Thermoplastic glazings, rubber gaskets, absorber coatings all can rapidly deteriorate unless they are carefully chosen to withstand ultraviolet radiation.

MOISTURE: The collectors are designed to be watertight. Moisture entering the collector can ruin the insulating value of the back and side insulation. It can cause blistering, scaling and lifting of the absorber plate coating. Or it can fog the glazing and cause light scattering. Any or all of these conditions lower the thermal efficiency of the solar system.

HEAT AND COLD: At sunrise on a cold winter's morning, the collector may be at -30° F. By noon on a bright day, with snow on the ground, it may have risen to well over 200° F. This large increase in temperature expands the metal and places a high strain on the gasketing, paints, and sealants. These materials must be free to move with the metal. They must stay flexible at high and low temperature.

Again in the summer, if the storage tank is not calling for heat, the collector temperatures may rise to over 400° F. If a sudden rain were to fall, the collector would be subjected to an immediate 300° F thermal shock. This can shatter improperly mounted glazings, create a sudden vacuum within an unvented collector, and contract the metal absorber plate. Again, sealants, paints, and gasketing must not soften or run under these conditions.

Excess heat can also cause thermoplastic glazings to soften and sag if they are not properly supported in the collector. This would result in permanently deforming them and lowering efficiency.

Improperly mounted collector absorber plates can expand and bow upwards and, in extreme cases, contact and shatter or melt the glazing.

WIND AND HAIL: Collectors should be able to withstand winds up to 130 mph by both construction and proper installation. Hailstones two-to-three inches in diameter may fall on the glazing in a freak storm. The collector must be engineered to withstand these environmental conditions over its lifetime.

So, the fifth rule of estimating solar system life is to recognize the extreme environmental conditions that the solar collector will encounter. The collector should be designed to withstand the environmental extremes.

Figure 6.3 Over-design pipe sizes by one size to minimize pumping losses.

ESTIMATING OPERATIONAL COSTS

In a solar energy system with a liquid heat-transfer medium, the major operating cost is incurred in running the circulating pumps. Electrically operated blowers may be used in the heat-delivery system. However, the costs for running these blowers would be incurred even if a standard heating system were used instead of a solar system.

The pumps in a solar energy system are used to move heat-transfer liquid through the collectors and through a series of heat exchangers. In this way, the solar energy can be brought from the roof to storage, to the hot water tank, and to the space-heating distribution system.

Liquids moving through pipes are subject to friction losses. The sides of the pipes slow down the liquid flow. This requires power to overcome the friction. The faster the speed of flow and the smaller the pipe, the greater the friction and thus the greater the power required.

Piping is an area where designers tend to size too small and to ignore the excess power losses. In a solar system design, this should not be done merely to save a few dollars. Piping is a very inexpensive part of the system. It pays to over design with a larger pipe as shown in Figure 6.3. As a result, small pumps — about 1/20 to 1/12 horsepower — can normally be used throughout most solar heating systems.

To estimate solar system pumping costs, you need to know the wattage of the pumps, the annual hours of pump operation, and the number of pumps. The estimated hours of pumping for various pumps in a solar system are shown in Figure 6.4. Both daily and annual estimates are given. The solar system will usually contain three or four pumps. And, as shown, these will be in the collector primary loop, collector secondary loop, water heating loop, and space heating loop.

The wattage of the pumps, as mentioned, will usually depend on the system size. The higher the horsepower, the higher the wattage. High wattage units use more electricity. Typical pumping costs for various sizes of pumps are shown in Figure 6.5. The costs have been calculated for various costs per kilowatt-hour.

USE	DAILY HRS	ANNUAL HRS
Primary	3- 4	1,278
Secondary	3- 4	1,278
Water Heating	6- 8	2,555
Space Heating	8-12 (120 days)	1,200
Total/year		5,968 hrs.

Figure 6.4 Estimated hours of operation for various solar system pumps.

PUMP HORSEPOWER	WATTS	ANNUAL KILOWATT HOURS	ANNUAL COST FOR PUMPS AT VARIOUS COSTS PER KWH		
			4¢	5¢	6¢
1/20	154	919	$36.76	$45.95	$55.14
1/12	180	1,074	42.96	53.70	64.44
1/4	420	2,506	100.24	125.30	150.36
1/3	530	3,163	126.52	158.15	189.78
1/2	790	4,715	188.60	235.75	282.90

Figure 6.5 Typical pumping costs for various sizes of pumps.

If the system is designed properly, smaller pumps can be used. So, in an average-sized system, the pumps might have an operating cost of $35 to $65 a year. If larger pumps are used, the costs are multiplied several times.

This is not the true pumping cost, however. Most pump efficiency losses are caused by friction within the pump body. This friction adds heat to the fluid. The heat stays in the system. It actually serves to reduce the pump operating cost by 50- or 60-percent.

Thus, the true cost of operating pumps in an average solar system runs about $15 to $30 a year, or only $1.22 to $2.44 a month. As electrical costs increase, these costs will also increase. That's another important reason to keep friction losses in the system piping at a minimum.

Figure 6.6 shows the estimated annual pumping costs for various sizes of collector panels. They range from a low of only $3 a year to a high of $30 a year.

SQ. FT. PANEL	PUMPING COST RANGES [Net Annual]
50	$ 3.00 - $ 6.00
100	4.00 - 8.00
200	6.00 - 15.00
500	15.00 - 30.00

Figure 6.6 Estimated annual pumping costs for various sizes of collector panels.

ESTIMATING MAINTENANCE COSTS

The type of system you choose will determine your cost of maintenance. Your system must perform for over 20 years so the choice of materials has an extremely important bearing on maintenance costs. There are basically 15 items in a solar collector loop to be kept in repair.

- Collector Glazing
- Collector Gasketing
- Collector Sealants
- Absorber Plate
- Absorber Plate Coating
- Collector Insulation
- Heat-Transfer Fluid
- Pumps
- Heat Exchangers
- Piping
- Valves
- Expansion Tank
- Connectors
- Storage Tank
- Manifolds

Some of these terms may be unfamiliar to you right now, but each will be detailed in the various equipment selection and system design sections of The Solar Decision Book. They are listed here only to show you that many items must be kept in good repair in a solar energy system.

That sounds like an enormous, costly task. Even a nightmare! And, quite frankly, some early solar systems were nightmares to maintain. Something was always in need of repair. Most of those early problems, though, were caused by a lack of knowledge in the young solar energy industry. It had not yet learned that only premium-grade materials could withstand the harsh conditions of the solar environment. This design necessity has now become clearly apparent.

To illustrate, the maintenance costs of three different systems will be estimated and compared. The ratings will be based on maintenance costs, and not on performance characteristics. The three systems and their key components are shown in Figure 6.7. The design specifics are not necessary for this discussion.

The estimated life of the components in each of these systems is shown in Figure 6.8. In studying the chart, you can quickly see that premium materials do make a big difference. The materials shown can be used in various combinations, so maintenance can vary considerably.

Comparing Maintenance Requirements

System 1. Maintenance on System 1 over a 20-to-25-year operating life will be minimal. The maintenance costs will be held to an annual service call to check the system operation and to make minor adjustments for performance improvements. Some contingency funds might be earmarked for unforeseen incidents such as vandalism, freak storm damage, or component malfunction.

System 2. Summer *stagnation* (no flow) will cause the heat-transfer fluid to degrade to acids and sludge. These lower thermal performance and attack gaskets and packings. To prevent this, a complete heat-transfer fluid replacement should be planned on a three-year average. Such replacement will vary with stagnation conditions. If copper is present in this system, degradation will be faster. Collector glazings will deteriorate and lower thermal performance. A

System 1
- Tempered glass glazings
- Gasketing and sealants of silicone rubber
- Black chrome-oxide absorber plate coatings
- A well-manufactured absorber plate (metal)
- High-temperature collector insulation
- Silicone heat-transfer liquid
- Canned wet-rotor pumps
- All copper piping and brass valving
- Heavy-duty-metal heat exchangers

System 2
- Fiberglass laminates or plastic-sheet glazings
- Ethylene propylene gaskets
- Butyl or polysulphide sealants
- Painted absorber plates
- Hydrocarbon oil heat-transfer fluid
- Canned wet-rotor pumps
- Copper piping and brass valving
- Heavy-duty metal heat exchangers

System 3
- Plastic film glazing
- Butyl gaskets and sealants
- Painted absorber plate coatings
- Glycol/water heat-transfer fluids
- Canned wet-rotor pumps
- Plastic or metal piping and valves
- Heavy-duty metal heat exchangers

Figure 6.7 Three types of solar systems used for maintenance cost comparison.

top coating renewal or replacement once during twenty years will most likely be required. Gaskets and sealants will have to be replaced at the time and the absorber plates should be repainted.

System 3. Glycol/water heat-transfer fluids have not proven satisfactory unless they are changed at very frequent intervals. Not any glycol can be used; special grades with special additives are required. At best, their effective life without corroding the system over twenty years is about two years. Assuming maintenance won't always be performed on time, absorber plate replacement in 5-15 years is indicated. Plastic films have relatively short lives compared to the other products and must be considered a frequent replacement item.

Comparing Maintenance Costs

Figure 6.9 shows the estimated annual maintenance costs for the three systems being compared. The savings for the system using all premium-grade materials are sizeable. Not to be forgotten, is the value you place on peace of mind.

ITEM	SYSTEM 1	SYSTEM 2	SYSTEM 3
Collector Glazing	20 - 25	10 - 12	5 - 6
Collector Gaskets	20 - 25	10 - 20	5 - 6
Absorber Plate Coatings	15 - 25	10 - 15	10 - 15
Absorber Plates	20 - 25	20 - 25	5 - 15
Heat Trans. Fluid*	20 - 25	2 - 4	1 - 2
Pumps	20 - 25	20 - 25	15 - 20
Piping and Valves	20 - 25	20 - 25	15 - 20
Heat Exchangers	20 - 25	20 - 25	10 - 15
Gaskets & Packings	20 - 25	2 - 4	5 - 10

*If the heat transfer fluid is changed to another type, the life of operation is completely changed. Heat degradation of the heat-transfer fluid is the major contributor to internal panel failure through corrosion and sludge buildup.

Figure 6.8 Estimated life of components used in three systems for comparing maintenance costs.

MAINTENANCE ITEM	ESTIMATED COST/YEAR 200 FT² SYSTEM		
	SYSTEM 1	SYSTEM 2	SYSTEM 3
Annual Service Call	25	25	25
Contingency Fund	25	25	25
Heat Transfer Fluid	0	33 ($5/gal)	40 ($3/gal)
Labor to Replace Fluid (4 hours)	0	33	67
Gaskets & Packings	0	3	1
Collector Glazing Renewal	0	20	22
Glazing Renewal Labor (8 hours)	0	6	40
Leak Sealing Labor & Materials (2 hours)	0	2	4
Absorber Plate Replacement	0	0	100
	$ 50	$147	$324

Figure 6.9 Estimated annual maintenance costs on three systems in comparison study.

Figure 6.10 shows the estimated costs of maintenance for a twenty-year period. The differential becomes much greater. It's obvious that the maintenance costs can easily detract from your investment. Sizeable costs can eat away fuel savings in a hurry. And, added up over 20 years, the dollars could have been put to better use.

HOW GOOD IS THE INVESTMENT

There are many variables involved in determining the value of any solar investment. In later sections of The Solar Decision Book, you will read about the many variables that go into designing the right system for your building. Is it an existing structure or is it being planned for construction? What area of the country, what is the weather, how much heat will be required from solar? The answers to these questions will help size the system and help lead to a basic cost. The materials and local labor rates may affect this cost.

The materials and size of the system will also affect the system life, operational costs, and maintenance costs.

The system costs may require financing and interest charges. Added taxes for increased building value. And, quite likely, added insurance coverage.

YEAR	MAINTENANCE COSTS		
	SYSTEM 1	SYSTEM 2	SYSTEM 3
1	50	147	324
2	53	156	343
3	56	165	364
4	60	175	386
5	63	186	409
6	67	198	434
7	71	209	460
8	75	221	487
9	80	234	516
10	84	248	547
11	90	263	580
12	95	279	615
13	101	296	652
14	107	314	691
15	113	333	733
16	120	353	776
17	127	374	823
18	135	396	872
19	143	420	924
20	151	445	980
	$1,841	$5,411	$11,916
% of Est. System Cost	37%	108%	238%

Figure 6.10 Estimated costs of maintenance for 20 years at six-percent inflation on three systems in comparision study.

The savings will depend on the prevailing rates for conventional fuels, possible property tax credits or income tax deductions, and other factors.

Also, the salvage value, or real estate appreciation must be considered in weighing the investment.

Simple calculations to show that solar energy systems are sound investments do not exist. However, detailed computer analyses of the variables, costs and savings, are now possible.

The argument for solar energy is stronger than ever. For instance, payback periods ranging from as few as five years to as many as 12 years. Savings from a few hundred dollars to many thousand dollars. In some cases, the investment appears huge, but the savings quickly pay it back many times over.

In any cost analysis, the savings with solar are sizeable. The easiest way to determine this would be to obtain a cost for the system needed. Calculate its monthly cost in terms of loan payback with interest. Add the per-month operational and maintenance costs. And figure the total costs for the expected life of the system.

Compare that figure then with what you would pay for conventional fuels for the same time period. The savings will surprise you. And they do not take into account the added value of your building nor the savings you may gain from tax deductions.

Your specific system can also be thoroughly analyzed for performance and economic impact.

MAKING A DECISION

In this section of The Solar Decision Book, you have learned about some basic considerations for choosing solar energy for existing and new structures. You have learned that the system must be durable, and that durability costs money. You have learned that there are five rules for estimating solar system life. These rules should be followed to insure designing a system with the desired minimum 20-year life. You have learned how to estimate operational costs, and that maintenance costs are variable and significant if the right materials are not used. You have also learned that the savings with solar energy can be substantial.

The actual savings you can gain depend on many variables. And the costs and savings both cannot be determined accurately until the system is designed and priced. However, if the system life is 20 years or more, the operational costs low, and the maintenance costs reasonable, the savings will definitely be substantial.

Solar energy systems are good investments. It's a decision you must make for your own situation. And, of course, to insure the level of comfort you desire in future years.

DECISION 7

Negotiate An Intelligent Loan

Solar does offer advantages. It will have a significant impact on tomorrow's energy planning. So, what now?

If you are a potential owner of a solar energy system, you will need to decide if the system is a good investment. Can you afford to pay for it? If you are a contractor, you will need to decide if you can offer custom-designed systems. Will you be able to tailor the costs and performance to the owner's budget? If you are a lender, you will need to decide if the risk is reasonable and the value sufficient. Can you provide financing for this new energy technology?

This section of The Solar Decision Book will help you to make the decision that solar systems are good investments. You will learn that:

- Financial planning for the investment is needed.

- The effects of the system on cash flow and taxes must be considered.

- The system cost, performance, and life can help "sell" the investment.

FINANCING A SOLAR ENERGY SYSTEM

Regardless of the type of solar energy system being planned, the materials and labor costs for construction may require financing. The extent of the financing needed will depend on the type and size of the system.

Solar System Costs

The cost of a solar energy system may vary from a minimal amount to a sizeable portion of the building's value. For simple passive solar energy systems, such as the addition of awnings or south-facing windows, the costs may be very little. Many types of active solar systems can also cost little. Yet, if the system is a major addition to an existing structure or a major factor in a new structure's design, the costs can be considerable. These costs as well as the system design can be tailored to match the purchaser's financing restrictions and energy needs.

Sources of Capital

Whether the cost is large or small, a solar energy system will most likely require financing. The small building owner will need to plan the capital investment carefully. In the case of an addition to an existing structure, the solar energy system may require financing either as a short-term consumer loan or as an add-on to an existing mortgage.

As shown in Figure 7.1, the small building owner has several sources for investment capital. Consumer loans are available from credit unions and commercial banks. Real-estate mortgage loans are available from commercial banks, mutual savings institutions, and savings and loan associations. Some financing may also be available through credit card plans and retail installment credit plans.

Regardless of the source of capital, the lender will carefully examine the borrower's credit. A typical credit application is shown in

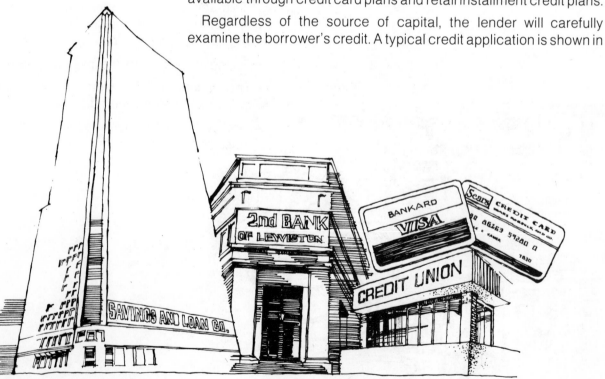

Figure 7.1 Sources of financing capital.

Date ______________ Loan No. ______________

READ – IMPORTANT – IF YOU ARE MARRIED, YOU MAY APPLY FOR EITHER JOINT OR INDIVIDUAL CREDIT. YOU ALSO HAVE THE RIGHT TO REQUEST THAT THE CREDIT HISTORIES OF YOU AND YOUR SPOUSE BE MAINTAINED IN SEPARATE CREDIT FILES. You are not required to disclose any information relating to marital status if you are applying for unsecured credit in your name alone; nor are you required, in any instance, to disclose income from alimony, child support, or maintenance payments.

I HEREBY MAKE APPLICATION FOR AN INSTALLMENT LOAN ☐ BANKCARD ☐ FIRST CLASS ACCOUNT ☐ OF $ ______________

Purpose of Loan ______________

Social Security No. ______________ Driver License No. ______________

Applicant ______________ Age ______ Spouse's Name ______________

Home Address ______________ Phone ______________ No. of Dependents ______

City ______________ County ______________ State ______ Zip ______ How Long ______

Previous Address ______________ How Long ______

Applicant's C/S ______________ Address ______________ Phone ______________

Employed by ______________ Position ______________ Year Started ______ Dept. No. ______

Business Address ______________ Phone No. ______________ Income $ ______ Wk. ☐ Mo. ☐

Previous Employment ______________ Position ______________ Years There ______

Address ______________ City ______________

Spouse's Employment ______________ Position ______________ Years Here ______

Business Address ______________ Phone No. ______________ Income $ ______ Wk. ☐ Mo. ☐

Other Income $ ______________ ☐ Mo. ☐ Yr. Source (Explain) ______________

LOCATION/DESCRIPTION OF REAL ESTATE OWNED	REAL ESTATE IN NAME(S) OF	PURCHASE PRICE	AMOUNT OF MORTGAGE	MONTHLY PAYMENTS OR RENTAL PAYMENTS	MORTGAGE HOLDER OR LANDLORDS NAME & ADDRESS

Bank Account With ______________ ☐ Saving ☐ Checking

Name of Nearest Relative Not Living With You ______________ Street City ______________ How Related ______

List All Debts Now Owing Or Recently Paid, Including Alimony, Support Payments, Stores, Banks, Loan Companies And Credit Unions.

NAME OF COMPANY	DEBT IN NAME(S) OF	PRESENT BALANCE	MONTHLY PAYMENT	SECURED BY
	TOTALS			

______________ SIGNATURE OF THE APPLICANT ______________ SIGNATURE OF THE APPLICANT

Figure 7.2 A typical credit application.

Figure 7.2. The borrower's current assets and liabilities will be examined. The impact of the loan on the borrower's cash flow will also be studied. And, in the case of a real-estate mortgage, the real-estate appraisal department of the lending institution will make an assessment of the value and the risk of the investment.

The borrower should be ready to "sell" the lending institution on the system's value. And, the borrower should be ready to show that the risk is reasonable. Since solar energy systems are a relatively new consideration in the real-estate market, the potential value and risk will be closely scrutinized.

The lending institution reserves the decision as to whether or not the investment is sound. As such, the real-estate appraisal is very important to the cost, size, and risk of the investment. The sytem will need to offer good potential savings on energy costs, and it must not detract from the value of the structure.

LOAN PURPOSE	TERM	AVERAGE INTEREST RATE
New autos	36 mo.	11.62%
Mobile homes	84 mo.	11.71%
Consumer goods	24 mo.	13.27%
Personal loans	12 mo.	13.60%
Credit card plans	—	17.21%
Finance companies	—	21.11%

Figure 7.3 Average simple interest rates for various types and sources of short-term consumer loans. (Detailed by Federal Reserve Board in December 1974.)

Consumer Loans

For amounts under $5000, the borrower will normally look for a short-term consumer loan. Credit unions and commercial banks specialize in such loans. Credit unions are nonprofit institutions, usually operated by a church or a business, so their interest rates tend to be lower than commercial banks. Consumer loans are also available from finance companies or through retail credit plans. Interest rates from these sources are usually much higher than those from banks and credit unions. Figure 7.3 shows the average simple interest rates as detailed by the Federal Reserve Board in December of 1974 for various types and sources of short-term consumer loans.

Figure 7.4 is a consumer loan check list. It contains a series of questions that the borrower should have answered before making a loan.

Mortgage Loans

Real-estate mortgage loans are generally made by savings and loan institutions, commercial banks, mutual savings banks, and life insurance companies. Figure 7.5 shows the percentage of real-estate loans by various lending institutions.

There are many types of real-estate mortgage loans. The most familiar type and the one most commonly used is the direct-reduction, fully-amortized loan. Equal payments are made over the life of

☐ Should I save in advance for this purchase or should I borrow the money to make it now?

☐ Have I shopped for the best interest rates available?

☐ Do I belong to a credit union where the rates may be lower?

☐ What is the annual simple interest rate of the loan?

☐ What is the amount of the monthly payments and are they equal level payments over the loan's life?

☐ Are there any prepayment penalties should I elect to pay off the loan early?

☐ Do I have to pay an application fee to make the loan?

☐ Is credit life insurance on the loan available or included?

☐ Does the lending institution comply with the Federal Equal Credit Opportunity Act which prohibits discrimination on the basis of sex or marital status?

☐ Do I have any recourse if the merchandise is faulty?

☐ Can I afford the loan and do I know where the funds to repay it will come from?

☐ Is a finance company or a consumer credit plan involved? If so, do I understand the interest rates and the prepayment rights?

Figure 7.4 Consumer loan check list.

the loan and the entire sum is paid at the end of the loan period. As each monthly payment is made, it is first credited to the interest on the outstanding balance and then any sum remaining is used to reduce the outstanding debt.

A second type of mortgage loan is known as the limited-reduction-plan, partially-amortized loan. Another name for it is the "balloon" mortgage. The balloon mortgage is generally written for a shorter term, and the unamortized balance is paid in a lump sum at the end of the loan period. Normally however, the balloon payment is not made. Instead, the balance of the loan is rewritten at the prevailing interest rate at the time of the rewriting.

The straight-reduction, fully-amortized loan is a third type of mortgage loan. In this loan, a specified amount is paid on the principal plus the interest on the outstanding balance. The payments become smaller as the debt is reduced.

Figure 7.6 shows the typical monthly payments for various fully amortized loans. The payment amounts are calculated for each $1000 borrowed. And, several rates of interest and a number of loan lengths are given.

Mortgages are also written "open-ended." With these loans, additional money can be borrowed against the same mortgage. Such borrowing is usually limited to the amount of principal repaid.

LENDING INSTITUTION	TOTAL HELD
Savings and Loan Institutions	56.9 percent
Commercial Banks	22.5 percent
Mutual Savings Banks	12.6 percent
Life Insurance Companies	8.0 percent

Figure 7.5 Percentage of real-estate mortgages held by various lenders. (Data as of September 30, 1974.)

TERM, YEARS	MONTHLY COST TO AMORTIZE $1000 AT						
	8.0%	8.5%	9.0%	9.5%	10%	11%	12%
2	45.23	45.46	45.69	45.92	46.15	46.61	47.08
3	31.34	31.57	31.80	32.04	32.27	32.74	33.22
5	20.28	20.52	20.76	21.01	21.25	21.75	22.25
7	15.59	15.84	16.09	16.35	16.61	17.13	17.66
10	12.14	12.40	12.67	12.94	13.22	13.78	14.35
15	9.56	9.85	10.15	10.45	10.75	11.37	12.01
20	8.37	8.68	9.00	9.33	9.65	10.33	11.02
25	7.72	8.06	8.40	8.74	9.09	9.81	10.54
30	7.34	7.69	8.05	8.41	8.78	9.53	10.29

Figure 7.6 Typical monthly payments for fully amortized loans.

- ☐ Does a consumer loan or a real estate loan best serve my needs for this size debt?
- ☐ Can I borrow against my current mortgage or is it necessary to obtain a new loan, refinancing the property?
- ☐ If I have to refinance, what will my total interest bill become considering the outstanding balance on my old debt?
- ☐ What type of real estate loan best suits my needs?
- ☐ What are the current rates of interest at the three types of lending institutions in my particular area?
- ☐ Do I have the details of the "extra costs" such as appraisal fees, points, loan application fees, taxes, preparation of legal instruments, etc?
- ☐ Will refinancing change my tax appraisal or otherwise affect my tax assessment?
- ☐ Am I eligible for a FHA and VA insured loan and can I obtain it at less cost?
- ☐ How large a down payment will I have to make. Will a larger down payment decrease the interest rate?
- ☐ Are there any prepayment penalties if I need to move before the term of the loan expires?
- ☐ How are late charges handled?
- ☐ Do I have to deposit taxes, insurance etc. in escrow and do they earn interest?
- ☐ Am I required to provide any additional security such as a compensating balance in savings or securities or a note on other property?
- ☐ Does the mortgage contain a "due-on-encumberance clause" preventing me from using my equity in the property as security for other short term loans I might need to make?
- ☐ Is disability and life insurance available? Is it optional or required? How do the rates compare to term insurance?
- ☐ Can the loan be assigned or sold to another lending institution? Can they change the terms without prior approval?
- ☐ What is the local reputation of the lending institution with other borrowers? How well do they service their customers?
- ☐ Have I shopped well for my loan and obtained the best loan available in terms of rates, length, and general terms?

Figure 7.7 A checklist for real-estate loans.

There are many factors to consider when making a real-estate loan. Figure 7.7 shows a real-estate-loan checklist to help you in making a wise loan.

General Borrowing Considerations

For security, the lending institution normally requires a mortgage on the property. In some cases, other property may have to be assigned as security on the loan. This allows the lender to recover the investment if the borrower is unable to repay the loan for some reason.

For residential buildings, the loan or mortgage is normally written for a repayment term of 20 to 30 years. Depending on the risk, the loan may carry an interest rate of 8- to 10-percent per annum. Some loans are insured by such government agencies as FHA (Federal Housing Administration) or VA (Veteran's Administration). The lender will also require adequate insurance on the structure, possibly insurance on the life of the borrower, a possible extra payment (points) for making the loan, a separate appraisal fee, and some means of guaranteeing payment of real-estate taxes on the structure.

For commercial buildings, the loans generally carry shorter repayment terms of 10 to 20 years. And they are usually written at higher interest rates of 10- to 12-percent. The lender may require a full review of company assets and liabilities, as well as an adequate forecast of projected business growth.

Loans up to 80-percent — those with a downpayment of 20-percent or more — are considered prime or first class loans by most lending institutions. Loans of greater amounts are considered more risky and carry higher rates of interest. However, in today's inflating economy, some lending institutions will loan up to 95-percent of the building's *appraised value.*

Appraised value is the value that the loaning bank places on the investment, not the market cost of it. The two may or may not agree. The loan committee of the bank is guided only by its real-estate department's appraisal, not by the market price.

In the case of a small investment on the existing building, the lending institution uses the shorter-term, higher-rate-of-return consumer loan, which is not secured by a mortgage. These loans are normally written for periods of three to five years at 11- to 14-percent interest. The bank's security is generally a note from the borrower. Again, many consumer loans are FHA-guaranteed.

IMPACT ON CASH FLOW AND TAXES

A solar energy system — and for that matter, any capital expenditure on a building — will have an impact on the owner's cash flow and taxes. The repayment of the financing loan must be considered. And the effect the investment may have on monthly energy costs, personal or business taxes, and real-estate taxes must be considered.

Capital Investment Considerations

The borrower must consider making a loan that is reasonable and within the personal or business budget requirements. The right balance of system performance and cost must be made according to the individual's financial capabilities.

Cash Flow

Cash flow for our purposes is defined as the amount of money spent each month by the owner on the building. Mortgage and energy payments are normally made from the monthly income.

For a solar energy system to be considered an attractive investment, it must offer a reduced cash flow over its lifetime. Unless it lowers the cost of living or the cost of doing business, it becomes a burden rather than an investment.

In other words, the solar system has to generate energy savings equal to or greater than its cost. It will then have a positive impact on available monthly income.

During the early years of operation, many solar systems will have a negative impact on cash flow. The amount of money spent will be greater than it would be if conventional fuels were used. However, as the years pass and energy prices rise, the system will show an ever-increasing positive impact on cash flow. This is what makes solar appear so attractive from an investment standpoint today.

Taxes

How the solar system affects two types of taxes must be examined. These taxes are those on income and real-estate. Savings on income taxes can be generated through the interest paid on the borrowed money. Added expense will be generated by the property tax incurred by increasing the assessed value of the building.

The income tax savings generated are a function of the owner's tax bracket and the size of the loan. A person in the 25-percent tax bracket paying $300/year in interest could generate $75.00 annual income tax savings. This would amount to an increased monthly cash flow of $6.25.

If the assessed value of the solar system is $2,000 and the property tax rate is two-percent, the increased property taxes would generate a negative cash flow of $40/year or $3.33/month. Of course, these added property taxes could result in some additional income tax savings.

Additional tax credits and property-assessment exclusions for solar systems are either already available or are the subject of legislative action both at the state and federal level. These tax laws vary from state to state. They also vary in effective date. Such laws can serve to increase cash flow.

The availability of tax credits and property-assessment exclusions should be carefully investigated when making the solar investment. You should consult your tax advisor concerning the impact of a solar expenditure on your personal as well as real estate taxes.

WHAT A BANKER NEEDS TO KNOW

Most solar energy systems for actively heating structures are a major investment for a building owner. As such, they need to be financed and paid for out of fuel savings and regular income either as part of the structure mortgage or as a consumer loan.

The bank that invests in an active solar energy system needs to know that its investment is protected if the investor is for some reason unable to meet his commitment to repay the loan.

The building owner should be prepared to answer questions relating to system performance, cost, life, and the system's effect on real-estate values for the banker. Investment in solar systems is new. The average lending institution has not had ample experience in assessing the solar system investment.

Solar System Costs

The cost of an active solar system will vary over a very wide range depending on what it is expected to do. A solar hot water heating kit that you install yourself can cost as little as $1200. A large fully installed, fully warranted system in a northern climate for a large family may cost as much as $3500. The costs for a solar energy system for space heating as well as hot water range higher. Systems costing from $5000 to $15,000 are not unusual.

Design and Construction Plans

The lending institution may require to see the solar system plans. However, the best way to proceed appears to be for the owner to obtain an estimate for a typical system first. And, to talk with the lender concerning the feasibility of any loan for solar. The lender can then request specific additional information from the building owner and, possibly, from the consultant or contractor.

Solar System Life

Solar system life and maintenance has been discussed previously. Some guidelines have also been given on system quality and maintenance costs. Depending on how well your system is designed and installed, you can expect from five to 25 years of life without major maintenance.

Solar System Performance

Solar system performance can be predicted as discussed. A square foot of solar panel, depending upon the location and the type of system, will give from 100,000 to 300,000 Btu per square foot each year.

CLP of the System

Cost, Life, and Performance can be combined into one figure. This figure can be used to measure the relative value of a solar system. The author has chosen to call this *System CLP*. It can be expressed as dollars per Btu per year.

As an example of CLP:

Cost   = $3000 for a 75-ft² system
Performance   = 200,000 Btu/ft² per year
Life   = 20 years

$$CLP = \frac{\$3000}{(75)\,(200{,}000)\,(20)} = \$10/\overline{M}\ Btu$$

In essence, CLP is showing the cost per million Btu of installing the solar system. If the system only lasted 10 years, then the CLP in this example would be $20 per million Btu. Obviously, the lower the CLP, the higher the value of the system.

Real-Estate Values

Life, aesthetics, and performance of a solar system will have a marked effect on the real-estate value of a building structure. A system designed to last more than 20 years . . . one which enhances or does not detract from the appearance of the structure . . . and one with a lower CLP will grow in value rather than depreciate. As fuel costs rise, the structure will become more and more desirable on the real-estate market.

MAKING A DECISION

In this section of The Solar Decision Book, you have learned how to make an intelligent loan if financing the solar investment is required. There are various sources for borrowing the required capital, as well as various costs involved. A potential owner of a solar energy system must consider the effects of loan payments, energy costs or savings, and tax costs or savings on monthly cash flow (spendable income). You have also learned how to be prepared to sell the value of a solar investment to a lending institution. The lender needs to know the answers to several key questions about the system.

A decision on financing solar is easy to make with the proper planning. Knowing the system cost, life, and performance is important. But you must decide that solar is a good investment before moving ahead.

DECISION 8

Start Planning The System

Solar energy is an attractive alternate energy source. And, thus far in The Solar Decision Book, you have read some strong arguments in favor of solar energy.

These have included the frightening predictions of future energy shortages. The expected and substantial increases in the costs of traditional energies. The hope that massive conservation can delay a catastrophic energy shortage. The dwindling supplies of domestic fuel sources and the increasing need for costly imports. The lack of sufficient development of new energy sources. The free energy from the sun. The low costs of operating and maintaining a properly designed solar system. The facts to use in negotiating a loan for the solar investment.

You may or may not have come to the same conclusions, or decisions, as the author. However, you have most likely decided that solar energy deserves your close examination. You may want to see what impact a workable solar system will have on your energy costs. To do so, some system planning must be done. This section of The Solar Decision Book will give you the basic requirements for such planning. It gives you a start toward planning a system especially for your building.

The remaining sections of the book then help you make the critical decisions for equipment selection, system sizing, system installation, and system pricing.

REVIEW YOUR OPTIONS

Some source of alternate energy is essential to your health, to your lifestyle, and especially to your financial well-being. If you feel that solar energy merits close examination, your first step would be to review your options. How does solar energy fit into an existing structure? What is needed for solar energy in a new structure? Is do-it-yourself feasible or should a contractor be consulted?

Solar Energy for Existing Structures

In making the decision to install a solar energy system in an existing structure, there are three major considerations. 1) Lowering heat losses through energy conservation. 2) Building modifications to increase thermal mass for collecting and trapping the sun's energy. And, 3) installing active solar systems.

LOWERING HEAT LOSSES. Depending on the particular structure, the conservation measures discussed in Decision 3 should be undertaken wherever possible. Such measures can reduce the energy demand to the lowest possible level.

BUILDING MODIFICATIONS. Careful planning and thought is needed here. What site and building modifications will increase the structure's ability to control heat loss and gain? This involves controlling the penetration of solar energy into the structure.

Simple modifications such as awnings and plantings may be quite reasonable in cost. Modifications such as installing new windows or increasing thermal mass may be more costly. These modifications should be priced to determine if they represent a wise investment. The energy conservation form in Appendix B will help you make these decisions.

INSTALLING ACTIVE SOLAR SYSTEMS. The integration of a solar system into the structure's existing heat and hot-water systems is a major consideration. The fewest problems will be encountered if the structure already contains a forced-air heat-delivery system. Only minor ductwork changes will be required. If the structure is currently heated with electrical resistance heat, major changes may be needed in the heat-delivery system.

Hot-water heating systems can usually be installed at little cost. The present hot-water tank becomes the auxiliary heater. It is fed by a solar preheater. If the present hot-water heater is nearing the end of its useful life, this would be an excellent time to replace it. A new unit could be matched to the solar system. And the cheapest possible backup fuel could be used.

Siting of the collector array may present architectural problems because of shading, structure orientation, and design. A knowledgeable solar contractor will be able to provide experienced and practical advice. Some design compromises may be needed to achieve pleasing aesthetics.

Space for solar heat storage may be limited or intrude into the available living space. Again, some compromises may be needed.

Active solar systems for space heating in existing structures will tend to be somewhat larger than those in new structures. However, if the system design and orientation are idealized for solar energy collection and storage, the two systems will be approximately the same size.

Solar Energy for New Structures

No new structure should be built today without giving careful consideration to solar energy. The energy shortage is permanent and fuel costs are rising at a 10- to 12-percent annual rate. So, the use of the structure as a solar collector and as a heat trap becomes a major building consideration. Structure design, siting, and orientation must be idealized to take maximum advantage of the available solar energy.

Purchasers of existing structures which will become "new-to-them" should carefully consider how adaptable the structure is to the utilization of solar energy. Improperly insulated, electrical-resistance-heated, low-thermal-mass structures are becoming poor investments for both the new owner and the lending institutions. Currently proposed governmental legislation could require energy conservation investments above and beyond the purchase price. Such legislation could drastically affect the future value of the structure on the real estate market.

The decision to install solar in a new structure is essential to reduce future cash flow, to increase future real estate value, and to insure the availability of "affordable" energy. In new structures:

• The building needs to be a passive solar collector.

• The building needs to be a high-thermal-mass heat trap.

• The building needs to be oriented and sited for an active solar system installation.

The decision to install an active solar system during initial construction is the only solar decision that can be put off or delayed. Delaying the active solar system decision until a later date will result in additional costs. These costs include inflation and the need to provide 100-percent fossil-fuel heat until a solar system is installed.

The new building owner should either become extremely knowledgeable in energy conservation and passive solar architectural considerations. Or, he should utilize the services of knowledgeable people before committing to a final investment.

ACTIVE SOLAR SYSTEM INSTALLATION. To integrate the active solar energy system into the final building design also requires knowledge. Knowledge of what the active system consists of. How the system is sized. How much solar energy can be economically used. And, most important, what solar energy cannot do.

Solar energy cannot provide 100-percent of your heat requirements and still remain economical. Some auxiliary heat will always be needed. This is a limitation that must be recognized in system design.

Active solar energy systems and passive devices must also be integrated. If the passive system is properly designed and utilized during sunny periods, then the active system can be storing energy for use during extended periods of no sun.

Careful consideration must be given to cooling needs as well as to heating needs during design and construction. In southern areas of the country, the space cooling considerations may be even more important than the space heating considerations. Air conditioning, humidity control, ventilation and heating should be integrated to obtain complete climate control in the building structure at the most economical cost.

THE CRITICAL PARAMETERS IN PLANNING THE SOLAR SYSTEM

The critical parameters which need to be given the most consideration in choosing a solar system are:

- Geographical location
- Size of the heat load
- The materials of construction
- The efficiency of the collectors
- The efficiency of the heat exchangers
- The size of the heat storage
- The design temperature of operation of the terminal sytem
- The siting of the solar collectors

GEOGRAPHICAL LOCATION. The analyses detailed in Decision 5 show that the amount of sunlight varies considerably from location to location. A solar collector installed in Denver, Colorado; Phoenix, Arizona; or Miami, Florida, will have much more energy available to work from than one installed in Seattle, Washington; Detroit, Michigan; or Boston, Massachusetts. Solar energy is readily available in all of these locations and a solar system will perform well in any location, but the correct size needs to be larger or smaller for economical performance.

HEAT LOAD. The heat load a solar system works against has a very measurable effect on the energy collected. The higher the load on a given size system, the better the performance. This is encouraging. It indicates that higher collection efficiencies are seen with systems in cold climates than in warm climates. It also indicates higher efficiencies for water-heater heat recovery. Because of this, the system designer must accurately calculate the correct heat load.

MATERIALS OF CONSTRUCTION. The analyses shown earlier use conservative fuel costs because the facts indicate that a conservative inflation scenario may be correct. Therefore, the system must be durable. A durable system will be economically competitive with other sources of energy; and it will become an asset rather than a liability. The system must be engineered with the best possible materials to ensure long life.

COLLECTOR EFFICIENCY. The effects of collector efficiency will be described later in The Solar Decision Book. No matter how much energy is available, the energy is useless if it cannot be efficiently collected. Ten-percent less collector efficiency means 10-percent more collector area to obtain the same amount of usable heat.

HEAT EXCHANGER EFFICIENCY. Too small a heat exchanger between the solar loop and heat storage will seriously lower the collector efficiency. Too small an exchanger between the storage tank and load will have the same effect. If heat cannot be transferred rapidly and efficiently, the collectors will operate at a higher temperature. They will be less efficient. Heat exchanger design will be covered in detail in a later section. Too small a heat exchanger can impose a 15- to 20-percent penalty in collection efficiency.

SIZE OF HEAT STORAGE. The larger the heat storage device, the greater the collection efficiency. However, studies have shown that beyond a certain point, efficiency gains become minimal. Too small heat storage again imposes severe penalties on collection efficiencies. Therefore, there is an optimum heat-storage size. This size will be discussed in detail later.

TERMINAL SYSTEM HEAT-DELIVERY TEMPERATURES. The fossil-fuel furnace and the electrical resistance heater operate at high heat *fluxes* (temperatures above temperatures desired). Most terminal delivery systems, either air or hot water, are designed to turn on between 140 to 180° F. The nature of solar energy is such that it provides low heat fluxes. Terminal systems need to be designed to operate at 100 to 120° F for efficient use of solar collected heat. This requirement necessitates a different design approach on the part of the heating contractor. This difference must be recognized.

SOLAR COLLECTOR SITING. Collectors must be faced in the right direction and tilted at the right angle to maximize energy collection. They must not be shaded by surrounding objects. The sun's path across the sky must be known and plotted to make optimum use of solar energy. Collectors facing north will never see the sun, and those on a vertical or horizontal surface will see less sun. The collector site will be discussed in Decision 9 of The Solar Decision Book.

MAKING A DECISION

In this section of The Solar Decision Book, you have reviewed your options regarding solar energy. You have also reviewed the basic parameters needed for planning a good, cost-effective solar system. Without these initial steps in planning, a serious design defect may occur. The system may exhibit poor efficiency, high maintenance costs, and a likelihood of premature failure.

Your decision to start planning a solar energy system is an important one. You will need some source of alternate energy to remain comfortable over the next 25 years.

DECISION 9

Site The Collectors

The sun's energy is beamed to earth across 93,000,000 miles. This energy strikes the earth at different angles, depending on the geographical area, the hour of the day, and the time of the year. For that reason, the collector site is one of the most important considerations in the solar system design.

Certainly, an efficient, properly sized collector area is a must. This is true, no matter what the location. But regardless of the type used and the size needed, the collectors must be placed on or near the building in the most pleasing, economical, and effective way. The collectors must be oriented in the proper direction to catch the sun during a good part of the day. And the collectors also must be tilted at the right angle to gather maximum energy during the months it is needed most.

Your geographical area, architectural tastes, and landscaping restrictions will enter into your decision on siting the collectors. This section of The Solar Decision Book will help you to make the decision. You will learn that:

- The collectors can be integrated into many building designs and landscaping plans.
- Solar energy reaches the collectors in three ways, and the collector position is critical to gathering this energy.
- The collector orientation depends on the geographical area and the building design.
- The collector tilt angle depends on the geographical area and your energy needs.

BUILDING CONSIDERATIONS

The use of solar energy for water heating, space heating, and cooling has become an attractive alternative to fossil fuels. Over the years, solar energy has been put to work in hundreds of buildings. But many of these early applications left much to be desired with regards to architectural design. Now, with increasing acceptance of the solar alternative in every area of the country, much more attention is being given to the architectural aspects of solar system design.

Many of the early solar buildings were experimental projects. They emphasized only the engineering needs to harness the sun. Very little architectural change was made in accepted building design. As a result, attempts at making the structure a passive solar collector might have involved unsightly window walls, unattractive masses of masonry, or unusual window treatments, landscaping, or roofing. Attempts at adding an active solar system usually involved mounting the collector panels on rooftops or in yards — without integrating the collectors with the existing architecture or landscape.

Fortunately, this is no longer the case. Many options are now available for both existing structures as well as new structures. In Figure 9.1, the solar collectors are attractively integrated with the structure design. These are just a sampling of the many attractive designs being used for today's solar homes and office buildings.

As a general rule, the collectors must be mounted on the building or within a reasonable distance of the building. This is necessary for construction economy as well as heat efficiency. Costs increase as do heat losses, if the solar energy must be piped any distance before it can be used. Such a restriction can be minimized with the proper design.

Figure 9.2 shows several options for mounting the solar collectors. Since the sun travels a certain path across the sky, the collectors must be oriented toward the sun. They must also be tilted upward. These considerations will be discussed.

With The Solar Decision Book you can determine the collector orientation and tilt angle for your solar energy system. You can also determine the correct size and equipment needed for an efficient system. The book, however, makes no attempt to detail the various architectural options available to you. There are many other fine publications — books as well as magazines — that tackle the system architecture. The decisions regarding system performance are most important. Once the system is selected, you can choose the architectural treatment that is most suited to your personal tastes.

This is logical. After all, a good-looking but improperly designed system may fail to heat your building.

THE SUN

For a workable solar energy system, you should understand how the sun's energy reaches the earth. You should understand how this energy varies according to the time of day. And you should also understand that your solar collectors must catch the sun's energy through an imaginary "window" in the sky above your building.

Figure 9.1 Three samples of attractive solar architecture.

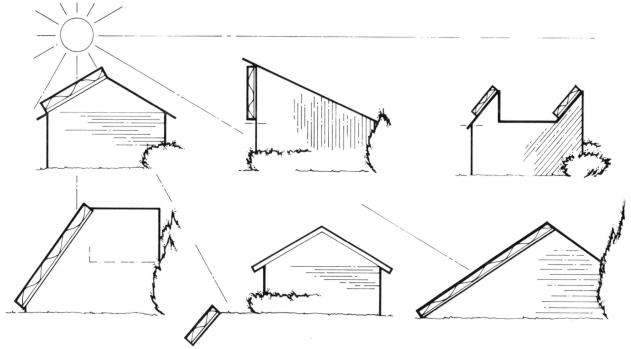

Figure 9.2 Several options for mounting the solar collectors.

Solar Radiation

The sun's energy can be collected by solar panels mounted on or near a building. This energy is called *solar* radiation. It reaches the panels in three ways — as direct, diffuse, or reflected radiation. These three types of radiation are shown in Figure 9.3.

- *Direct radiation* is made up of parallel rays coming straight from the sun. This radiation casts shadows on clear days.

- *Diffuse radiation* is scattered, nonparallel energy rays. This type of radiation makes the sky blue on clear days and grey on hazy days.

- *Reflected radiation* is solar energy that is sent to the collectors from adjacent surfaces of the building or ground. It depends a lot on the shape and texture of the surroundings.

A nearly constant amount of solar radiation strikes the earth's atmosphere: 429.2 Btu per square foot each hour. However, a large amount of this energy is lost in the earth's atmosphere by absorption and reflection as it passes to the earth's surface. Depending upon location and weather conditions, from 30- to 60-percent can be lost. Only about 170- to 300-Btu per square foot might reach the earth's surface each hour.

The purity of the atmosphere, vapor, dust, and smoke content all have an effect on this energy, as does the angle of the sun. The relative amount of radiation received on earth is diminished when the sun is lower in the sky.

Clouds and particles in the atmosphere not only reflect and absorb solar energy, but they also scatter it in all directions. Thus, part of the solar radiation may be diffused. Diffuse radiation, as opposed to direct radiation, is larger on hazy days than on clear ones. At most,

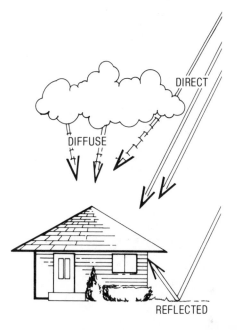

Figure 9.3 Three types of solar radiation.

TYPE OF RADIATION	AMOUNT OF ENERGY
Direct	250 Btu/sq ft/hr
Diffuse	50 Btu/sq ft/hr
Reflected	60 Btu/sq ft/hr
TOTAL	360 Btu/sq ft/hr

Figure 9.4 A typical example of "clear day" solar radiation.

Horizontal

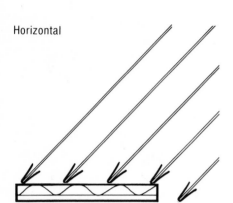

Vertical

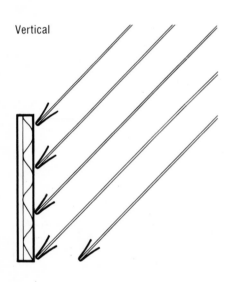

Perpendicular to
the sun's rays

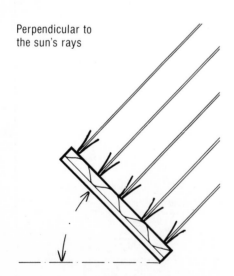

Figure 9.5 Collector tilt is important to
energy collection.

diffuse radiation can only be about 25-percent of the available radiation. About 75 Btu per square foot each hour.

Reflected radiation from adjacent surfaces normally amounts to about 20-percent of the direct and diffuse solar radiation. But with a bright snow-covered surface, the reflected radiation can amount to as much as 70-percent. Thus, reflected radiation from adjacent surfaces, can be a very important factor in collector sizing and placement.

Figure 9.4 shows a typical example of the solar radiation that might reach a collector panel on a clear day. Most of this energy is made up of direct radiation. On hazy or cloudy days, most of the energy might come from diffuse radiation. And, when the sun is low in the sky as in winter and the morning and evening, much of the energy might come from reflected radiation.

Most solar energy systems rely on direct radiation. Since direct radiation is a series of parallel rays coming straight from the sun, the angle of the collector is extremely important. When the collector is tilted perpendicular to these rays, the maximum amount of direct radiation can be collected. As shown in Figure 9.5, some energy is lost if the collector is not tilted.

Solar Movement

The sun rises roughly in the east in the morning, moves across the southern sky, and sets in the approximate west. Because of the tilt of the earth's axis, as the earth orbits around the sun during the year, the sun is higher and lower in the sky during the year. The actual position of the sun depends on the location of the observer. This solar movement can be determined for any day of the year, for any geographical area, with sun maps. These maps are available in several publications, including *Architectural Graphic Standards* published by John Wiley & Sons in 1972.

For solar-heating purposes, the degree of accuracy provided by sun path maps is sufficient. The use of these maps is discussed under "solar window."

Solar Window

Imagine the sky as a transparent dome, as shown in Figure 9.6. The center of the dome would be the collector on a house. The path of the sun can be drawn on the dome to outline a "solar window." This is a window which would outline the area through which a maximum amount of solar energy could reach the collectors during the days of the year.

The top of the window would be drawn by the sun's path at the start of summer (June 21). The sun travels its highest path across the sky.

The bottom of the window would be drawn by the sun's path at the start of winter (December 21). The sun travels its lowest path across the sky. The sides of the window would be drawn by the sun's position at three hours before and after solar noon. These positions might be found at 9 AM and 3 PM depending on the particular time zone. Solar noon can be calculated for various geographical areas and times of the year as shown in Figure 9.7.

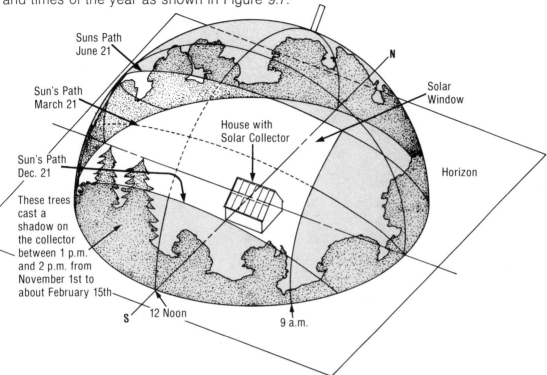

Figure 9.6 Imaginary dome above house with solar collector. Such a dome can be used for drawing a "solar window."

TO CORRECT LOCAL STANDARD TIME TO LOCAL SOLAR TIME

1. Determine the longitude meridian for your location.
2. Select the standard time longitude meridian for your location:

Standard Time Zone	Standard Time Longitude
Eastern Standard	75° longtitude
Central Standard	90° longitude
Mountain Standard	105° longitude
Pacific Standard	120° longitude

3. Multiply the difference between your longitude and the standard time longitude by four minutes per degree.
4. If you are EAST of the standard time longitude, ADD the minutes to the standard time.
5. If you are WEST of the standard time longitude, SUBTRACT the minutes from the standard time.

6. Correct for the time of year, by adding or subtracting the number of minutes shown:

Time Of Year	Number of Minutes
January 1	-5
February 1	-13
March 1	-13
April 1	-5
May 1	+2
June 1	+2
July 1	-3
August 1	-6
September 1	0
October 1	+10
November 1	+15
December 1	+12

Example:

1. Location: 72°
2. Standard time longitude: 75°
3. 4 minutes/degree × (75°-72°) = 12 minutes

4/5. Uncorrected solar noon = 12:00 + :12 = 12:12 PM
6. For November 1: 12 + :15 = 12:27

On November 1 for a location at 72° longitude, Solar Noon occurs at 12:27 EST.

Figure 9.7 Solar noon for various time zones.

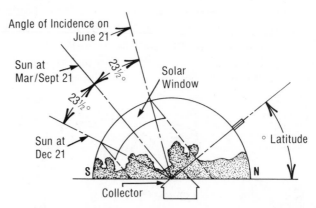

Figure 9.8 A side view of imaginary dome with solar window for 40°N latitude.

Almost all of the useful solar energy for a solar collector must come through this window. The window will show you which objects such as trees or other buildings might interfere with energy collection. Such objects will cast a shadow on the collector during certain hours of the day, at certain times of the year. With the sun lower in the sky during the winter — when the most solar energy is needed — shade becomes an extremely important consideration in locating the solar collectors.

The solar window will change considerably with the geographical area. The top and bottom of the window depend on the latitude, while the sides will depend on the longitude or time zone.

Figure 9.8 shows a side view of a solar window for a latitude of 40°N. The diagram illustrates that the solar energy can reach the collector during all times of the year.

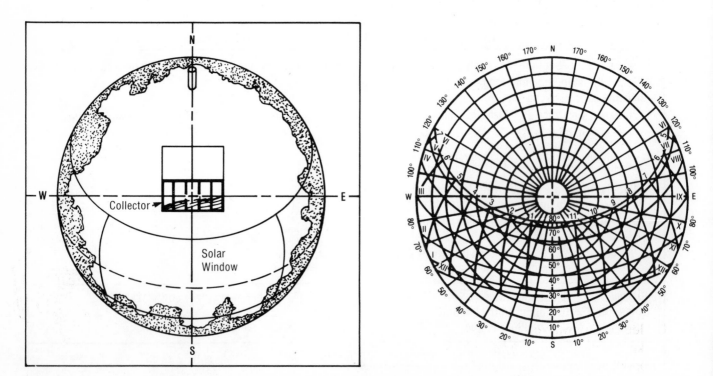

Figure 9.9 A top view of imaginary dome with solar window for 40°N latitude. Sun path diagram is used to draw window.

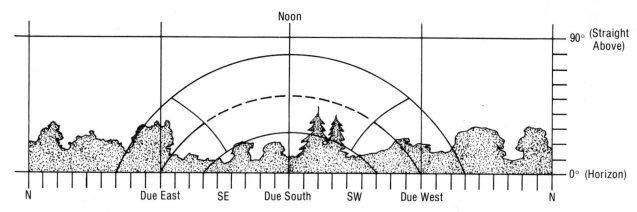

Figure 9.10 A typical Mercator's projection of skydome.

Figure 9.9 shows a top view of a sky dome with a solar window for 40°N. Also shown is a sun path diagram used to draw the window.

The same window can be plotted on a flat surface. This would be a *Mercator's Projection* of the skydome. The latitude and longitude lines are drawn as straight lines, and any obstacles surrounding the collector site can be shown. Figure 9.10 shows how the solar window might be drawn on a typical Mercator's projection of a skydome.

Understandably, each collector site must be studied. No general rule can be given because of the varying solar windows and shading possibilities. Solar windows, plotted as Mercator's projections for various latitudes, are shown in Appendix D. You can use these for identifying possible obstacles to solar energy collection on your property.

THE COLLECTOR POSITION

The location of the collectors for a solar energy system may depend on the structure design, shading, and geographical area. As discussed earlier, you have many options for integrating the collectors with the structure design. This is the case with both existing as well as new structures.

Plotting Solar Shade

A sextant is a very useful tool for plotting solar shade. Such an instrument can be used to measure the angle at which the sun would fall on your proposed collector location. Simple instruments such as that shown in Figure 9.11 can also be used. These instruments help you identify those objects which might shade your collector at different hours of the day and at different times of the year. With such instruments you can plot the obstacles on a Mercator's projection of the solar window.

By plotting the position and height of the shade on the solar window, you can begin making your decision on the collector location. You may have to change the collector location or eliminate the cause of shading, if possible.

Collector Orientation

Looking at the solar window, you can see that the collectors should be oriented to point due south. This is geographical south, not magnetic south. The magnetic lines radiating from the North Pole tend to

Figure 9.11 A simple instrument for plotting solar shade.

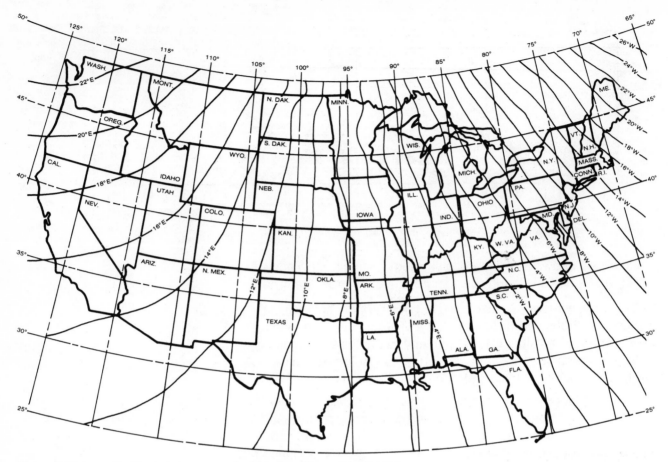

Figure 9.12 Isogonic Chart shows magnetic deviations for continential U.S.

Figure 9.13 The practical limits for collector orientation.

give a false reading when a compass is used to determine the direction of south. These readings vary according to geographical location.

To correct these readings, the "south" indicated by a magnetic compass must be adjusted according to the *Isogonic Chart* shown in Figure 9.12. Such a chart shows the magnetic compass deviation from true north. For instance, if the deviation is 10° east, true north will be 10° west of the indicated magnetic north. True south would then be 10° east of the indicated compass south.

Although a "true south" orientation is generally desired for the collectors, some variation is acceptable. A shift in collector direction may be necessary because of shading, local weather (AM/PM cloudiness), or other reasons.

Any shift from true south should not exceed 15° east or west of south. Such a change will reduce the energy collected to a certain extent. But, such a change will not drastically reduce the energy collected.

Of course, greater changes may be desired in some cases. However, such changes are not recommended. The energy collection is significantly reduced with collectors oriented beyond 15° to 20° east or west of south. Figure 9.13 shows the practical limits for collector orientation.

Collector Tilt

The angle between the collector and a horizontal or level surface is called the *collector tilt angle*. This, too, is an important design factor. The angle will vary according to your geographical area and your energy needs.

As shown in Figure 9.14, the optimum collector tilt angle for water heating alone is the same as the latitude of your geographical area. For instance, if the latitude is 40°N, the collectors would be tilted upward at 40°. This angle would insure maximum energy collection throughout the year.

As shown in Figure 9.15, the optimum collector tilt angle for space heating is the latitude plus 15°. For instance, if the latitude is 40°N, the collectors would be tilted upward at 55°. This steeper tilt is needed to collect maximum energy from a winter sun which travels a lower path across the sky.

These tilt angles can be used as a general guideline. The structure design may or may not require some variation in these angles. If so, variations of 10° on either side of the optimum are acceptable. The change will not significantly reduce energy collection. And, in some cases, a different angle may be desirable for architectural, weather, or other reasons. For example, in colder climates, a steeper angle than optimum may be desired because of increased reflected energy.

MAKING A DECISION

In this section of The Solar Decision Book, you have learned that solar energy systems — both active and passive — can be integrated with the structure architecture in many pleasing and practical ways. The possibilities are given in a variety of current publications. You have learned that knowledge of the sun's radiation, its movement, and how solar energy strikes your building through a "window" is important to collector siting. You have also learned that solar shade, collector orientation, and collector tilt angle are important considerations for collecting solar energy.

You should now be able to make a preliminary decision on the collector site. Such a decision will help you integrate any size and any type of collector into the architecture or landscaping you desire.

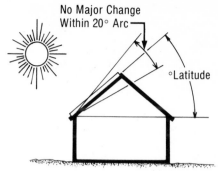

Figure 9.14 Optimum collector tilt angle for solar water-heating system.

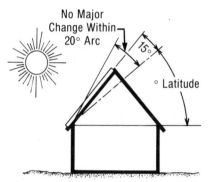

Figure 9.15 Optimum collector tilt angle for solar space-heating system.

DECISION 10

Catch The Sun With Flat-Plate Collectors

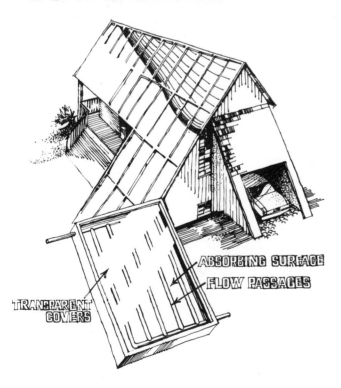

TRANSPARENT COVERS

ABSORBING SURFACE

FLOW PASSAGES

The sun can provide us with an enormous amount of energy. Various news stories have claimed that: if we could capture all of the solar energy striking only four-percent of the area in the United States, solar energy would provide all of our estimated energy needs at the turn of the century. That is estimated at about 105 quad of energy!

Four-percent of the area isn't much. Almost 15-percent is needed to produce our food. About four times the area that could produce our energy.

Unfortunately, the sun's energy does not fall equally on all areas of the country. And the devices for large-scale solar energy production have not been fully developed as yet.

The sun's energy can however, be gathered efficiently for individual energy needs such as water heating, space heating, and space cooling. The energy is still scattered, but a device called a solar collector can gather that energy and help concentrate it to provide usable heat. A heat-transfer medium, such as air or a fluid, can carry the heat from the collector to its point of intended use.

Obviously, a good collector is a very key component in your solar system. Any decision on the type of collector to use will affect the value of your investment. This section of The Solar Decision Book will help you to make the right decision. You will learn that:

- The flat-plate collector offers proven performance.

- The major components in a flat-plate collector use various materials of construction. Some are better than others.

- The thermal performance of various types of flat-plate collectors can be compared by standardized methods.

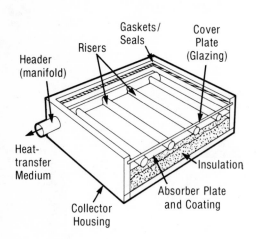

Figure 10.1 A typical flat-plate collector.

Labels in figure:
Header (manifold)
Risers
Gaskets/ Seals
Cover Plate (Glazing)
Heat-transfer Medium
Insulation
Absorber Plate and Coating
Collector Housing

TYPES OF SOLAR COLLECTORS

A solar *collector* is a device used to collect solar radiation (energy) and to convert it into usable heat. There are several types of collectors currently in use. The three most common types are *flat-plate collectors, evacuated-tube collectors,* and *concentrating* or *tracking collectors.*

Because of certain cost and performance advantages, the flat-plate collector is the workhorse of the solar energy industry. It has been used successfully for many years, on more solar energy systems than any other type of collector. Various designs of flat-plate collectors are currently manufactured by more than 175 companies.

In contrast, evacuated-tube collectors and concentrating collectors have seen limited use. The necessary technology has just recently become commercially feasible from a small number of manufacturers. For the most part, these collectors will not see the widespread application seen with flat-plate collectors.

The following sections will outline the operation and construction features of the three types of collectors.

Flat-Plate Collectors

The flat-plate collector has a very basic construction and an easy-to-understand operation. It converts the sun's radiation into heat on a flat surface within a simple box. It can be rigidly mounted on a roof or in a yard. It requires no special technology, reflecting surfaces or lens, nor mechanisms for changing its angle in relation to the sun's position.

A typical flat-plate collector is shown in Figure 10.1. There are seven major parts in a flat-plate collector. These are:

1. a cover plate or glazing;

2. an absorber plate coating;

3. an absorber plate;

4. passages for heat-transfer medium;

5. insulation;

6. a collector box or housing; and

7. gaskets or seals.

The *cover plate* is a transparent sheet of glass or plastic that is mounted above the absorber plate. It creates an air space in the collector. The sun's rays can penetrate the glass and be transformed into heat energy on the absorber plate. The cover plate then prevents this heat energy from escaping through the front of the collector. Some designs use double or triple glazings for added protection against heat loss.

The *absorber plate* gathers the heat energy which is transmitted through the cover plate. It has a blackened *absorptive coating* to improve its ability to absorb energy without reflecting it away. It also has *passages* in which the heat-transfer medium, either air or fluid, can flow and carry off the heat to storage. These passages include *headers* and *risers.* The headers are main passages or manifolds through which the heat-transfer medium enters into or exits from the collector. They are located at the top and bottom of the collector, or on both sides. The risers are flow channels or pipes that distribute the heat-transfer medium across the face of the collector. They are connected to the headers, evenly spaced from one end to the other.

Insulation is packed behind the absorber plate and around the perimeter of the absorber plate. This insulation protects against heat loss through the back and sides of the collector.

All of the components of a flat-plate collector are securely mounted in a weathertight box. This *collector housing* prevents moisture, dirt, dust, and air infiltration from entering the collector and adversely affecting its performance. Rubber seals or gaskets are used to fasten the cover glazing on the housing. These serve to seal out contaminants, but allow easy removal of the cover if collector repairs are needed.

Flat-plate collectors are classified according to the type of heat-transfer medium they use. *Liquid-type collectors* use a liquid as the heat-transfer medium. This liquid might be water, silicone fluid, or one of several other fluids. *Air-type collectors* use air as the heat-transfer medium.

A cross-sectional view of a liquid-type flat-plate collector is shown in Figure 10.2. The basic components of the collector and the collector loop are highlighted. This type of collector is most commonly used on solar systems that provide both water heating and space heating. Compared to air-type collectors, it offers advantages in heat storage and heat delivery for new construction as well as existing buildings.

The operation of a liquid-type flat-plate collector is quite simple. Solar radiation passes through the cover glazing and strikes the absorber plate coating. The coating helps the absorber plate absorb the radiation and turn it into usable heat. This heat, in turn, is absorbed by the heat-transfer medium in the plate's fluid passages. A pump in the collector loop circulates the heated fluid to a heat exchanger. This heat exchanger is part of a secondary pumping loop which removes the heat energy from the fluid and places it into a space-heating liquid storage tank or a water preheater tank. Thus, heated fluid can be pumped away from the collector and replaced with cooler fluid.

A cross-sectional view of an air-type flat-plate collector is shown in Figure 10.3. The basic components of the collector and the collector loop are highlighted. This type of collector is most commonly used on solar systems that provide only space heating and cooling. Its use for water heating is limited.

The operation of the air-type flat-plate collector is similar to that for the liquid-type flat-plate collector. However, air has a much lower heat capacity than water or any of the other heat-transfer liquids. About 3500 cubic feet of air are needed to transport the same amount of heat as one cubic foot of water. As a result, the air-type collector is usually much larger than a liquid-type collector of comparable capacity. The absorber plates are larger. Thin or narrow

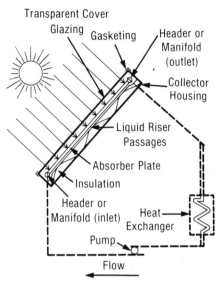

Figure 10.2 A cross-sectional view of a liquid-type flat-plate collector. The basic components of the collector and the collector loop are highlighted.

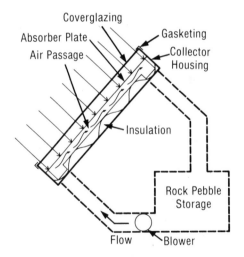

Figure 10.3 A cross-sectional view of an air-type flat-plate collector. The basic components of the collector and the collector loop are highlighted.

COLLECTOR COMPONENT	MATERIALS USED
Cover Plate or Glazing	Glass, fiberglass laminates, thermoplastic sheeting and film
Absorber Plate Coating	Selective metal oxides, nonselective black paints
Absorber Plate	Copper, aluminum, stainless or carbon steel
Fluid Passages	Aluminum or copper tubes, integral spaces in absorber plate
Insulation	Fiberglass, glass foam, foamed thermoplastics
Housing	Metal, honeycombed concrete, fiberglass laminates, extruded thermoplastics
Gasketing	Silicone, EPDM, butyl, PVC elastomers
Heat-Transfer Medium	Air; water, silicone fluid, hydrocarbon oils, water/glycol mixtures

Figure 10.4 Some of the materials being used for collector components.

fluid passages are replaced with much thicker air ducts. The underside of the absorber-plate is usually roughened and made with fins or other such baffles to promote turbulence in the heat-transfer air. The air will not efficiently transfer heat from the absorber plate if it flows in smooth layers under the plate.

With air-type flat-plate collectors, the pump in the collector loop is replaced by a blower. And the liquid storage tank is replaced by a much larger rock-pebble storage bed. A heat exchanger is not used between the collector loop and storage.

The design and performance of both types of flat-plate collectors is well known. Unlike other types of collectors, both collect all three types of solar radiation — direct, diffuse, and reflected. They are especially efficient at lower collection temperatures for water heating and space heating. They are not as efficient as some other collectors at the higher collection temperatures needed for space cooling.

Properly engineered and installed, the flat-plate collector is reliable, safe, and durable with known performance parameters. Designs do vary from manufacturer to manufacturer, however, Figure 10.4 lists some of the materials being used for collector components. The design and materials of construction can have an effect on collector performance. Later sections in this Decision detail the different materials used and show you how various collector designs can be compared for efficiency.

Evacuated-Tube Collectors

Figure 10.5 shows an evacuated-tube collector. This type of collector uses a vacuum to insulate against heat loss and to protect the absorber coating from deterioration. The collector is like an inverted

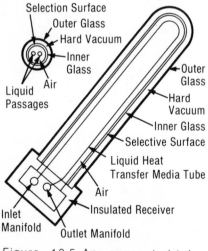

Figure 10.5 An evacuated-tube collector.

vacuum bottle placed over a hairpin-looped, liquid-filled tube. The double-glass bottle has an absorber coating on its inner glass. The sun's radiation comes through the outer glass and strikes the absorber coating. This heats the air contained in the bottle. The heated air, in turn, heats the liquid in the tube. The end of the vacuum bottle fits into an insulated receiver which contains the collector manifold.

This particular design uses both air and liquid for heat transfer. Other designs use a slightly different construction for either all-air or all-liquid heat transfer.

The evacuated-tube collector collects direct solar radiation very efficiently. Some designs show excellent efficiency for both direct and diffuse radiation. It is most efficient for high-temperature applications in which extremely hot water is needed for industrial processing or for operating absorption chillers in residential/commerial cooling. Its efficiency for low-temperature applications such as water heating and space heating is not as good as that of the flat-plate collector.

Concentrating Collectors

Concentrating collectors are sometimes called focusing collectors or tracking collectors. They all work on the same general principle: the sun's radiation is reflected off one or more mirrors to concentrate it onto a very small absorber area. There are many types of concentrating collectors. Most require mechanical devices to shift the collector position and track the sun in its travel across the sky. Some require special optical lens arrangements to help focus the sun's energy.

Figure 10.6 shows a *linear concentrating collector*. It collects direct solar radiation by reflecting the energy off a large curved mirror to a receiver that contains a heat-transfer liquid. This type of concentrating collector must track the sun, and it can collect only direct radiation from a clear sky.

Figure 10.7 shows a *linear-trough, fresnel lens collector*. Solar radiation passing through the lens is bent to strike a small absorber plate at the bottom of a trough which contains a heat-transfer liquid. Again, a tracking mechanism must be used and only clear-sky direct radiation can be collected.

Figure 10.8 shows a *compound parabolic mirror collector*. The unique mirror shape was developed by Dr. Roland Winston, a physicist at the Argonne National Laboratory. This type of mirror has the ability to gather both direct and diffuse solar radiation without tracking the sun. Some periodic changes in tilt angle may be necessary however. In the collector shown, two compound parabolic mirrors are combined with an evacuated tube to make a "fixed" focusing collector. Not all of the mirror is in focus at any one time, and radiation can be gathered from all directions.

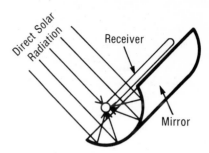

Figure 10.6 A linear concentrating collector.

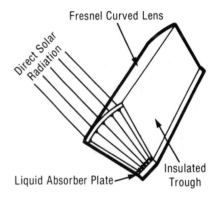

Figure 10.7 A linear-trough, fresnel lens collector.

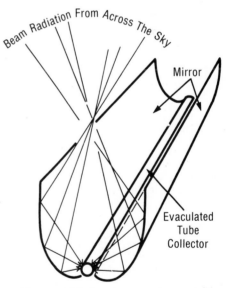

Figure 10.8 A compound parabolic mirror collector. This design uses two unique mirrors and an evacuated tube.

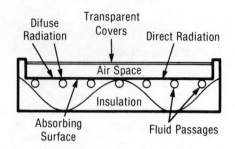

Figure 10.9 A cross-sectional view of a basic flat-plate collector.

Many other types of concentrating collectors have been developed. Most, like the three discussed, show the most promise for industrial-type solar systems. All can produce extremely high temperatures at good efficiencies. Their cost and complexity rule out their use for most residential space-heating applications. Also, most can collect only clear-sky radiation. Such radiation may be infrequent in areas where space-heating is needed most. They do offer high-temperature energy collection for solar cooling and process water heating.

THE FLAT-PLATE COLLECTOR

The flat plate collector is designed to deliver energy at temperatures up to approximately 150°F over outdoor (ambient) temperatures. Its top operating temperatures under flow conditions are in the area of 150° to 240°F. It collects direct, diffuse, and reflected radiation. It does not need to be oriented directly toward the sun at all times of the day, and it requires minimal maintenance over its lifetime. Properly designed and engineered, flat-plate collectors have a life expectancy of 20 to 25 years, or longer depending on the design. The cost of energy delivered from a flat-plate collector depends upon its thermal performance, its installed cost, and its effective life.

The performance of flat-plate collectors is well known and predictable. Performance, or *collector efficiency*, is usually measured as a ratio of the useful energy collected to the incident (available) energy striking the collector cover. As a formula:

$$\frac{\text{Energy Collected}}{\text{Energy Available}} \times 100 = \% \text{ Collector Efficiency}$$

Three major factors affect efficiency of a flat-plate collector:

1. The rate at which heat is removed from the collector. This is labelled "F_R".

2. The heat losses from the collector. This is labelled "U_L".

3. The amount of energy transmitted through the cover and absorbed by the absorber plate. This is labelled "$\tau\alpha$".

When these three factors are known, the collector performance can be predicted with accuracy. They are usually set and controlled by the design of four major collector parts:

- The transparent covers (glazing).
- The absorber plate coating (absorber surface).
- The absorber plate design.
- The collector insulation.

Figure 10.9 shows a cross-sectional view of a basic flat-plate collector.

Cover Plates Or Glazings

The energy striking a transparent surface must be absorbed by the surface, reflected away from the surface, or transmitted through the surface. In other words:

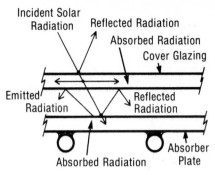

Figure 10.10 The paths of energy radiation in a collector.

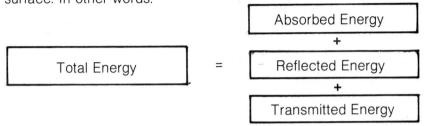

Whether the energy is absorbed, reflected, or transmitted depends on:

- The energy *wavelength*, or the length of each pulse.
- The energy's *angle of incidence,* or the angle at which it strikes the surface.
- The material's *refractive index*, a relative measure of how much the surface will bend the energy beams as they pass through the material.
- The material's *absorptive index*, a relative measure of how much energy the surface will absorb.

An effective collector glazing must transmit the maximum amount of the sun's energy. It must transmit that energy at all angles of incidence. And it must not bend that energy so that it cannot strike the absorber plate.

But an effective collector glazing must also reflect the maximum amount of heat energy which might be given off by the absorber plate. Since this heat energy usually has a different wavelength than the sun's radiation, this can be accomplished with the same material that might transmit the sun's energy.

At the same time, an effective collector glazing must not present a reflective surface or one that would absorb a large amount of energy. Energy reflected off the outside of the glazing is lost for collection purposes. The same is true for energy absorbed by the glazing. However, absorbed energy will increase the glazing temperature. This helps somewhat in maintaining temperatures inside the collector.

Figure 10.10 shows the paths of energy radiation in a collector.

The sun gives off shortwave radiation, with energy at wavelengths of 0.2 to 3.0 micrometers. The heat energy given off by the absorber plate inside the collector is longwave radiation, with wavelengths greater than 3.0 micrometers.

The best collector glazings would have the following characteristics:

- High shortwave transmittance (low refractance).
- Low longwave transmittance (high reflectance).
- Low absorptance at all wavelengths.
- Excellent weatherability and durability.

Figure 10.11 shows a comparison of various materials used for collector glazings. Low-iron-content tempered glass offers a good combination of economy and performance.

Of the nine materials listed, six appear highly satisfactory. Three appear to have some weaknesses that should be looked at carefully. Early polyester film appeared to weather poorly, but recent developments have increased their weatherability. Polyester has high infrared transmittance (poor reflectance). Polycarbonate sheeting appears to have poor solar transmittance. FEP-Teflon appears to have high infrared transmittance.

The physical and mechanical properties, as well as the cost, must be taken into consideration in making a final choice. Tensile, tear, burst, flexural, and impact strengths need to be adequate. The cost per square foot has an important impact on initial installed cost.

Absorbers

The absorber plate in a collector is the portion which gathers the energy transmitted through the glazing. It must be efficient in gathering and holding that energy. And it must be constructed in such a way that the energy can be efficiently removed by the heat-tranfer medium. Obviously, the absorber plate coating and the flow configuration on the plate are extremely important for an efficient collector.

ABSORBER COATINGS. A surface coating is placed on the absorber plate to improve its ability to gather and hold energy. Two general types of coatings are used. These are selective surfaces and nonselective surfaces. Selective surfaces will absorb most of the sunlight hitting them and will emit very little thermal radiation. Nonselective surfaces will also absorb most of the sunlight, but they will emit a high level of thermal radiation.

Selective surfaces will usually be defined in terms of energy wavelengths. The surface will absorb a very high amount of short-wave solar energy. And it will emit a very low amount of longwave heat (infrared) energy.

Glazing Type	Solar (Shortwave) Transmittance, Percent	Infrared (Longwave) Transmittance, Percent	Index Of Refraction	Weatherability And Durability
White Crystal Glass	91.5	2	1.50	Excellent
Low-Iron Tempered Glass	87.5	2	1.51	Excellent
Low-Iron Sheet Glass	87.5	2	1.51	Excellent
Tempered Float Glass	84.3	2	1.52	Excellent
Fiberglass	77 to 87	0.1 to 0.3	1.54	Fair to Good
Sheet Acrylic	80 to 90	2	1.49	Average to Good
Sheet Polycarbonate	73 to 84	2	1.59	Poor to Fair
FEP Teflon	90 to 92	25 to 26	1.34	Fair to Good
Polyester Film	80 to 87	20 to 21	1.64 to 1.67	Fair to Good

Figure 10.11 A comparison of various materials used for collector glazings.

Figure 10.12 shows how an ideal selective surface would perform. Less than five-percent of the solar radiation would be reflected, or 95-percent absorbed. But, in the infrared range, most of the energy would be reflected.

Ideal surfaces do not exist. Real selective surfaces do not have a well-defined critical wave length. Nor do they have uniform properties in the longwave and shortwave ranges. Consequently, emittance values are usually more sensitive to absorber plate temperatures than to energy wavelengths.

If coatings with high-solar-radiation absorptance and high-infrared-radiation transmittance are applied to absorber plates that have low emittance, the result will be efficient collection with low reradiation. Low longwave emittance is normally obtained by giving up some solar absorptance. An efficient balance is made between the two properties. Costs and the life of the coating must also be carefully considered.

Many collectors are designed with nonselective surfaces such as black paint. They are quite efficient. A selective surface is not essential to building a good collector, but it will improve the efficiency over that seen with nonselective surfaces.

Figure 10.13 shows a widely used type of selective surface. This surface appears to have excellent life in the solar system environment.

The absorber plate is first coated with a metal such as nickel. This provides corrosion protection and low thermal emittance. Black chrome is then electroplated onto the nickel. This provides an absorber coating which has high absorption for the solar radiation wavelengths but is transparent in the infrared. Such a coating, properly deposited in the correct thickness, will give 95- to 96-percent absorptivity and 9 to 12-percent emissivity. Its breakdown temperature exceeds 800°F and it appears unaffected by humidity.

In contrast, a black paint nonselective surface will have an absorptivity in the 97-percent range with similar 97-percent emissivity. Selective paints are being formulated, one of which has been reported as having 90-percent absorptivity and only 30-percent emissivity.

You need not be overly concerned with emissivity/absorptivity values and ratios. The thermal performance curve for the collector will show the overall thermal efficiency of the collector including the absorber plate coating. However, you should be quite concerned about the life of the absorber plate coating in the collector design you choose.

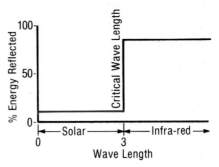

Figure 10.12 The hypothetical performance characteristics of an ideal selective surface.

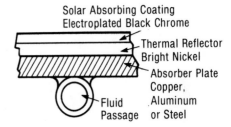

Figure 10.13 A widely used type of selective surface.

ABSORBER PLATES. An absorber plate can be any plastic, rubber, or metal material which will absorb solar radiation and provide passages for a liquid or air to carry off heat collected.

For solar heating of buildings and service water, metal plates have been found to be the most practical. They are almost universally used in flat-plate collectors for medium-temperature applications.

Copper, aluminum, carbon steel, stainless steel, and combinations of these are successfully used in good quality collectors. Each metal has its advantages and disadvantages. No one metal is superior when all factors of performance, life, economics, and weight are taken into consideration.

The absorber plate carries out a number of functions within the collector:

• It gathers and holds solar radiation.

• It transmits the heat generated by the solar radiation to a liquid or air.

• It provides channels or passages to carry the liquid or air through the collector panel to gather the heat.

PLATE CONFIGURATIONS. For liquid-type flat-plate collectors, there are a number of reliable absorber plate configurations. Some of the more popular types are shown in Figure 10.14. These include:

• Tube in strip.

• Tube in panel.

• Tube on strip.

• Tube on panel.

• Waffled panel.

• Fin on tube.

• Finned tubing.

A. *Tube in Strip* — In this method of production, a long strip is extruded with a tube integral within the construction. A typical collector might contain approximately 100 feet of tube and strip which is bent into a serpentine form with the edges of the adjacent fins mechanically screwed or bolted together. This is not a widely used technique. It has the disadvantages of widely separated tubes and a single passage through the panel. If it should become clogged, the liquid will not circulate. Fin efficiencies tend to be low. Tube in strip can also be utilized with parallel risers welded to the top and bottom headers.

B. *Tube In Panel* — In this configuration, a stop-weld pattern is silkscreened onto a sheet of copper or aluminum. Another sheet is placed over the first and the sandwich is sent through a hot rolling mill where the sheets are bonded. No bonding takes place where the stop-weld was silkscreened. The annealed sandwich is placed between two platens and high-pressure air is used to inflate the channels. This system is characterized by extreme passage flexibility. By varying the silkscreen pattern, any tube configuration or size may be employed to vary the wetted surface and fin efficiency. The tube-in-panel approach is the most popular method available in today's market. Improvements are constantly being introduced for greater collector efficiency.

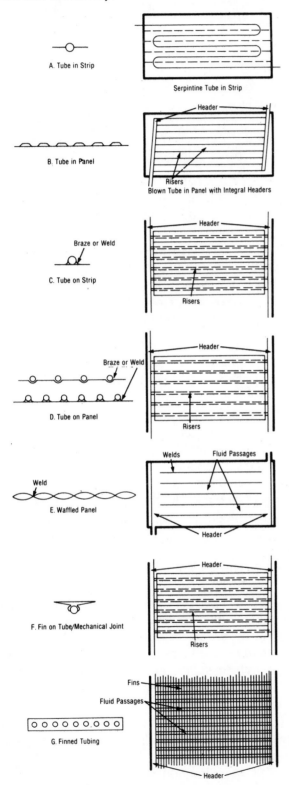

Figure 10.14 Seven of the more popular types of absorber plate configurations.

C. *Tube on Strip* — A metal tube is brazed or welded onto an absorber strip. These strips are then brazed to a top and bottom header to form a parallel set of fluid risers. Tube-on-strip is not popular. For the small shop desiring to build its own absorber panels, it represents a small investment in automatic brazing equipment. It makes a satisfactory panel.

D. *Tube On Panel* — This technique is very similar to tube on strip. It is a popular and proven method of building absorber plates. It has the advantage that, if desired, headers and risers may be preassembled and tested. Also, the absorber plate can be extended over the header. Quite often, the absorber plate is preformed into channels to accept the risers and headers. This appears to be the second most popular method of producing absorber plates at present.

E. *Waffle Panel* — Known by a variety of names and having an infinite number of variations, waffle panel consists of two separate pieces of metal, usually steel, spot welded in a number of places. This construction results in a very strong panel with a high wetted area (i.e. most of the panel is wetted by the heat transfer fluid). It is definitely a high quality type of construction. Its drawbacks are the weight of steel; its much lower heat conductivity; and, in carbon steel, its tendency to rust readily unless the surface is protected. The panels are heavy and have a slow *response time*, the length of time the absorber panel takes to heat up or cool down.

F. *Fin On Tube* — In this method of production, a separate fin is mechanically clamped to the riser tubes. No metal bond exists between the tube and the fin. Consequently, losses in heat-transfer efficiency can be experienced across the bond. If such losses occur in a given collector, the result will show up in the collector's thermal efficiency. The fin and the tubing are usually dissimilar metals such as a copper tubing and an aluminum fin. Galvanic corrosion under moist conditions is a definite possibility with this design and must be guarded against. Mechanically, the panel design is a sound one despite the differences in expansion when dissimilar metals are used.

G. *Finned Tubing* — In the finned tubing design, aluminum fins are placed on copper risers which are then expanded to form a firm mechanical bond. This design represents presently known heating and air conditioning technology at work. The design is unique in that no flat absorber panel exists. Instead the solar radiation falls into the fins which act as reflective traps to catch and hold the energy. This configuration is said to suffer only a two- to four-percent loss in efficiency when the surface coating is deliberately left off for test purposes. This suggests excellent lifetime thermal performance, despite any possible degradation of a surface coating. No corrosion problems between the fins and the risers have yet been reported but long-term performance (10-20 years) is not documented as yet. The design appears to be quite good.

SELECTION CRITERIA. Before choosing a solar collector absorber panel, you might check the design by asking a few key questions. These include:

- Will the panel withstand temperature cycling from -40°F to over 400°F without loosening mechanical bonds or losing strength along soldered, brazed, or welded joints?

- Is there good mechanical adhesion of the surface coating and is it flexible enough to withstand the expansion and contraction of the absorber plate over the same wide thermal range?

- If the panel contains dissimilar metals in contact with each other, what precautions have been taken against corrosion and how many corrosion failures has the manufacturer had?

  (Note: a history of corrosion failures does not indicate that a design should be thrown out of consideration. During the early days of solar, a number of corrosion problems arose and they have been satisfactorily solved. However, some detailed discussion of the subject of corrosion and its problems definitely is in order. The subject is extremely important and part of Decision 11 in The Solar Decision Book is devoted to corrosion and its prevention.)

- Has the absorber coating been throughly tested against thermal failure and moisture failure? Many coatings will not withstand heat and moisture.

- Is the absorber panel mounted in the collector in such a manner that it will not buckle or split during thermal cycling? A hot panel improperly mounted can buckle and either melt or break the surface glazing.

There are many good absorber panel designs from which to choose. You should understand the differences between them and the relative advantages and disadvantages of each. The expected life, the thermal efficiency over that life, and the initial cost are the most important factors in choosing between a number of readily available and excellent designs.

Insulation

For maximum collector efficiency, the back and sides of the collector must be insulated.

The back losses are a function of the thermal conductivity of the insulation and its thickness. The ambient temperature at the back of the collector is normally much lower than at the front. The back is shaded and is receiving no solar radiation.

In a well-designed collector using edge insulation equivalent in R-value to that on the back, the losses are small. They can be approximated by assuming heat flow out through the area of the perimeter.

A set of design requirements for the insulation in a good flat-plate collector should include the following:

1. No degradation, outgassing, or fuming at a temperature of 400°F.
2. No degradation under repeated thermal cycling from –30°F to to +250°F.

3. Thermal conductance less than 0.1 Btu/hr/°F (R = 10 or better).
4. Structurally fabricated to be nonslumping, noncompacting, and nonsettling at a 90° angle under repeated thermal and humidity cycling.
5. Hydrophobic (non-water loving) so it does not pick up and hold water.

There are four basic types of insulation you can consider. These are:

- Mineral Fiber
- Ceramic Fiber
- Foamed Glass and Thermoplastics
- Fiberglass

Mineral and ceramic fiber insulations, with the exception of mineral wool, are materials which are generally designed for higher temperatures than those encountered in flat-plate collectors. They are usually not used because of their high cost. Mineral wool is a loose fill which loses its insulating qualities under humidity cycling. It is not usually considered acceptable.

Urethane foam and expanded polystyrene do not have good temperature stability, are prone to outgassing, and have less than satisfactory flammability characteristics. Their use should be restricted to collectors in which they are completely encased in their own enclosure separate from the glazing and absorber plate. Foamed glass has good characteristics and is generally considered an excellent insulation.

Building-construction-grade fiberglass insulation is generally unsatisfactory. It is formulated with large amounts of phenolic binders which have an upper use temperature below the stagnation temperatures possible in collectors.

High temperature fiberglass board is manufactured with little or no binder and is a very satisfactory insulation. It is made in different densities, so the R-factor should be checked for the particular thickness being utilized.

Collector Housings

The collector housing performs three functions in a properly designed collector. These functions are:

- Provide a weathertight enclosure for the absorber plate and the insulation.
- Provide a stable mounting of the collector module to the supporting structure (building).
- Provide a support mechanism for a weathertight and secure cover glazing.

Like absorber plates, collector housings are many and varied. They can be built of metals, wood, plastics, concrete, and other materials. The most common types are made of:

- Aluminum
- Galvanized sheet metal
- Fiberglass laminates
- High-temperature thermoplastics
- Wood
- Honeycombed lightweight aggregate concrete shells

All six structural materials are satisfactory if properly utilized.

The normal trouble spots in the collector housing are located wherever assembly takes place. This primarily involves securing the back to the sides and the cover to the sides. Remember, particularly with metals, that gross expansion and contraction takes place during thermal cycling. This must be allowed for in the design or assembly.

Gaskets And Seals

The most troublesome part of the collector is the interface between the cover glazing and the collector box. Generally, the collector box has a different rate of thermal expansion than the glazing. If the seals fail, moisture will enter the collector. The glazing will fog and the insulation may slump. These problems can drastically lower the thermal performance of the collector.

There are many ways to seal the glazing satisfactorily. No one method meets the requirements of all applications. However, certain principles should be kept in mind when designing or examining collector gaskets and seals. The gaskets and seals must:

- Resist ultraviolet light for many years.

- Resist outdoor weathering for many years.

- Not harden or become brittle.

- Have excellent adhesion to all surfaces.

- Withstand temperature cycling from –30 to 400°F.

- Have sufficient elongation and compression properties to withstand expansion and contraction without destruction.

Figure 10.15 shows a typical sealing method for either single or double glazings. U-gaskets are employed to absorb expansion/contraction, and a primary weather sealant is applied to insure that no moisture enters the housing. In Figure 10.16, a single E-gasket is utilized on a double glazing. Another common method is to build double-glazed units in much the same manner as "thermopane" windows. The glass is sealed together and then mounted in a U-gasket. In this construction, a primary weather sealant is still recommended.

Many other constructions are practical and possible, but make sure the seals satisfy the requirements shown above.

The choice of gasketing and sealing materials is quite critical. Many elastomers will not take the weathering and temperature demands of the application. For gasketing, both EPDM and silicone rubbers have been found adequate. EPDM rubber is limited to temperatures of 300° to 350°F, while silicone has a much higher temperature limit. For sealants, the industry has settled almost exclusively on silicones. With the use of silicone sealants, several precautions should be taken: three-sided adhesion should be avoided, a thin bead with a 2:1 width-to-depth ratio is best, a sealant

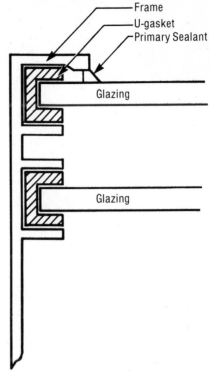

Figure 10.15 A typical sealing method for either single or double glazings.

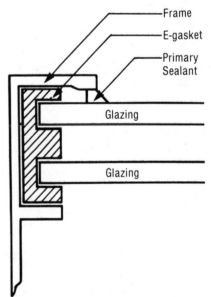

Figure 10.16 A single E-gasket is used to seal and cushion this double glazing. A primary weather seal is also used.

DOW CORNING SILICONE RUBBER SEALANT
SURFACE PREPARATION AND PRIMER RECOMMENDATIONS*

Substrate	Surface Preparation	Recommended Primer
Glass, glazed surfaces, tile	Oil-free solvent wipe	None
Anodized and mill finish aluminum	Oil-free solvent wipe	Dow Corning® 1200 prime coat
Steels: carbon, stainless, weathering	Oil-free solvent wipe	Dow Corning® 1200 prime coat
Plastics such as acrylic, polycarbonate, PVC	Oil-free solvent wipe	Dow Corning® 1205 primer

*Surfaces should be sound, clean and dry, and free of dust, dirt, oils, laitance or other materials which could impair adhesion.

Figure 10.17 Recommendations for primers and surface preparations when using silicone sealants.

bead thinner than ⅛-inch or thicker than ½-inch should not be used. Primers are necessary, insuring maximum adhesion of the silicone sealant to certain surfaces. Dow Corning's recommendations for the primers and surface preparations are given in Figure 10.17.

Silicone sealants are well known as a high-quality construction material and have been widely used for almost 20 years. They have exceptional weathering resistance, as shown in Figure 10.18. This weathering resistance, coupled with high-temperature resistance to more than 450°F, make silicone rubber gaskets and sealants the logical choice for reliable, long-lasting collector designs.

Mechanical Property	Weathering Time*			
	1 year	2 years	5 years	20 years
Hardness, points change	+3 to −6	+2 to −6	+8 to −9	+7
Tensile-strength, percent change	+8 to −25	+4 to −22	+22 to −27	−31
Elongation, percent change	0 to −30	+4 to −28	+14 to −34	−55

*20-year values are for rubber samples aged in Florida; the 1-, 2-, and 5-year results are for samples aged in Michigan.

Figure 10.18 Data that illustrates the exceptional weathering resistance of silicone sealants.

THERMAL PERFORMANCE COMPARISONS

Basic Considerations

The value of two or more competing solar collectors can be determined by considering the:

- End use of the collector
- Cost of purchasing each collector
- Anticipated life of each collector
- Cost of maintaining each collector in operating order
- Thermal performance of each collector
- Geographical location where the collector will be installed

This section will discuss collector thermal performance and compare the generally found operating characteristics of different types of flat-plate collectors.

The thermal performance of a solar collector can be determined in one of two ways. One way is to test it under a number of conditions. This is a time-consuming and expensive task. The other way is to choose a set of standard conditions and mathematically extrapolate the results. This predicts the collector performance under various conditions.

Hottel-Whillier determined a mathematical equation governing the thermodynamic performance of collectors. It permits the use of instantaneous efficiency test methods to adequately rate the efficiency of solar collectors.

The *American Society of Heating, Refrigerating, and Air Conditioning Engineers, Inc. (ASHRAE)* sponsored the development of a uniform method of testing solar collectors for rating purposes. The method uses the Hottel-Whillier equation. This ASHRAE sponsorship has resulted in a standard test method generally accepted in the solar industry. It is titled, *ASHRAE STANDARD 93-77: Methods of Testing To Determine The Thermal Performance of Solar Collectors.*

When considering the thermal efficiencies of the different collectors, you should insist that the collectors to be compared be tested by this standard method. This will insure an accurate comparison.

Collector Efficiency

Collector efficiency is defined as:

$$\frac{\text{Actual Useful Energy Collected}}{\text{Solar Energy Striking the Collector}} = \frac{\text{Solar Collector}}{\text{Efficiency}}$$

As the collector temperature increases above the temperature of the surrounding air, the heat losses from the collector become larger and the useful energy collected becomes less. This results in a lower collector efficiency at the higher temperatures.

The rate at which the collector efficiency decreases is an important measure of the solar collector performance. To determine this efficiency loss rate, the collector efficiency must be measured at different collector temperatures. In Figure 10.19, the collector efficiency is shown dropping off as the collector plate temperature above ambient increases.

The collector used in this example had an insolation (I), or total energy striking its surface, of 250 Btu per square foot each hour. If the incident solar energy changes, the efficiency drop-off rate also changes. The curves shown in Figure 10.20 illustrate this.

The ASHRAE method of comparison allows producing a single curve to represent all conditions of solar radiation. The collector temperature axis (horizontal) is changed to:

$$\frac{\text{Temperature (Inlet) - Temperature (Ambient)}}{\text{Incident Sunlight}}$$

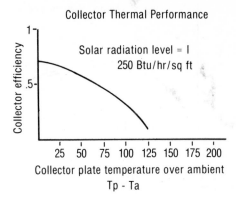

Figure 10.19 The collector efficiency drops off as the collector plate temperatures above ambient increases.

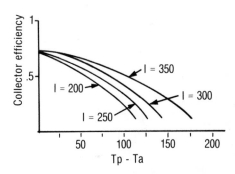

Figure 10.20 The rate of collector efficiency drop-off changes, if the incident solar energy changes.

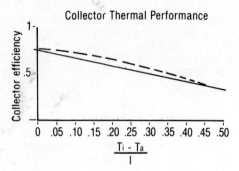

Figure 10.21 A typical ASHRAE thermal performance chart.

Note that the inlet temperature of the collector is used rather than the average temperature across the plate. The inlet temperature can be measured directly and is, thus, more accurate and easier to obtain. The average temperature must be calculated by observing the inlet and outlet temperatures and averaging them.

Figure 10.21 shows a typical ASHRAE thermal performance chart. The plot of collector efficiency is made at a given temperature divided by the incident sunlight. The plot has now become a straight line. Some flat-plate collectors and most concentrating collectors do not follow this straight line. Instead, they follow a curved line indicating a variation of heat loss with receiver temperature. This possibility is indicated by the dashed line on the same graph.

Obviously, when no temperature differential exists, the collector is operating at its theoretical maximum performance. This performance is the product of:

(Heat Removal Factor) (Effective Transmittance Absorptance Factor)

and is designated as:

$$F_R \tau \alpha$$

As the temperature differential increases, efficiency decreases at a rate which is the product of:

(Heat Removal Factor) (Collector Heat-Transfer loss Coefficient)

and is designated as:

$$F_R U_L$$

Thus, the major factors dictating the performance of a collector, F_R, U_L, and $\tau \alpha$ have been described by an accurate test method. The performance of competing collectors can be compared reliably.

The value of the product " $F_R \tau \alpha$ " is found at the intersection of the efficiency curve and the vertical axis in Figure 10.21. So, for this example:

$F_R \tau \alpha = 0.75$

The value of " $F_R U_L$ " is the slope of the efficiency curve. This can be calculated mathematically. First, choose a point on the curve and draw a connecting line to the vertical axis. This forms a triangle. The slope is calculated by dividing one leg (vertical axis) by the other leg (horizontal axis). In the example, if the end point of the curve is used:

$$F_R U_L = \frac{.425}{.50} = 0.85$$

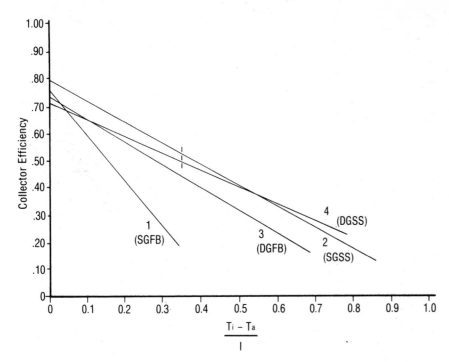

Figure 10.22 Four representative ASHRAE 93-77 curves for liquid-type collector performance.

Figure 10.22 shows four representive ASHRAE 93-77 curves for collector performance. These curves are numbered according to the collector tested. The collectors were all liquid-type with the following differences:

1. Single-glazed; flat-black-paint absorber coating

2. Single-glazed; selective-surface absorber coating

3. Double-glazed; flat-black-paint absorber coating

4. Double-glazed; selective-surface absorber coating

Some interesting observations can be made. Comparing ② with ④, single- and double-glazed selective-surface collectors, the single-glazed collector outperforms the double-glazed collector until about 0.525 on the temperature/radiation axis (horizontal). At radiation levels of 200 Btu/sq ft/hr and a 50°F ambient temperature:

$$\frac{T_i - 50}{200} = 0.525 \qquad T_i = (200)\,(0.525) + 50 = 155°F$$

#	Glazing	Absorber Coating	$F_R \tau \alpha$	$F_R U_L$
1	Single	Flat Black	0.77	1.73
2	Single	Selective Surface	0.80	0.78
3	Double	Flat Black	0.74	0.84
4	Double	Selective Surface	0.72	0.63

Figure 10.23 The relative performance of the four collectors plotted in Figure 10.22.

Radiation (I)	Ambient Temperature	Inlet temp Crossover Point
150	20°F	98°F
250	20°F	151°F
350	20°F	204°F
150	90°F	169°F
250	90°F	221°F
350	90°F	274°F

Figure 10.24 Collector inlet temperatures calculated using various radiation (I) levels and ambient temperatures.

So, at inlet temperatures of 155°F with these radiation and ambient temperature conditions, performance is equal. Below that temperature, the single-glazed collector performs better. Above that temperature, the double-glazed collector performs better.

Using this crossover point, the collectors can be compared under conditions of varying ambient temperatures and radiation levels. Figure 10.24 shows how the performance might be compared.

Where radiation values are low and winter heat is desired, the double-glazed collector is better ... assuming you want 160°F storage water.

Conversely, where radiation values are high, the single-glazed collector would perform very adequately.

If you desired to collect 120°F service water year-round, the single-glazed collector would be very adequate except in low radiation areas. If the cost differential is large, it should definitely be considered.

Many preliminary judgements about which collector should be considered for further thermal analysis by computer programs can be made by similar curve comparisons.

Figure 10.25 shows representative ASHRAE curves for three air-type flat-plate collectors. The collectors in the comparison were:

1. Single-glazed; flat-black-paint absorber coating

2. Double-glazed; flat-black-paint absorber coating

3. Triple-glazed; flat-black-paint absorber coating

Similar calculations and observations as those made for the four liquid-type collectors can be made for these.

The ASHRAE 93-77 standard provides a means of comparing thermal performance of different collectors.

When thermal data is combined with data on the geographical location, use, maintenance, life and cost, the best economic decision can be made. How many Btu can be obtained per dollar?

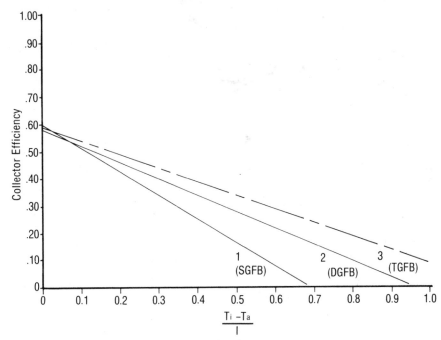

Figure 10.25 Representative ASHRAE curves for three air-type collectors.

MAKING A DECISION

In this section of The Solar Decision Book, you have learned how the scattered energy from the sun can be collected for an active solar system. You learned about three basic types of solar collectors. The flat-plate collector for low-temperature collection and use for water and space heating. The newer evacuated-tube collector for high-temperature collection and probable use for space cooling. And the more costly, complex concentrating collectors for high-temperature applications.

You learned about the design details of various components in the flat-plate collector. The quality, or lack of quality, in the components can affect the collector performance and life. The most popular materials and methods of construction were detailed.

You also learned about a standardized method for comparing the efficiencies of various flat-plate collectors. As the industry grows, such standardized comparisons will become commonplace for all components.

The flat plate collector is recommended for the systems in The Solar Decision Book because of its proven, measurable performance. The decision as to which flat-plate collector to use is yours. Your decision should be based on the intended use, the geographical area, the cost, the expected life, the required maintenance, and the thermal performance for the desired collectors.

DECISION 11

Charge The System With Its Life Blood

All types of solar energy systems have a heat-transfer medium. It is the component that readily absorbs the sun's energy and releases it into storage or into the building.

In active solar energy systems, the heat-transfer medium is one of the key reasons the system can be called active. It is usually air or a liquid which can be circulated to the collectors where it absorbs energy. It can then carry that energy away from the collectors and transfer it to a storage system or a heat-delivery system. The energy collection, storage, and delivery can be continuous or only on demand. The heat-transfer medium is truly the lifeblood as it circulates through the system carrying the sun's energy to the point of intended use.

A liquid offers many advantages over air as a heat-transfer medium. Much more flexibility is possible in system design. However, the wrong liquid, inadequate system design, or improper system installation can result in expensive mistakes when using a liquid heat-transfer medium. Fortunately, such problems can be easily avoided.

This section of The Solar Decision Book will help you to make a decision on the heat-transfer fluid. You will learn that:

- Corrosion can be deadly in a solar system, but several simple steps can be followed to minimize corrosion possibilities.

- The proper choice of gasketing and sealing materials can help prevent troublesome leaks.

- Some liquids are better than others, and the strengths and weaknesses of each can be easily compared.

CORROSION IN SOLAR SYSTEMS

Types Of Corrosion

Several types of corrosion are possible in solar energy systems.

GALVANIC CORROSION. Galvanic corrosion is a type of corrosion which is caused by an electrochemical reaction between two or more different metals. A chemical reaction between the metals causes a small electrical current. This current erodes material from one of the metals.

Solar energy systems generally contain a number of different metals such as aluminum, copper, brass, tin, and steel. This makes the solar system a prime candidate for galvanic corrosion. If the dissimilar metals are physically joined or if they are contacted by a common storage or heat-transfer fluid, the possibility of galvanic corrosion becomes much greater.

Corrosion control thus becomes an important factor in the design and operation of a multimetal solar energy system. Without proper corrosion control, premature system failure may result.

Figure 11.1 shows an elementary setup that demonstrates the principles of corrosion. An aluminum plate and a copper plate are suspended in salt water. An external electrical connection is made between the plates. Salt water is an *electrolyte*, capable of carrying an electrical charge. Because the metals are different, an electrical potential or voltage will exist between them across the electrolyte. This voltage will cause a current to flow through the external circuit. The voltage acts as a force to push metal ions from the *anode* into solution in the electrolyte. The anode is the more electrically positive metal while the *cathode* is the more electrically negative metal.

A metal is more positive (anodic) or more negative (cathodic) than another metal because of its chemical structure. The various metals can be ranked from positive to negative in a *galvanic series*. The more positive the material, the more it will corrode. Also, the corrosive action between two metals next to each other in a galvanic series is small. The corrosion action increases to a high level between two metals widely separated in the series. There is a greater electrical potential. A galvanic series of common metals and alloys is shown in Figure 11.2.

In the simple example of galvanic corrosion shown in Figure 11.1, the aluminum ions will go into solution. The aluminum will become corroded.

If magnesium is substituted for the copper, the reaction shown in Figure 11.3 takes place. The magnesium is more positive than aluminum in the galvanic series. So, the magnesium serves as the anode and the aluminum becomes the cathode. Magnesium ions flow into solution.

The relative "corrodability" of metals in the galvanic series can be used to the designers' advantage. If different metals are needed in a system, they can be chosen to be close in electrical charge. The corrosion will be slow. If two widely separated metals must be used, a

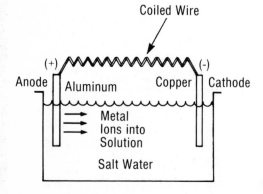

Figure 11.1 An elementary setup that demonstrates the principles of galvanic corrosion.

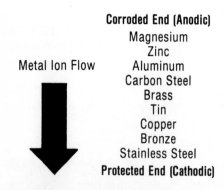

Figure 11.2 A galvanic series of common metals and alloys.

third metal might be added to the system. This metal would be chosen as the most positive of the three. It will be sacrificed as the next most positive material is protected.

This is a typical solution for hot-water tanks, as shown in Figure 11.4. The tank is carbon steel and the water lines are copper. Water is a good electrolyte since it usually contains some amount of dissolved salts. If not protected, such a steel tank would rapidly become corroded due to galvanic action between the steel (anodic) and copper (cathodic).

To prevent this corrosion, a metal which is more anodic than carbon steel is placed in a hot-water tank when it is manufactured. Magnesium is most anodic and is usually chosen. The magnesium must be consumed before the carbon steel becomes the anode and begins to corrode. This prolongs the life of such hot-water tanks.

Many factors affect the rate at which the corrosion takes place. If the electrolyte is agitated increasing the flow, if the temperature is increased, if more oxygen is introduced, if the electrolyte is made more active; the rate of corrosion will generally increase.

The relative size of the anodic metal to the cathodic metal is also very important. If the anode is extremely small and the cathode is extremely large, corrosion will be rapid. If the cathode is small and the anode is large, corrosion will be slower.

In the solar energy system, the most anodic metal must be protected to prevent premature system failure.

PITTING CORROSION. In this type of corrosion, the metal ions leave localized areas causing a pitted surface or uneven corrosion such as shown in Figure 11.5. When heavy metal ions such as iron or copper, plate out on a more anodic metal such as aluminum, a small local galvanic cell can be formed. This will cause a local "pit" or corrosion spot. As the anode is "capped" by the cathodic plating, pitting will usually continue until the metal is perforated.

Heavy metal ions can either come as a natural impurity in a water-mixture heat transfer fluid or from corrosion of other metal parts of the solar system. Pitting corrosion can also be aggravated by the presence of chloride or other chemicals which can be part of the water mixture or a contaminant from solder fluxes.

Aluminum is very susceptible to pitting corrosion, while copper generally is not, except on rare occasions.

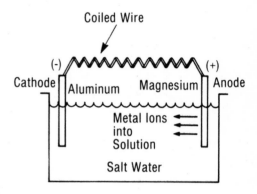

Figure 11.3 Galvanic action between magnesium and aluminum.

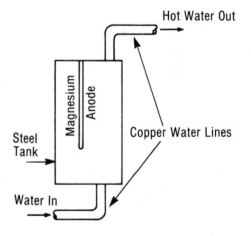

Figure 11.4 A typical design solution for hot-water tanks. A magnesium rod in the tank serves as a sacrificial metal to prevent rapid corrosion of the steel tank.

Figure 11.5 An exaggerated sample of pitting corrosion on a metal surface.

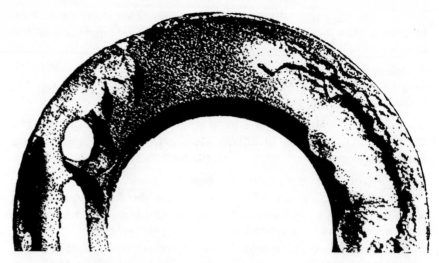

Figure 11.6 A typical example of crevice corrosion on a flange under a leaky gasket.

Figure 11.7 An example of erosion/corrosion caused by localized turbulence.

CREVICE CORROSION. Like pitting corrosion, crevice corrosion occurs in localized areas. Figure 11.6 shows a typical example of crevice corrosion on a flange under a leaky gasket. Crevice corrosion is generally associated with bad gasketing, poorly fitting joints, internal blockages, scale deposits from hard waters, and poor design. Both aluminum and copper are susceptible to crevice corrosion.

EROSION/CORROSION. A metal placed in the atmosphere quickly develops a protective coating due to its interaction with oxygen. A surface metal oxide is formed. High-velocity liquid flow, particularly when coupled with air bubbles or abrasive debris, can mechanically remove this protective film and cause the metal to erode/corrode. An example of such erosion/corrosion is shown in Figure 11.7.

Guidelines For Corrosion Prevention

A practical solar energy system cannot be built using a single type of metal throughout. All solar energy systems incorporate many types of metals. Thus, corrosion prevention is important in all types of systems.

Galvanic corrosion and localized pitting have caused the most failures in solar collector systems. Problems with crevice corrosion and erosion/corrosion have been minor, but these types of corrosion should be guarded against. While there are other forms of corrosion, they have not appeared in solar energy systems.

Since aluminum is usually the most anodic metal in the system, it requires the most corrosion protection. It offers too many advantages not to be used. It is light in weight, high in strength, and easily fabricated. Possibly most important: aluminum is an economical material that has a high thermal conductivity.

AQUEOUS SYSTEMS. When water is used as the collector heat-transfer medium in a closed loop (recirculating system), the water should be deionized, demineralized, and neutralized. A *"getter"* should be installed in the loop as shown in Figure 11.8. It should be galvanically isolated from the panels and directly before them.

A getter is very simply a column or cartridge containing an active metal, such as aluminum, which will be sacrificed to protect some other metal in the system. Any heavy metal ions developing in the system will plate out on the "getter" metal and corrode it. Getters are not 100-percent effective and they must be periodically replaced.

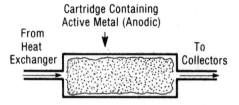

Figure 11.8 A "getter" for corrosion protection in the collector loop.

In addition to the getter, inhibitors should be added to the water. Anodic inhibitors, which are primarily oxidizing agents that halt corrosion, can be used. Chromates, for example, are extremely effective with aluminum. Acidic water and chloride irons, in combination with an insufficient concentration of chromate ions, can stimulate corrosion. This must be considered dangerous, unless the mixture is rigorously maintained at the correct concentration and pH throughout the life of the system.

Anodic inhibitors which form insoluble films can also be used. Phosphates, arsenates and silicates are effective. Filming anodic inhibitors can also aggravate localized corrosion when used in too small quantities. However, they are not as dangerous as oxidizing inhibitors (chromates).

The cathodic inhibitors normally used with iron and steel are generally not used in the solar collector loop. They are not effective for aluminum.

Continual maintenance is the key for successful prevention of corrosion in aqueous solar collector loops. The getter column cartridge must be periodically inspected and replaced. The pH and the inhibitor level must be constantly monitored and adjusted as required. Generally, the services of a water treatment company should be employed to fill and monitor the system properly throughout its life. If maintenance is neglected, just once, localized corrosion can develop. Once started, corrosion usually cannot be stopped.

AQUEOUS/ANTIFREEZE SYSTEMS. An aqueous system must be drained down during freezing weather to prevent mechanical damage. Otherwise, an antifreeze must be added. Ethylene and propylene glycols are the most commonly used antifreezes. When either of these are mixed 50/50 with water, freeze protection down to -30°F is provided while the boiling point is raised to about 230°F.

The addition of glycols to the collector heat-transfer loop presents a new corrosion problem not seen in aqueous systems. At temperatures close to the boiling point, glycols can break down to form glycolic acid. Further breakdown to oxalic acid may also occur. The formation of these acids reduces the pH of the heat-transfer fluid. This makes the fluid corrosive to most all metals including aluminum, copper, and steel. In automotive applications, the normal practice is to add pH buffers such as borates to slow the acidification of the heat transfer medium. However, solar collectors may see temperatures as high as 400°F, while automotive systems operate under 230°F. At these high solar-system temperatures, breakdown is more rapid and the buffer is more quickly depleted.

Anodic inhibitors are still required in the system. However, oxidizing inhibitors such as chromates are not suitable. They promote rapid degradation of the glycol. Extreme care must be exercised in selecting inhibitors for water-glycol systems. Toxicity can be a consideration, particularly with ethylene glycol. Again a getter column would provide additional corrosion protection.

The strict schedule of maintenance mentioned for aqueous systems is also required for water-glycol systems. However, because of the buffer depletion and subsequent acid formation problem, the system must be monitored for pH changes continually and drained and refilled as soon as the pH begins to turn acid.

NONAQUEOUS FLUIDS. Fluids which are non-electrolytes appear to be a practical solution to the multimetal corrosion problem. Current practice indicates that there are several promising candidates of this type in the marketplace. These include silicone heat-transfer fluids. To date, no corrosion problems have been seen with this fluid. The various heat-transfer media, aqueous and non-aqueous, will be compared later in this decision.

OTHER CONSIDERATIONS. "Internal corrosion" within the collector loop fluid passages is not the only area for prevention measures. There are also two other places where corrosion prevention must be carefully practiced:

● Between solar storage and the heat load.
● On the external surfaces of the solar system metals.

Solar storage is usually accomplished with water held in large tanks. These tanks cycle from 45° to 200°F and can be made from a variety of materials. Solar storage water must be properly inhibited and maintained. The corrosion problem differs, depending upon the metal combinations, and therefore cannot be generalized. A local water treatment company should be consulted for details.

For the external surfaces of the solar collector loop, the following corrosion-prevention techniques should be practiced. Regardless of what medium is chosen for internal heat transfer, external failure is generally much less likely to occur.

● Two widely dissimilar metals such as copper and aluminum should never be directly connected. A nonconducting joint or flange should be used. An example would be a high-temperature flexible rubber hose. This, too, should be carefully chosen for compatibility with the heat-transfer agent and the temperature conditions. Generally, steel-to-brass, copper-to-steel, and copper-to-brass connections do not cause serious problems.

- Moisture from condensation or leakage should be carefully avoided. Without an aqueous medium present, corrosion rarely occurs. Contamination from salt spray and atmospheric pollutants such as sulphur dioxide must be avoided.

- Collector surface paints and platings must be chosen and applied with care to prevent galvanic effects and crevices. The rear of the panel must be protected against insulation decomposition corrosion. This is normally accomplished with good design in the manufacture of the panel.

GASKETING/SEALING IN SOLAR SYSTEMS

A number of elastomeric (rubbery) gasketing and sealing materials are used on solar energy systems. Some are excellent, some average, and some poor. Even the smallest leaks should be avoided to insure proper performance of the system with minimal maintenance.

The more common gasketing materials include:

- Natural rubber
- Styrene-butadiene rubber (SBR)
- Butyl
- Nitrile
- Polysulfides
- Neoprene® elastomers
- Silicone
- Acrylics
- Hypalon® elastomers
- Fluoroelastomers

Natural rubber has a maximum service temperature of 225°F, with good mechanical properties. It is impervious to water, has fair resistance to acid and alkalies, poor resistance to oils and gasoline. It has poor weathering and aging properties. It is probably a poor choice for most systems.

Styrene-butadiene rubber (SBR) has a maximum service temperature of 250°F. Its water resistance is excellent, alkali and acid resistance is fair to good. It has poor resistance to gasoline, oils, and solvents.

Butyl rubber has a maximum service temperature of 300°F. Like SBR, it has good resistance to water, alkalies and acids, but poor resistance to oils, gasolines, and most solvents.

Nitrile rubber also has a 300°F service temperature. It has excellent resistance to water, oils, and gasoline; but, only fair resistance to acids and alkalies.

Polysulfides have maximum service temperatures of only 150°F. They are usually poor choices on collector glazings. They do however, have excellent resistance to oils, gasoline, hydrocarbon solvents, water, and alkalies. They have fair acid resistance and poor mechanical properties.

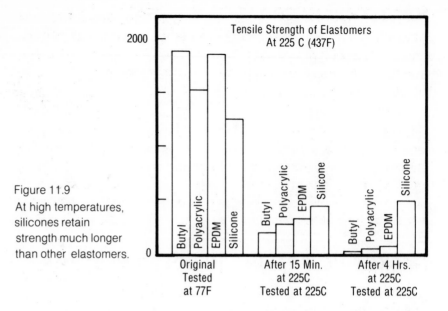

Figure 11.9
At high temperatures, silicones retain strength much longer than other elastomers.

Neoprene® elastomers will withstand a 250°F maximum surface temperature. They have excellent mechanical properties and good resistance to nonaromatic petroleum oils, fatty oils, and most solvents except for aromatic, chlorinated, or ketone types. They have good water and alkali resistance, but only fair acid resistance.

Various silicone polymers withstand service temperatures up to 600°F. They have excellent heat resistance, good water resistance, poor resistance to high-pressure steam, fair to good acid/alkali resistance, and poor resistance to oils and solvents.

Although silicones are not as strong as certain other elastomers at room temperature, they retain their strength much better at high temperatures. As shown in Figure 11.9, the silicone is stronger than other elastomers at temperatures in the range of collector panel temperatures. For that reason, silicone sealants are especially valuable as long-lasting adhesives and sealants on collector glazings. A typical use for silicone rubber seals on collector panels is shown in Figure 11.10.

Acrylics have maximum service temperatures of 450°, but poor cold resistance.

Hypalon® rubber has a maximum service temperature of 250°F with excellent resistance to oxidizing chemicals, ozone and weathering. It also has relatively good resistance to oils and grease, but poor resistance to aromatic or chlorinated hydrocarbons. Its mechanical properties are good.

Fluoroelastomers such as Viton® rubber have a maximum service temperature of 450°F and can be used at those high temperatures with many fuels, lubricants, hydraulic fluids and solvents. They are highly resistant to ozone weathering and they have good mechanical properties. They rank with the fluorosilicones as the premium materials for a combination of solvent, weather, and high-temperature resistance. Their mechanical properties are excellent.

®Neoprene, Viton, and Hypalon are registered trademarks of E.I. duPont de Nemours.

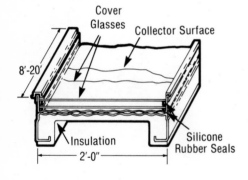

Figure 11.10 Silicone rubber seals on collector glazings.

HEAT-TRANSFER LIQUIDS

Analysis of the system load and operating conditions will lead to the choice of a heat transfer fluid. The system components and controls are then designed based on the load, operating conditions, and properties of the fluid.

A general checklist of fluid properties can be used to select a fluid that will give the optimal solar system in terms of dollars per Btu of energy supplied. The choice of a heat-transfer fluid should not be made unless its effect on total solar system cost is clearly understood.

Identify Real-Time Service Load

A liquid solar system can be looked at as being no different than any other liquid heat-transfer system, with two exceptions. First, the fuel is different and characteristically quite dispersed in comparison to conventional fuels. Secondly, for nontracking solar systems, the fuel is uncontrolled. The low heat flux of the sun requires a large-surface-area collector.

The first step in heat transfer system design is to identify the real-time service load. A determination of the desired storage temperature will lead to a determination of maximum panel operating temperature. Weather conditions determine minimum fluid temperatures in the panel. Service load and seasonal load fluctuations determine elapsed time at minimum (night), operating (load), and maximum (stagnation) conditions. Thus, a solar space-heating system in Chicago may experience minimum temperatures of -20°F, panel operating temperatures of 75° to 180°F and stagnation temperatures of 400°F. Stagnation will likely occur from April to August with the heat-transfer fluid experiencing 300 to 800 hours per year at high temperatures.

Fluid Capabilities

Before selecting a heat-transfer fluid to handle these conditions, several other requirements must be considered. The fluid should be essentially nontoxic and environmentally acceptable. It should be compatible with multimetal systems, including iron, aluminum, bronze and copper. Also, for residential systems, the *flash point* of the fluid should exceed the system stagnation temperatures. The flash point is the temperature at which the fluid vapors will flashover if an ignition source is present.

With these requirements in mind, select a fluid that will provide the desired level of safety and reliability. The fluid's physical properties then form the basis for specific system design. The fluid heat-transfer capacity will determine the required flow rates. The fluid viscosity and density will dictate proper piping size in the collectors, transfer loop and heat exchangers. After pumping requirements are determined, choose the pump. Then match the resulting configuration with system demand, design the control system, and the planning is complete.

While none of this is new or very sophisticated, the flow of events is critical. You cannot select a high-efficiency solar collector with ⅜-inch diameter fluid channels, design a system, and then look for a premium fluid that will not freeze or boil, and is thermally and oxidatively stable at 400°F. The results are complaints that the fluid is too thick to pump, and requires too high a ΔT in the heat exchanger. Time has shown that it is more practical to look for a heat exchanger to fit the chosen heat transfer fluid.

Solar System Economics

Putting the transfer fluid selection in its proper place in the design sequence: it is important to understand what impact this choice has on the total system. Solar systems must be cost effective. Of course, safety and reliability must be looked at as essential ingredients in a cost effective solar system. The equation in Figure 11.11 lays out the major points of the solar system economics.

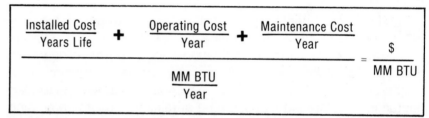

$$\frac{\dfrac{\text{Installed Cost}}{\text{Years Life}} + \dfrac{\text{Operating Cost}}{\text{Year}} + \dfrac{\text{Maintenance Cost}}{\text{Year}}}{\dfrac{\text{MM BTU}}{\text{Year}}} = \frac{\$}{\text{MM BTU}}$$

Figure 11.11 A formula for determining economics of solar system cost per one million Btu.

Property	Silicone	Water	Water/Glycol	Hydrocarbons
Viscosity, –40 F 180 F				
Flash Point-COC				
Fire Point				
Toxicity				
Decomposition Temperature				
Stability — Thermal Oxidative				
Vapor Pressure 400 F				
Metal Compatibility				
Products of Decomposition				
Specific Heat				
Thermal Conductivity				
Specific Gravity				

Figure 11.12 A checklist for comparing heat-transfer fluids.

Fluid selection has a major effect on both the installed cost and the maintenance cost.

Most points of concern for solar systems are related to fluid properties. Freezing, boiling, corrosion, scaling and required homeowner attention all relate to the properties of the heat-transfer fluid. These are design considerations only in that any deficiency in the chosen fluid must be taken care of by system hardware and controls — often at much additional expense.

A properties checklist is helpful in examining various heat tranfer fluids for possible use. The four basic types of heat transfer fluids are identified in the checklist shown in Figure 11.12.

Some Other Important Considerations

Two other important items when considering residential solar systems are (1) fluid odor, and (2) the effect of the fluid on materials of construction such as shingles, paint, floor tile and carpeting.

Of all the properties, a few are worth highlighting.

FLASH POINT. The flash point is a critical safety consideration. The flash point should be well above the stagnation temperature of the collectors. For safe operation, if the collectors stagnate at 380°F, choose a fluid which has a flash point of 425°F or higher.

TOXICITY. Distilled water in a drainback system cannot be considered to be a nontoxic fluid if you are using toxic corrosion and scale inhibitors. Also, consider the products of decomposition. If, upon aging, the fluid breaks down into strong acids, its toxicity may change.

STABILITY. Differentiate between thermal and oxidative stability. Many heat-transfer fluids offer good service life at 500°F when the system is blanketed with dry nitrogen. In a non-blanketed system they degrade rapidly, due to oxidation, at much lower temperatures. The presence of certain metals, such as copper, can greatly accelerate degradation of some fluids. Also, every fluid has some temperature at which the molecules will decompose. Some fluids used today in many solar systems have decomposition temperatures in the range of 280° to 320°F.

SCALE. Inside your collectors, scale can cost many Btu per year. In the cost equation, this greatly affects the cost effectiveness of the total system.

PRODUCTS OF DECOMPOSITION. A fluid that degrades 10-percent, with a resulting increase in fluid viscosity, is probably preferable to a fluid that degrades one-percent with the resulting formation of scale and hydrochloric acid.

Comparison Of Fluids

An increasing number of solar system problems related to heat-transfer fluids has led more and more people in the solar industry to choose their fluids with great care. The following overview of the four main classes of fluids is offered as a starting point in selection of a fluid, always remembering that any fluid can be made to work with proper design and sufficient quality control to protect against its shortcomings. The goal, however, is to end up with the safest, most reliable and most cost-effective solar system.

WATER. Untreated water has the strengths of being nontoxic, environmentally safe, available and inexpensive. The thermal efficiency of water is high but this property is of little cost benefit other than reducing heat exchanger area. On the negative side, water will freeze, support galvanic corrosion, boil at low temperature, and promote scale formation. These properties require the use of more expensive metals, more complicated controls and periodic addition of corrosion inhibitors — a costly procedure, especially if it is forgotten! Where water is used, many designers now specify inhibited distilled water in a carefully designed and properly installed drainback system.

WATER/GLYCOL. Water/glycol mixtures will not freeze down to –35°F. Various additives can help prevent scale formation and offer corrosion protection for the short term but the fluid must be replaced frequently. This is not only costly, but also results in an environmental problem: how to dispose of significant volumes of water/glycol safely.

Other negative properties of water/glycol: it boils at temperatures only a little higher than the boiling point of water, it supports galvanic corrosion, it is difficult to seal, and most importantly, it has low thermal stability. The glycol decomposes rapidly at 280° to 300°F, forming sludge and organic acids. This can lead to corrosion if the fluid is not replaced, even in copper systems. The sludge can decrease the efficiency of the solar collectors. In system design these characteristics lead to the use of more expensive metals and more complicated controls.

Drainback is a questionable answer to these problems with glycols. The fluid film left behind can bake under stagnation temperatures and scale up the collector. Under any design, the reliability and durability of a water/glycol solar system depends solely on how well the homeowner maintains the system.

HYDROCARBONS. Hydrocarbon heat-transfer fluids — typically highly refined mineral oils — are low cost, nonvolatile, relatively nontoxic, environmentally acceptable, and they offer no direct damage due to freezing. However, they have relatively poor oxidation stability and thermal stability at high temperatures, resulting in sludge and acid formation. Excessive thickening at low temperature and incompatibility with copper are also problems. They harm some materials of construction (roofing, shingles), and have relatively low flashpoints.

Their low-temperature viscosity can overload pumps and lead to missed solar energy during periods of low temperatures. Severe damage is unlikely, though.

The question of fluid stability is a complex one. The rate and method of decomposition is a function of fluid volume, amount of oxygen exposure, temperature, time and the presence of catalytic metals. A hydrocarbon exposed to copper and significant air for 72 hours at 250°F can significantly degrade and become quite acidic.

In addition to stability, the flashpoint of hydrocarbon heat-transfer fluids is a concern. Typical closed-cup flashpoints run from 300°F to 420°F, but the higher flashpoint fluids have a high viscosity. To insure safe operation, these fluids should be used only in lower efficiency panels that have a maximum stagnation temperature from 250° to 375°F.

The risks of damage to roofing and their materials due to spills or leaks may be acceptable to obtain the protection from freeze damage and pressure at a moderate cost. Fluid replacement will be less frequent than with glycol/water.

SILICONE FLUIDS. Silicone heat-transfer fluids have four technical strengths that have a direct bearing on total costs of closed flat-plate collector solar systems:

1. They do not freeze.
2. They do not boil.
3. They do not corrode common metals, including aluminum.
4. Current evidence indicates that they should last the life of a closed-loop, flat-plate collector, solar system stagnating under 400°F.

Silicone fluids are also environmentally acceptable, virtually nontoxic, have no odor, will not harm common materials of construction, and have high flash and fire points.

Using silicone heat-transfer liquids, designers can create sealed solar systems with minimum hardware and the simplest of controls. Since there is no need to protect against freezing or boiling, the basic solar loop consists of a pump that is turned on or off by the appropriate controls. Additional hardware such as solenoid valves, resistance heaters, radiators and associated controls are unnecessary. The system owner need not monitor, replace, or dispose of used fluid periodically, and there's no risk of system damage if this maintenance is not done by the owner. Finally, solar collector efficiency will not degrade with time since there is no scale and sludge buildup. In short, the use of silicone heat-transfer fluid results in safety, simplicity, reliability and sustained performance.

Of course, silicone fluids are not ideal. The heat capacity and viscosity are not like those of water. In the early days of solar systems, this raised much concern in the industry over "pumping problems" and system "inefficiency". If you try to use a silicone in a system designed around water, the concern may be justified. Proper design techniques on hundreds of solar systems now using silicone heat-transfer liquids have shown them to be safe, reliable, and efficient. One system sat stagnant in New England for eight months with no ill effect on the fluid. Installation errors have led to spills on roofing and carpets, and the nonaggressive nature of the silicone paid off handsomely.

Field experience with silicone heat-transfer fluid has been favorable. However, one economic objection and one technical problem have emerged: high initial cost and seepage of fluid at pipe joints. High initial costs of the fluid, however, are offset by lower system costs and lower operating expense. Some of the systems did have slow seepage; surprisingly, most often in soldered joints. Poor workmanship and failure to air-pressure test the system for leaks before use proved to be the big problem. These installation problems are discussed in Decision 21.

MAKING A DECISION

In this section of The Solar Decision Book, you learned that corrosion protection, proper gasketing, and selection of the proper heat-transfer fluid are important for system performance. You learned about the different types of corrosion normally seen in solar energy systems. You have some guidelines to follow in protecting your system against corrosion. You learned about the general properties of various gasketing and sealing materials. In choosing a certain material you should select the one that best meets your system's operating conditions. You also learned about general design considerations for heat-transfer fluids. You should be able to compare the strengths and weaknesses of the various choices. The right fluid is the one which gives the maximum performance for the longest period of time without frequent maintenance and replenishment or replacement.

DECISION 12

Pump The Energy Indoors

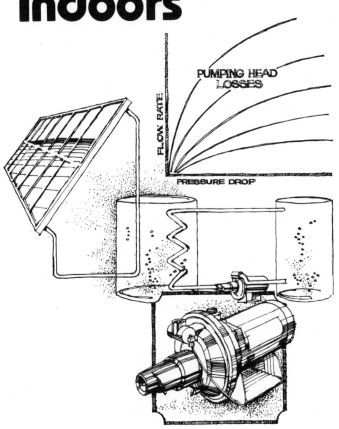

The human body is a mass of living cells. Each has its own special function. And each has its own special need for life-sustaining nutrients.

With the right diet, you can collect the nutrients needed by each and every cell daily. Food and drink can be converted into usable energy. This nutrient energy can then be transported by your blood to where it is needed. For this to happen however, you need a heart. A mechanism that continuously pumps the life-giving blood to and from the cells.

The pumps in an active solar energy system play a similar role. They circulate the fluid that transports usable energy to key components in the system. A pump in the collector loop circulates heat-transfer fluid to a water preheater tank or storage tank. A pump in the storage loop circulates water to a collector-loop heat exchanger to pick up collected energy from the heat-transfer fluid. A pump in the heat-delivery loop circulates heated water from solar storage or from an auxiliary heater to a load heat exchanger.

The pumps should be properly selected and sized for the system design. They are the heart of the system. This section of The Solar Decision Book will help you to make the right decision on pumps for your solar system. You will learn that:

- Certain pump designs can be used for open-loop systems, others for closed-loop systems.
- Pumps can be used in combination to gain flow and possible economic advantages.
- Collector flow rates and pumping friction losses can be calculated to aid pump sizing.

GENERAL CONSIDERATIONS

Pumps are used in solar energy systems to move heat-transfer fluids from one part of the system to another. Usually, *centrifugal pumps* of various designs are used. This type of pump has blades that rotate and whirl the fluid around so that it acquires sufficient momentum to discharge from the pump body. The fluid is thrown outward by centrifugal force. Hence, the name: centrifugal pump.

Pumps are used in several loops of the solar energy system. A typical solar system for heating water would have a pump in the collector loop. Depending on the type of water preheater tank, this pump would be in the line from the tank to the collectors or from a heat exchanger to the collectors. For solar systems using an external heat exchanger between the water preheater tank or solar storage tank, another pump would be placed on this secondary loop. It would be in the line from the tank to the collector loop heat exchanger. For systems that have space-heating capabilities, a third pump would be included to move heated water from solar storage or the auxiliary heater to the load heat exchanger. And for systems with cooling capabilites, the system might include as many as four pumps.

For pumping purposes, there are two basic types of pipe circuits or loops to consider. These are *open loops* and *closed loops.* In selecting pumps, you must first determine the type of loop in which it will be operating. The two types call for different pump designs.

Pumps For The Collector Loop

OPEN-LOOP SYSTEMS. If the water in the system is open to the atmosphere ... anywhere; or if the water will be used as drinking water, you have an open loop. Open loops require a pump in which all water-wetted surfaces must be bronze or stainless steel to prevent corrosion and a resultant short pump life.

Open loops require sufficient horsepower to overcome the *vertical head.* This is the vertical rise to the highest point in the system. The horsepower must also be sufficient to overcome friction losses within the system.

Figure 12.1 shows a typical draindown system with an open loop. In this system, the pump turns on and lifts the water from the tank's internal heat exchanger to the highest point in the system. Once there, some of the water drains, by gravity, back into the heat exchanger through the downleg. When the pump stops, the water drains back through the pump and the downleg, putting all the water back into the heat exchanger.

The pump must be designed to overcome friction losses in the heat exchanger, piping, and collector. It also must overcome the vertical head between the top of the water in the heat exchanger and the highest point in the system.

The level of water in the heat exchanger drops when the pump charges the system. So, the designer should calculate vertical head from the pump inlet to the highest point.

Centrifugal pumps will not operate without some head at the pump inlet. Such a system must be sized so that the volume of the water in

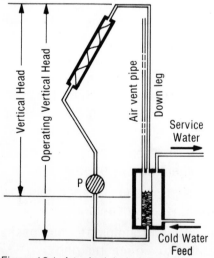

Figure 12.1 A typical draindown system with an open loop. Open loop is caused by air vent in water tank.

the heat exchanger is larger than that which can be contained in a collector system. Also, the line with the pump should be connected to the bottom of the heat exchanger. These two design considerations help insure pump inlet head under all conditions.

The vertical head can be calculated quite simply. Measure the vertical distance from the pump inlet to the highest point in the system, but ignore the total length of pipe and its size. Horizontal pipe runs do not add vertical head, nor does the amount of water in the pipe affect the head. Head is measured in vertical feet of water. Suppose the vertical rise is 22-feet. Even though the total pipe run may be 150-feet, the vertical head is 22-feet of water. Only the vertical rise. During operation, the pump constantly works to overcome this head.

There are also friction losses caused by pumping the liquid through the system pipes, elbows, tees, and other components. In this open system, these losses are incurred from the bottom of the heat exchanger to the highest point in the system. There are no friction losses for the pump to overcome in the downleg. However, the downleg should be larger in diameter than the riser to the collectors.

Friction losses in the system are a function of fluid velocity and total pipe length. They will be discussed further in a later section of this Decision.

CLOSED-LOOP SYSTEMS. Closed-loop systems are not open to the atmosphere. They circulate the same liquid month after month through the loop.

Depending upon the heat-transfer fluid used, the material requirements for the pump can be less stringent than those for open-loop systems. A pump with an iron housing and impeller can be used. Long pump life can be expected provided that noncorrosive heat transfer liquids are utilized.

Figure 12.2 shows a pump in a closed-loop system. In this system, the loop consists of the heat exchanger, the collectors, the pump, and the associated piping. The system is filled with heat-transfer liquid and the air is purged.

There is no vertical head in this closed system. The weight of the liquid in the downleg balances the weight of liquid in the riser. Only friction losses need to be considered. Friction losses in the entire system, including the downleg, must be included.

This closed-loop system takes far less pump horsepower to operate than an open-loop system.

COMBINATION SYSTEMS. There are also combination systems. During start up, these systems must pump the liquid to the top of the collectors. After start up, they operate as closed loops. These systems generally employ draindown for freeze protection and are usually made in many configurations. The rule to remember is: if at any time the loop is open and the vertical riser is not counterbalanced by downleg liquid, an open system for pump-designing purposes exists. The pump must then be sized large enough to overcome the vertical head during start up. Also, a bronze or stainless steel pump must be used.

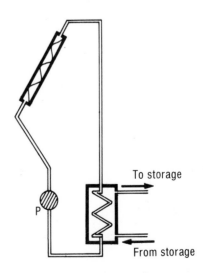

Figure 12.2 A pump in a closed-loop system.

Pumps For The Storage Loop

The closed system is the most attractive design for the collector loop. The other pump locations in the solar system must be examined to determine whether they are open or closed loops.

Figure 12.3 shows a storage loop with a tank for service water purposes. It uses an external heat exchanger.

This system must be considered as an open-loop system for pump design purposes. The pump is circulating constantly replenished water which can contain dissolved oxygen and corrosive salts or impurities. Its pH is generally either acid or alkaline, rarely neutral. The system normally operates under pressure from the well or city water supply. Thus, the pump must be bronze or stainless steel to insure adequate life.

If the system is properly purged of air, no vertical head will exist. The pressurized tank exerts equal pressure upon the inlet and outlet, and head can be ignored. Only friction losses need to be considered:

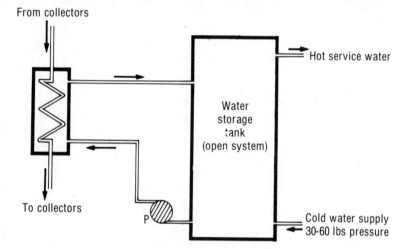

Figure 12.3 A storage loop with a service water storage tank and an external heat exchanger.

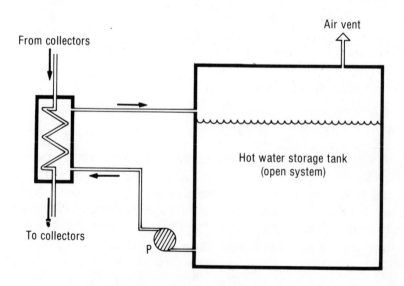

Figure 12.4 A storage loop with a hot-water storage tank for space heating.

Figure 12.4 shows a storage loop with a hot-water storage tank for space heating. This particular configuration is vented to the outside air and represents a commonly used storage system. It must be treated as an open system. While it circulates the same storage liquid, most likely inhibited and demineralized, fresh oxygen is available to the pump. Again, a bronze or stainless steel pump is required. Any vertical head between the inlet of the pump and the highest point in the system must be included in the pump design. In addition, the friction losses must be calculated.

Figure 12.5 shows a closed storage tank. No air is contained in the system and the same treated water is recirculated. This can be considered a closed-loop system.

Load Loop Pumps

Whether the loop going to the load is closed or open will usually depend upon the type of storage tank.

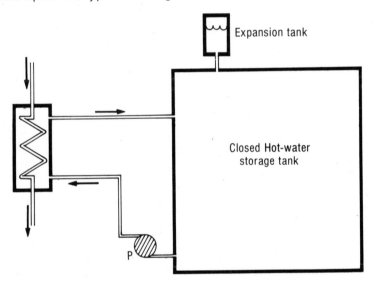

Figure 12.5 A closed-loop storage system.

PUMP SELECTION AND USE CRITERIA

Types of Centrifugal Pumps

There are three types of centrifugal pumps to consider:

- External-motor-driven pumps with a mechanical shaft seal
- Canned wet-rotor pumps
- Magnetic-drive pumps

Figure 12.6 shows a simplified cutaway view of a pump with an external motor and a mechanical shaft seal. There are four basic parts to a mechanical seal:

- Shaft seal
- Spring loading with bellows
- Pump seal
- Pump seal seat

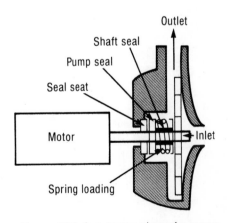

Figure 12.6 A cutaway view of a pump with an external motor and a mechanical shaft seal.

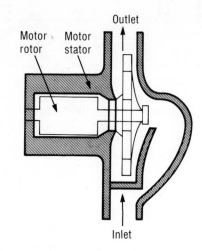

Figure 12.7 A canned wet-rotor pump.

The mechanical seal is fastened to the motor shaft and turns with the pump. A tight seal fit, utilizing Teflon or a similar material, fastens the mechanical seal to the shaft and to the pump seal. This entire assembly is spring-loaded. It runs against a seal seat which does not rotate and is fixed to the pump body. The seal wear takes place between the seat and the spring-loaded seal.

The mechanical seal and seat in this type of centrifugal pump come in various qualities. They are designed for various end-use purposes and temperatures.

Unless high-quality mechanical seals are utilized, these seals are a common source of leaks. Wherever high temperatures are encountered and heat-exchanger fluids other than water are used, mechanically sealed pumps should be avoided.

Figure 12.7 shows a canned wet-rotor pump. In this pump, the mechanical seal is not required. The field windings of the motor (stator) are contained in the pump body while the rotor turns in the pump liquid. Pumps of this type are highly reliable and are not prone to leakage.

Figure 12.8 shows a magnetic-drive pump. Magnets in the motor shaft attract and drive magnets in the impeller shaft. Again, the mechanical seal is not needed. This is also a very reliable pump.

Only canned wet-rotor and magnetic-drive pumps are recommended for the collector loop. All three types of pumps are satisfactory for pumping water in the storage and load loops.

Body And Bearing Gaskets

Most pumps contain both body gaskets and bearing gaskets. All gasketing materials should be designed to operate at the extreme temperatures that the pump will see. They should not swell or shrink from exposure to the particular heat transfer fluid being employed.

Pump manufacturers are aware of gasketing problems. They usually can supply the correct materials, *if* the designer takes time to specify them.

Pump Operation

A pump should be thought of as a device to do work. It converts electrical energy into mechanical energy to drive a liquid through an array consisting of pipes and associated parts.

A typical centrifugal pump is shown in Figure 12.9. It provides the energy by sucking liquid into the center of a rapidly rotating disc which has a series of projections or blades on it. Then, through centrifugal force, it slings the water off the tips of the blades under high velocity. This rapidly rotating disc, called the impeller, is located in a close-fitting case except at the discharge outlet. The water is contained at the tips of the blades until it reaches the discharge outlet.

If the discharge outlet is deliberately closed off, the impeller continues to rotate in the liquid. The water slips between the case and the impeller. The energy created is dissipated as frictional heat and radiated out the pump body.

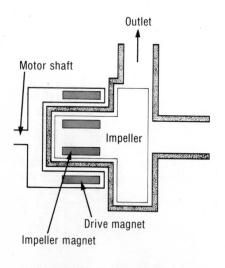

Figure 12.8 A magnetic-drive pump.

The centrifugal design provides no suction at the center of the impeller when running in air. It does not create enough vacuum to lift the liquid. Thus, centrifugal pumps are nonpriming.

As such, the liquid supply to the pump must be higher than the inlet of the pump. Once the pump is loaded with liquid and operating, it will lift liquid until an air pocket is encountered. It will stop if air is let into the pump. Thus, centrifugal pumps must always be located where they have an adequate head to sustain pumping on start-up.

The pump's capacity to do work is expressed as the amount of material it will move against a given resistance in a given period of time. Normally, the resistance is expressed in feet of head (height) and the amount of flow in gallons per minute (gpm).

The work the pump will do is usually measured under experimental conditions. The data is placed on a graph. The feet of head are on the vertical axis and the flow rate is on the horizontal axis.

Figure 12.10 shows such a performance graph for a hypothetical pump. Four scales are shown on this graph. First, concentrate on scales A and C, ignoring B and D.

The graph shows that if a 20-foot high pipe was erected and pumping attempted, the water would just reach the top of the column and stop. Zero flow would result. The pump only has the capacity to lift water to that 20-foot height. The diameter of the pipe makes no difference. The pump would lift the water to the same height in a pipe of one-inch or one-foot diameter.

If the head is lowered to 15-feet by shortening the pipe, 10-gpm would flow. With a 10-foot pipe or head, 18-gpm would flow. And with no head, 31-gpm would flow. By drawing a curve connecting these four points, the flow at any head can be obtained.

Staging Pumps

Figure 12.11 shows how staging the pumps can affect flow rate. Scales A and C on the graph in Figure 12.10 represent one pump.

If two pumps were placed together one after the other, *series staged*, the exit velocity of the liquid from the first pump would become the inlet velocity for the second pump. The exit velocity of the second pump would be double that of one pump. This staging would allow the pumps to pump against twice the head as shown on the graph by using scales C and B. At a 20-foot head, the pumps would produce a flow of 18-gpm. The same flow one pump produced against a 10-foot head before.

Two pumps placed beside each other are *staged in parallel*. If the inlet and outlet pipes are enlarged so as not to produce additional head, then the results shown by scales A and D would be obtained. There would still be no flow at a 20-foot head, but now a 36-gpm flow at a 10-foot head.

In many cases, two small pumps can be staged in either parallel or series to outperform a single larger pump. Quite often, two smaller units will be cheaper to purchase and will require less energy to run. In addition, one pump can be turned off when it is not required. It can

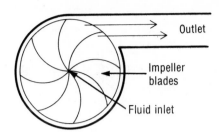

Figure 12.9 A typical centrifugal pump.

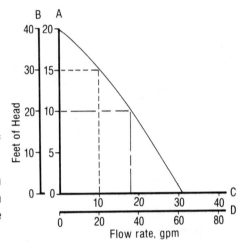

Figure 12.10 A performance graph for a hypothetical pump.

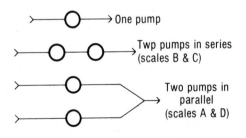

Figure 12.11 Pump staging can affect flow rate.

be utilized when high flow is needed in the collector loop such as on hot sunny days.

There are three key points to remember:

1. Two pumps placed in series will pump against approximately double the head that one pump will pump against for a given flow rate.

2. Two pumps placed in parallel will pump approximately double the flow rate of one pump at a given head.

3. Two or more pumps staged are often cheaper to purchase and run than a single large pump.

Sizing Pumps

Sizing pumps is a question of knowing the flow rates required and the resistance that the pumps must overcome. Once these factors are known, the manufacturer's curves for the various pumps can be consulted to select the correct pump.

Some representative pump curves are shown in Figure 12.12.

The calculation of pressure drops (feet of head) will be covered later in this decision.

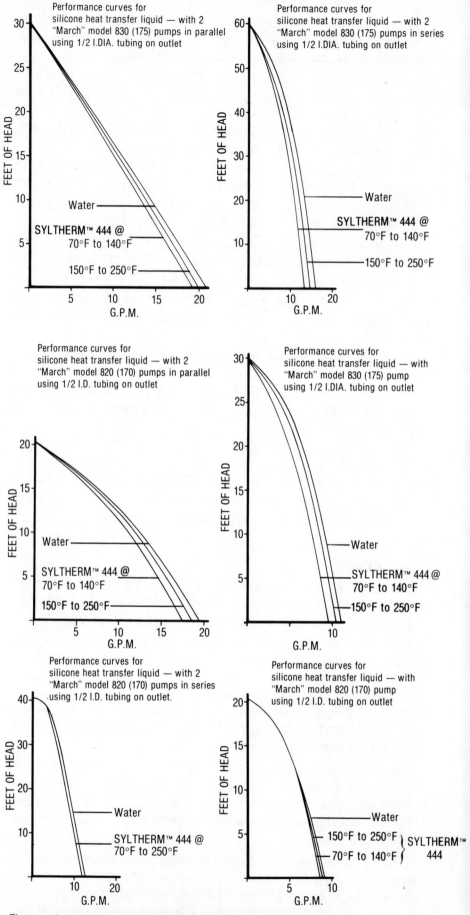

Figure 12.12 Representative pump curves from manufacturer's data.

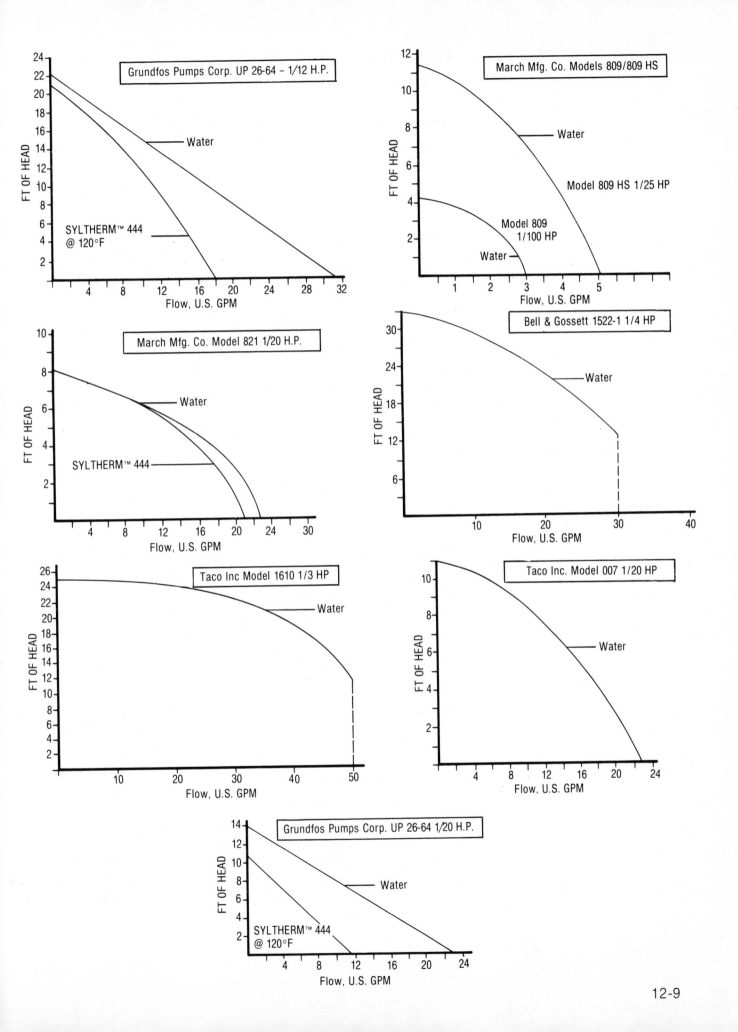

DETERMINING FLOW RATES

Collector Loop

The rate at which the heat-transfer fluid should move through the collector must be determined for sizing the pump.

When the maximum energy is reaching the panel, the pumping system should be capable of removing this maximum amount of energy. Proportional pump control will allow slower pumping speeds to handle the other conditions which can exist at the collector.

The maximum energy that must be removed from the collector is about 225 Btu/sq ft/hr. The inlet temperature of the collector should be optimized at less than 5°F above the lowest tank temperature.

As the collector temperature rises above ambient, collector efficiency drops. Hence, pumping rates should be established to minimize collector panel temperatures and maximize collector efficiencies. The maximum flow rate should keep the collector temperature close to the lowest tank temperature for good efficiency.

The inlet temperature of the collector will approximate the lowest storage temperature plus 5°F. The outlet temperature of the collector should be from 25°F to 35°F higher at maximum radiation intensity for efficient solar collection.

Using these parameters, the idealized flow rate through the collectors can be calculated as shown in Figure 12.13.

From the chart data, the idealized flow rate for maximum energy removal would be:

- WATER — Collector Sq. Ft. x 0.015 gpm = fluid flow rate

- SYLTHERM™ 444 Liquid — Collector Sq. Ft. x 0.039 gpm = fluid flow rate.

Under the design conditions described using a tank temperature shut off of 200°F, the collector's maximum operating temperatures with both heat-transfer fluids would be 230°F. Their collection efficiency would be equal.

IDEALIZED FLOW RATES — MAXIMUM ENERGY REMOVAL (225 Btu/sq ft/hr)	
	When temperature rise across collector is: T = 30
Water (Cp = 1)	
LBS/hr to remove heat	7.5/ft²
LBS/min to remove heat	0.125/ft²
GPM required to remove heat	0.015/ft²
SYLTHERM™ 444 Liquid (Cp = 0.4)	
LBS/hr to remove heat	18.75/ft²
LBS/min to remove heat	0.312/ft²
GPM required to remove heat	0.039/ft²

Figure 12.13 Calculating idealized flow rates through the collectors.

The design procedure employed may be utilized for any fluids and any desired conditions.

Storage Loop

The flow rate for the storage loop is determined by the heat-exchanger manufacturer.

Heat-Delivery Loop

The flow rate for the heat-delivery loop is determined by the manufacturer of the load heat exchanger. It is a function of the load demand and the exchanger design.

PUMPING FRICTION LOSSES

In closed-loop systems, the fluid moving through the piping, collectors, heat exchangers, and other associated parts meets resistance to flow. Friction is created between the fluid and piping walls. The amount of friction encountered is a function of the:

- Configuration of the device
- Velocity of the liquid
- Type of liquid
- Size of pipe

SIZE IN INCHES	INSIDE DIAMETER	CROSS SECTION SQUARE INCHES	% INCREASE OVER LOWER SIZE
1/4	.315	0.78	—
3/8	.430	.145	86%
1/2	.545	.233	61%
5/8	.666	.348	49%
3/4	.785	.484	39%
1	1.025	.825	71%
1 1/4	1.265	1.260	53%
1 1/2	1.505	1.780	41%

Figure 12.14 Various sizes of Type L copper pipe.

The amount of pressure drop is directly proportional to the square of velocity. If velocity is doubled, then pressure drop becomes four times as great. So, as velocity increases, the pipe diameter must increase to prevent excess pressure drop ($\triangle$P).

Figure 12.14 shows various sizes of Type L copper pipe. The cross-sectional area increase from one size to the next is considerable.

Small changes in pipe size will have a marked effect on flow velocity and, thus, on head losses. Figure 12.15 shows this to be true. The flow rate versus head loss is plotted for five sizes of pipe. Figure 12.16 then shows how the flow rate at two different head losses vary for the five pipe sizes. Small systems utilizing water as the heat-transfer liquid can be sized for pumping requirements directly from this graph.

Other heat-transfer fluids such as SYLTHERM™ 444 Silicone Heat-Transfer Liquid have different viscosities and densities. Thus, a different chart is required to determine their head losses at given flow rates.

A chart for SYLTHERM™ 444 Liquid is shown in Figure 12.17. This may also be used for collector loops. The pressure drops are tabulated at 150°F. A multiplier for correcting to other temperatures is shown in the upper-right-hand corner.

Pipe fittings also cause friction losses. These must be included in the total friction losses for the system. The piping should be converted to the equivalent length of straight pipe. For example: one ½-inch 90° elbow equals 1-foot of straight ½-inch pipe.

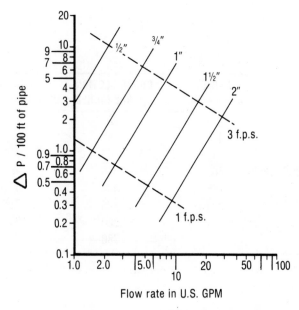

Figure 12.15 Water head losses in five sizes of Type L copper pipe.

PIPE DIAMETER	FLOW RATE	
	10-FT HEAD	5-FT HEAD
3/8″	1 gpm	0.75 gpm
1/2″	2 gpm	1.40 gpm
5/8″	3 1/2 gpm	2.5 gpm
3/4″	5 1/2 gpm	3.75 gpm
1″	—	8.0 gpm

Figure 12.16 Flow rates at different head losses.

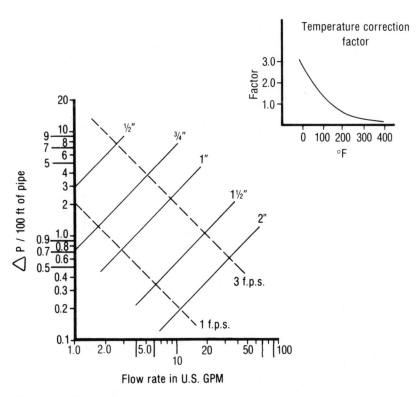

Figure 12.17 Head losses at various pipe sizes, flow rates and collector temperatures for SYLTHERM™ 444 Silicone Heat-Transfer Liquid.

The equivalent pipe lengths for copper sweat fittings are shown in Figure 12.18. These allowances should be used for all heat-transfer liquids.

HEAD LOSSES

To estimate the total pressure drop across the piping, a table such as that in Figure 12.20 is useful. Assuming all parts of the loop are connected in series, the equivalent length in straight pipe is figured and the results inserted in the table. Adding these gives the total length of pipe of each size. The pressure drop is then read from the graphs shown in either Figure 12.15 or 12.17. The individual pressure drops can then be added to arrive at a total.

FITTING SIZE INCHES	EQUIVALENT LENGTH OF PIPE IN FEET					
	STD 90°	ELLS 45°	90° Tee STRAIGHT RUN	PIPE COUPLING	GATE VALVE	GLOBE VALVE
3/8	0.5	0.3	0.15	0.15	0.1	4
1/2	1.0	0.6	0.3	0.3	0.2	7.5
3/4	1.25	0.75	0.4	0.4	0.25	10
1	1.5	1.0	0.45	0.45	0.3	12.5
1 1/4	2	1.2	0.6	0.6	0.4	18

Figure 12.18 Equivalent pipe lengths for copper sweat fittings for use in calculating friction losses.

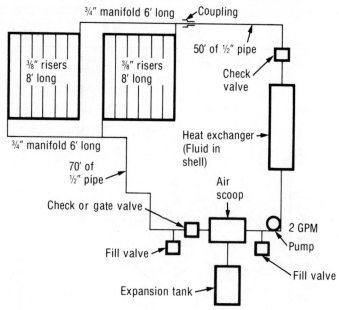

Figure 12.19 A typical parallel collector loop.

Solar system loops are not all series-connected loops, however. There are paralleled piping arrangements in solar loops, particularly in the collector loop. Series flow and parallel flow are handled differently. An example of a typical series-parallel collector loop is shown in Figure 12.19. The calculations for the total pressure drop are shown in Figure 12.20.

Refer to the system diagram, and note entries made in the calculations chart. With the pump running at two-gpm, the fluid circulates through:

1 - Tee	1 - Tee
1 - Air Scoop	4 - Elbows
1 - Gate Valve	70 ft. - ½" pipe

The fluid then is supplied to six feet of ¾-inch manifold in series with the supply riser.

From the manifold, the flow divides across 14 risers situated in parallel. So, the flow rate divides across these risers to 2 gpm ÷ 14 = 0.142 gpm/riser. There are 14 risers of 8-feet in length, or 112-feet of pipe resisting a 0.142 gpm flow.

These couple to a six-foot ¾-inch manifold. The flow rate again becomes two-gpm. And the fluid goes through:

1 - coupling	1 - check valve
50 ft. - ½" pipe	1 - heat exchanger (shell)
1 - elbow	

To determine the pressure drop in this loop, with SYLTHERM™ 444 Heat-Transfer Liquid, proceed as shown in Figure 12.20.

For design purposes, assume a 10-percent efficiency loss in pumping over the life of the system. Add this additional head, giving a total 10.36 ft. of head.

PUMP TO DELIVERY MANIFOLD

Item	No.	Equivalent Length in feet of pipe	Pump Rate	$\triangle$ P/100' (From Graph)
½" Pipe	70 FT	70 FT	2 GPM	
Air Scoop	1	7.5 FT	2 GPM	
Gate Valve	1	0.2 FT	2 GPM	
Tees	2	0.06 FT	2 GPM	
Elbows	4	4 FT	2 GPM	
Total		81.76		5.4'

$$\triangle P_1 = \frac{81.76 \times 5.4}{100} = 4.40 \text{ FT}$$

MANIFOLDS

Item	No.	Equivalent Length	Pump Rate	$\triangle$ P/100'
¾" Piping	12 FT	12 FT	2 GPM	1.5

$$\triangle P_2 = \frac{12 \times 1.5}{100} = 0.18$$

DOWN LEG

Item	No.	Equivalent Length	Pump Rate	$\triangle$ P/100'
½" Pipe	50 FT	50 FT	2 GPM	
Elbow	1	1 FT	2 GPM	
Check Valve	1	7.5 FT	2 GPM	
Coupling	1	0.3 FT	2 GPM	
Heat Exchanger	1	10 FT*	2 GPM	
Total		68.8		5.4

$$\triangle P_3 = \frac{68.8 \times 5.4}{100} = 3.72 \text{ FT}$$

*Mfg'rs Data

Collectors

Item	No.	Equivalent Length	Pump Rate	$\triangle$ P/100'
⅜" Risers	112 FT	112 FT	0.14 GPM	1'/100'*

$$\triangle P_4 = \frac{112 \times 1}{100} = 1.12'$$

*Mfg'rs Data

Total

$\triangle$	P_1	4.40
$\triangle$	P_2	0.18
$\triangle$	P_3	3.72
$\triangle$	P_4	1.12
		9.42' Pressure drop
10%		.94
		10.36 FT of fluid

Figure 12.20 Calculations for the total pressure drop for the system shown in Figure 12.19.

Referring back to the pumping graphs in Figure 12.12, a flow rate of two gpm cannot be obtained with a Grundfos UP 25-42. Nor will a March Model 821 handle this load. But the head is easily achieved with a Grundfos UP 26-64 or a March Model 820. These pumps are the logical choices for this collector loop.

CALCULATING FLUID REQUIREMENTS

Calculating the fluid required to fill a given system is a simple procedure. Enough fluid is needed to:

- Fill the piping
- Fill the heat exchanger
- Fill the collectors
- Fill approximately one-half of the expansion tank

One gallon of fluid occupies 0.133 cu. ft. or 3785 cc. Usually the amount of fluid held in the heat exchangers, collectors, and expansion tank is specified in the manufacturer's literature.

To estimate the amount of fluid needed to fill different sizes of copper Type L piping, use the graph in Figure 12.21.

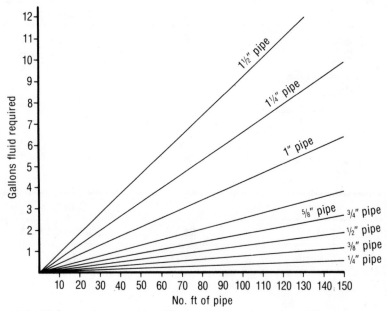

Figure 12.21 Fluid requirements for different sizes and lengths of Type L copper piping.

MAKING A DECISION

In this section of The Solar Decision Book, you learned about open-loop and closed-loop systems, the types and operation of centrifugal pumps. You also learned about methods used to determine collector flow rates, calculate pumping friction losses, and estimate fluid requirements. Your decision on which pump to choose can be made after looking at the design requirements outlined. The principles shown apply to load pumps, as well as to collector-loop pumps. Your decision should be an easy one if the various principles are carefully applied.

DECISION 13

Select Efficient Heat Exchangers

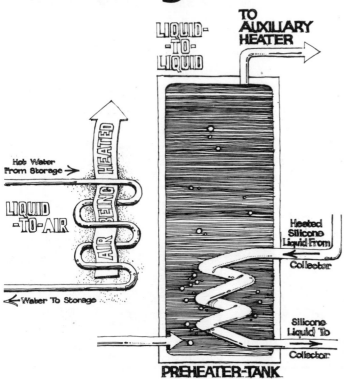

LIQUID-TO-LIQUID

TO AUXILIARY HEATER

LIQUID-TO-AIR

AIR BEING HEATED

Hot Water From Storage

Water To Storage

Heated Silicone Liquid From Collector

Silicone Liquid To Collector

PREHEATER-TANK

Solar energy can be stored for when you need it. That energy can then be delivered on demand. Two heat exchangers in the solar energy system make such storage and delivery possible. Each is a device which transfers energy from one substance to another without mixing the two substances.

One heat exchanger is in the collector loop. It pulls energy from the heat-transfer fluid and puts it into the storage water or the hot-water pre-heater tank. The other heat exchanger is in the space-heating heat-delivery system. It takes energy from the storage water and puts it into the space-heating system.

There are different types and sizes of heat exchangers. But, for any particular system, the heat exchangers must be carefully matched to the system's collectors, storage capabilities, and heat load. Otherwise, solar energy cannot be efficiently stored or delivered. As such, the selection of heat exchangers is an important decision. This section of The Solar Decision Book will help you to make that decision. You will learn that:

- Heat exchangers are made in a number of flow configurations.

- The heat exchanger effectiveness can be calculated.

- Specifying a heat exchanger for the collector-to-storage loop involves determining the maximum amount of energy which can be received by the collector array.

- Specifying a heat exchanger for the storage-to-load loop involves determining the maximum amount of heat which will be required by the building.

BASIC CONSIDERATIONS

What Is A Heat Exchanger?

A *heat exchanger* is any device which transfers heat from one substance to another substance without mixing the two. The device may be something simple or it may be complex. A building wall acts as a heat exchanger between the outside air and the inside air. A solar collector acts as a heat exchanger between the sun's rays and the heat-transfer medium. Your car's radiator acts as a heat exchanger between the hot engine coolant and the cooler outside air.

Most every device in a solar energy system serves as a heat exchanger. But, the primary function of the device might be something other than transferring heat. There are devices in the system however, that have the sole function of transferring heat. These are the heat exchangers. One is used to transfer heat from the collector loop to the storage tank. The other is used to transfer heat from the storage tank to the heat-delivery system.

These heat exchangers may transfer heat from air-to-air, liquid-to-air, or liquid-to-liquid. In Figure 13.1, the three basic methods used for such heat transfer are shown.

For air-to-air heat exchangers, cool air may be warmed by passing it through or around containers of warm air. The heat exchanger may be something as simple as a metal wall or plenum in rock-pebble storage bed. The cool air is heated as it is pushed across the metal wall or through the plenum.

For liquid-to-air heat exchangers, cool air may be warmed by passing it over coils containing warm collector fluids or storage water. The heat exchanger may be like your car's radiator. It will have many finned tubes in which the warm fluid or water can be circulated. Heat from the coiled tubes spreads quickly to the thin metal fins. When cool air is pushed through the mass of finned tubes, the heat is easily transferred to the air.

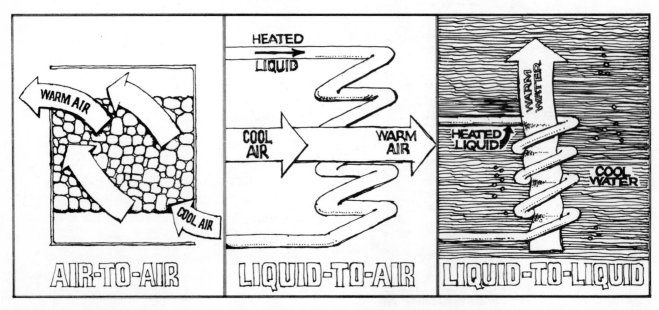

Figure 13.1 The three basic methods used for heat transfer in solar system heat exchangers.

For liquid-to-liquid heat exchangers, cool water may be warmed by piping it around coils containing warm collector fluid or storage water. The heat exchanger may be a simple coil inside a water tank or it may be a complex device with coils or tubes inside a container or shell. Cool water, held in the tank or circulated in the shell, is heated as warm fluid or water flows through the coils.

No matter what type of heat exchanger is used, heat transfer can take place only if a temperature difference exists between the two substances. Heat will always move from hot to cold. And this movement will continue until the two substances become the same temperature. If the two substances are not circulated, they will eventually reach temperature equilibrium. For that reason, solar system pumps circulate the warmer substance to the heat exchangers. Energy is removed. Then, the substance is sent back to the collectors to absorb more energy or back to the storage tank to be reheated.

The rate at which the heat will be transferred depends on the type of heat exchanger and the temperature difference between the two substances. There are several types of heat exchangers, and their performance varies considerably. High efficiency heat exchangers, of course, can transfer large amounts of heat in a short time. The temperature difference acts as the driving force which pushes energy from the warmer substance to the cooler substance. The greater the temperature difference, the faster the heat transfer.

As discussed in Decision 10, a maximum amount of energy can be collected if the heat-transfer fluid is at the lowest temperature possible upon return to the collector. This means that the heat the collector absorber plate usually sees only 75-percent of the total radiation. As such, the maximum heat flux for design purposes is about 225 Btu per square foot an hour.

Collector efficiency is also improved if usable heat can be drawn from storage at very low temperatures. The solar energy system may be able to provide 100-percent of the building's heating needs even on very cold, partly sunny days. For this to happen, the heat exchanger in the storage-to-load loop must be very effective in transferring stored energy to the heat-delivery system.

Heat Exchanger Flow Configurations

The Solar Decision Book is primarily concerned with the liquid-type solar energy systems. A liquid-to-liquid heat exchanger is recommended for the collector-to-storage loop. A liquid-to-air heat exchanger is recommended for the storage-to-load loop.

There are four basic flow configurations which can be used in a liquid-to-liquid heat exchanger. These are: coil-in-tank, counterflow, mixed-flow, and parallel-flow. Some heat exchangers use a combination of these. However, a brief look at the four basic types will show why certain types are preferred.

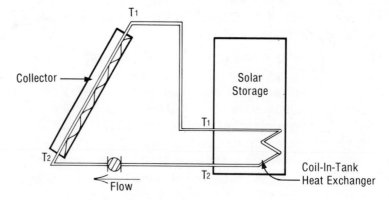

Figure 13.2 A coil-in-tank heat exchanger.

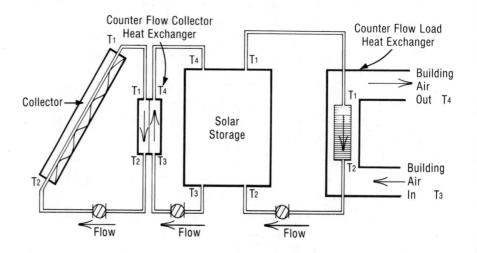

Figure 13.3 A counterflow heat exchanger.

Figure 13.2 shows a *coil-in-tank heat exchanger*. This type of heat exchanger is a finned coil in the bottom of the water tank. It is most commonly used on solar water-heating systems. The tank water is coldest at the bottom of the tank. As it is heated, it rises to the top of the tank by convection. A maximum amount of energy can be removed from the heat-transfer fluid before it is sent back to the collectors.

Figure 13.3 shows a *counterflow heat exchanger*. This type of heat exchanger is a self-contained device in which the two substances flow in opposite directions. It is used for both solar water heating and for solar space heating. The coldest substance on the supply side (collector) always sees the coldest substance on the side being heated (storage). The driving force is highest at the inlet to storage. The collector temperature is governed by the storage tank temperature before any heat is added.

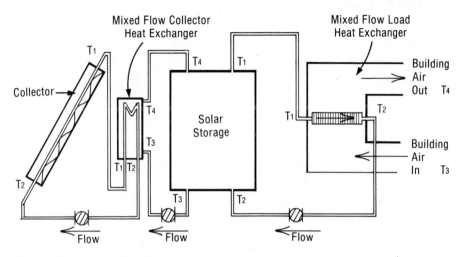

Figure 13.4 A mixed-flow heat exchanger.

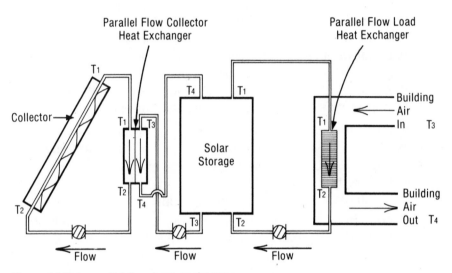

Figure 13.5 A parallel-flow heat exchanger.

Figure 13.4 shows a *mixed-flow heat exchanger*. This type of heat exchanger is a device in which one substance sees the average temperature of the other substance. The supply substance may see the average temperature of the substance being heated, or the substance being heated may see the average supply temperature. The collector temperature will fall somewhere between the tank inlet and outlet temperatures. This design can be used in the collector loop or load loop, but it is less effective than the counterflow design.

Figure 13.5 shows a *parallel-flow heat exchanger*. This type of heat exchanger is a self-contained device in which the two substances flow in the same direction. It is unsatisfactory for solar energy collector systems. The hottest supply substance always sees the coldest substance on the side being heated. The driving force tends to be lowest at the inlet to storage. The heat added to the storage fluid governs the collector temperature. This type of heat exchanger is very inefficient.

Heat Exchanger Effectiveness

Heat-exchanger effectiveness is defined as: the ratio of the actual rate of heat transfer to the theoretical maximum rate of heat transfer in an infinitely large heat exchanger.

Referring to Figure 13.3, the effectiveness would be calculated using the formula:

$$\frac{T_1 - T_2}{T_1 - T_3} = E, \text{ or}$$

$$\frac{\text{Supply Inlet Temperature} - \text{Supply Outlet Temperature}}{\text{Supply Inlet Temperature} - \text{Secondary Inlet Temperature}} = E$$

In a counterflow heat exchanger where the exchanger is large enough to make $T_2 = T_3$, the heat exchanger effectiveness is 1. This is often expressed as percent effectiveness, or % E = 100. The heat exchanger would have to be infinitely large for % E to be 100. There would be no resistance to heat flow across a 100% E heat exchanger. Such a heat exchanger cannot be built. There is always some resistance to heat flow across the heat-exchanger walls.

If the heat exchanger configuration is not counterflow or coil-in-tank, T_3 can never closely approach T_2. In the mixed-flow heat exchanger T_2 must become the average of T_4 and T_3. And, in the parallel-flow heat exchanger, T_2 cannot possibly be less than the hottest temperature of the secondary substance.

Recognizing these heat exchanger limitations is extremely important. The efficiency at which the collector operates is determined by the collector inlet temperature or T_2. As T_2 rises, the efficiency of the collector drops. Therefore, T_2 must be kept as close as possible to T_3 without spending an inordinate amount of money on a heat exchanger. The same logic applies to the building load heat exchanger. T_2 from the load exchanger determines T_3 for the collector exchanger. A counterflow heat exchanger is essential to keep T_2, load as low as possible. A mixed-flow design can be used for the load heat exchanger, but it will have a negative effect on the collection process.

Figure 13.6 shows the maximum effectiveness for the four basic types of heat exchangers. These values were calculated using typical conditions found in solar energy systems. Counterflow designs, which include coil-in-tank heat exchangers, offer the highest effectiveness.

Heat Exchanger	%E Maximum
Coil-in-tank	≈ 100
Counterflow	96-97
Mixed flow	85
Parallel flow	66-67

Figure 13.6 The maximum effectiveness for four types of heat exchangers.

DESIGN FOR THE COLLECTOR-TO-STORAGE LOOP

Flat-plate collectors rapidly lose efficiency as their operating temperature rises above ambient. The coolest possible fluid should be introduced to the inlet of the collector. Figure 13.7 shows a system that contains no heat exchanger. The storage water is also the collector heat-transfer medium. This offers the best set of conditions. In this system, the collector inlet temperature is equal to the lowest temperature of the storage tank. The collector operates at its coolest possible temperature.

However, solar collection usually demands a different fluid than storage water. A heat exchanger is then needed between the collector and the storage tank to keep the fluid and water separated. Figure 13.8 shows a simple system with a counterflow heat exchanger.

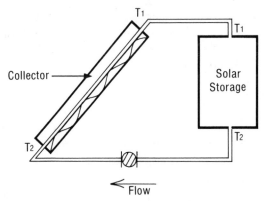

Figure 13.7 A solar collector loop with no heat exchanger.

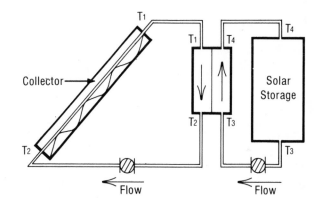

Figure 13.8 A collector-to-storage loop with a counterflow heat exchanger.

Conditions Of Operation

Adding a heat exchanger to the collector-to-storage loop introduces a different set of operating conditions. These conditions are highly dependent on the size of the heat exchanger and its flow configuration. Unless the heat exchanger is infinitely large, it offers some resistance to heat transfer. Because of this, the collector inlet temperature cannot be equal to the lowest temperature in the storage tank. The inlet temperature will be higher, and this will serve to reduce the collector efficiency somewhat. This loss is minimized by using heat exchangers with high effectiveness and counterflow configurations.

As a result, the design of a heat exchanger for the collector-to-storage loop is usually a compromise. There must be a tradeoff between the cost of the heat exchanger and the penalty imposed on energy collection. A counterflow design helps keep this cost down.

$$E = \frac{T_1 - T_2}{T_1 - T_3}$$

$$\%E = \frac{T_1 - T_2}{T_1 - T_3} \times 100$$

EFFECTIVENESS. As discussed briefly earlier in this section, a simple set of temperature ratios defines the effectiveness of a heat exchanger.

The effectiveness equals the difference in temperature across the collector divided by the difference in temperature between the collector outlet and the storage tank outlet. This is generally expressed as percent effectiveness. If $T_2 = T_3$, then $\% E = 100$ and in effect, there is no heat exchanger resistance. Such is rarely the case. Unless the heat exchanger is grossly oversized, which is economically not feasible, then T_2 is always higher than T_3 and $\% E$ is less than 100.

Figure 13.9 shows a comparison of two heat exchangers. The operating conditions affect the percent effectiveness.

The counterflow heat exchanger, previously shown in Figure 13.3 and 13.8, offers excellent efficiency. A mixed-flow heat exchanger is less effective, and a parallel-flow heat exchanger is worse. The loss of collector efficiency would be significant in both.

Temperatures	Operating Conditions	
	Heat exchanger A	Heat exchanger B
T_1	153°F	153°F
T_2	130°F	123°F
T_3	120°F	120°F
% E	70	90

Figure 13.9 The effectiveness of two heat exchangers with different conditions of operation.

COLLECTOR RISE FACTOR. The effectiveness of a counterflow heat exchanger can also be mathematically determined by another method.

The temperature difference across the collector can be compared to the temperature difference between the collector inlet and the storge tank outlet. This results in a ratio which can be called the *collector rise factor* (CRF). It describes the temperature rise between collector inlet and storage tank outlet in relation to the temperature rise across the collector. Using the same operating conditions as in Figure 13.9, the CRF for the two heat exchangers can be calculated. The results are shown in Figure 13.10.

$$CRF = \frac{T_2 - T_3}{T_1 - T_2}$$

The collector rise factor can be determined for any heat exchanger of known percent effectiveness. And the CRF remains constant with effectiveness. Some typical CRF values for heat exchangers with different % E ratings are shown in Figure 13.11. The temperature difference between the collector inlet and the storage tank outlet can be calculated if the temperature difference across the collectors is known.

FLOW RATE. Collector loops are usually designed to have a 25° to 35°F temperature difference between the collector inlet and outlet under maximum flux conditions. Generally, the maximum solar flux

Temperatures	Operating Conditions	
	Exchanger A	Exchanger B
T$_1$	153°F	153°F
T$_2$	130°F	123°F
T$_3$	120°F	120°F
% E	70	91
CRF	0.43	0.10

Figure 13.10 Collector rise factors for two different heat exchangers.

available does not exceed 300 Btu per square foot each hour. Also, the absorber usually sees only 75-percent of the total radiation. As such, the maximum heat flux for design purposes is about 225 Btu per square foot an hour.

With this in mind, some of the design parameters for the collector-to-storage loop can be determined. For the sake of illustration, suppose the collector array is 100 square feet and the loop is filled with SYLTHERM™ 444 Heat-Transfer Liquid. This heat-transfer fluid has a specific heat of 0.4 Btu per pound per degree F and a weight of eight pounds a gallon.

% E	CRF
60	0.65
70	0.43
80	0.25
85	0.18
90	0.11
95	0.05

Figure 13.11 Some typical CRF values for heat exchangers having different % E ratings.

The maximum heat which needs to be removed is 22,500 Btu per hour.

$$\begin{array}{r} 225 \text{ Btu/sq ft/hr} \\ \times\, 100 \text{ sq ft} \\ \hline 22,500 \text{ Btu/hr} \end{array}$$

At a one degree temperature rise, the fluid flow required to remove the heat is 56,250 pounds per hour.

$$\begin{array}{r} 1°F \\ \times\, 22,500 \text{ Btu/hr} \\ \div\ 0.4 \text{ Btu/Lb/°F} \\ \hline 56,250 \text{ Lb/hr} \end{array}$$

At a 30°F temperature rise across the collectors, a fluid flow of 1875 pounds per hour is required.

$$\begin{array}{r} 56,250 \text{ Lb/hr/°F} \\ \div\ 30°F \\ \hline 1,875 \text{ Lb/hr} \end{array}$$

If the fluid weighs eight pounds per gallon, then the flow required becomes 3.9 gallons per minute.

$$\begin{array}{r} 1875 \text{ Lb/hr} \\ \div\ (60 \text{ min/hr})(8 \text{ Lb/gal}) \\ \hline 3.9 \text{ gal/min} \end{array}$$

Expressed as flow rate per square foot of collector for any size of collector array, the flow rate per square foot equals 0.039 gallons per minute.

$$\begin{array}{r} 3.9 \text{ gal/min} \\ \div\ 100 \\ \hline 0.039 \text{ GPM/sq. ft} \end{array}$$

Heat Exchanger		Temperature difference (T₂ - T₃) for 30°F collector rise
% E	CRF	
95	0.05	1.5°F
90	0.11	3.3°F
85	0.18	5.4°F
80	0.25	7.5°F
70	0.43	12.9°F
60	0.65	19.5°F

Figure 13.12 The temperature difference between the collector inlet and storage outlet for heat exchangers of varying effectiveness.

As previously discussed, the temperature difference across the collector inlet and storage outlet for a heat exchanger of a given effectiveness can be determined. The formula for collector rise factor needs to be rearranged to read:

$$T_2 - T_3 = CRF(T_1 - T_2)$$

Using this formula and the data from Figure 13.11, the temperature differences for various heat exchangers can be calculated. The results are shown in Figure 13.12. For heat exchangers with a high % E, the temperature difference is small. Most of the energy is removed and placed in storage. For heat exchangers with a low % E, the temperature difference is large. Only a portion of the energy is removed for storage.

Basically, the collector rise factor determines this inlet-outlet temperature difference as a percentage of the actual collector rise. For instance, if the heat exchanger effectiveness is 90-percent, the collector inlet temperature will be the tank temperature plus 11-percent of the collector rise. In a 30°F rise design, this would amount to 3.3°F.

Because the collector will only operate at design conditions around solar noon on a clear day, a 90-percent effective heat exchanger would appear to be very satisfactory. An 80-percent effective heat exchanger would appear not to impose too severe a collection penalty. But, a less effective heat exchanger would appear to be unsatisfactory with most collectors. The fast efficiency drop-off with the climb in temperature imposes too severe of a penalty in energy collection.

Specifying The Collector-Loop Heat Exchanger

You should now be able to generate the majority of the data required to specify a collector-loop heat exchanger. Only two other pieces of necessary information are missing. Does the heat exchanger need to be single-wall or double-wall? And, what should the flow rate of the storage water be on the secondary side of the heat exchanger?

Double-walled heat exchangers are used when a nonpotable collector fluid must be separated from a potable water such as domestic hot water. Figure 13.13 shows a double-walled heat exchanger. The resistance to heat transfer per unit of area is higher in a double-walled heat exchanger. Also, the construction is more

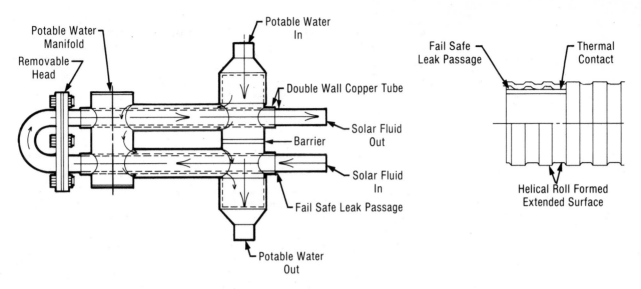

Figure 13.13 Construction details of a double-walled heat exchanger.   (Reprinted courtesy of Doucette Industries, York, Pa.)

HEAT EXCHANGER SPECIFICATIONS	
Collector Side	
Heat Transfer Fluid	SYLTHERM™ 444 Liquid
Specific Heat	0.4 Btu/lb/°F
Weight	8 pounds/gallon
Maximum collector flow rate	3.9 gpm
% E desired	90%
CRF	0.10
Double or single walled	Double
Typical operating mid-range	120-160°F
Max/Min Operating Temperatures	45-250°F
Flow Configuration	Counterflow
Heat Flux in Btu/hr	22,500 Btu/hr
Desired collector temperature rise, max	30°F
Pressure drop at maximum flow	(manufacturer specifies)
Storage Side	
Heat Transfer Fluid	Water
Specific Heat	1 Btu/lb/°F
Weight	8.33 pounds/gallon
Minimum flow rate	(manufacturer specifies)
Min/max operating temperature	45 to 200°F

Figure 13.14 Typical specifications for heat exchanger used in collector-to-storage loop discussed.

complex. Thus, a double-walled heat exchanger must be larger to maintain the % E and this makes it more expensive. A single-wall unit should be chosen wherever practical. This is possible when the storage water is not used to meet hot-water needs.

The flow rate on the secondary side of the heat exchanger should be left for the manufacturer to specify. A minimum flow rate will generally be specified to meet the required effectiveness. A faster-than-specified flow rate is usually acceptable, as long as the velocity at which erosion-corrosion starts is not exceeded.

The specifications for the heat exchanger in the collector-to-storage loop discussed would be as shown in Figure 13.14.

DESIGN FOR THE STORAGE-TO-LOAD LOOP

The design of a counterflow liquid-to-air load heat exchanger requires that a number of operating conditions and coil characteristics be set first. Then, the size of the heat exchanger can be calculated.

Operating Conditions

The operating conditions are set by the heat requirements of the building and the terminal or heat-delivery design temperature.

Figure 13.15 shows a load heat exchanger with the following conditions of operation:

T_1 (Minimum Water Inlet Temperature) = 120°F
T_2 (Minimum Water Outlet Temperature) = 65°F
T_3 (Average Air Inlet Temperature) = 55°F
T_4 (Minimum Air Outlet Temperature) = 110°F

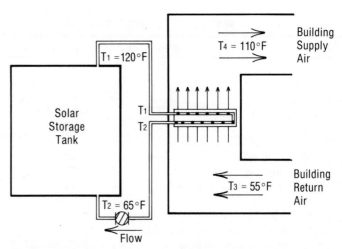

Figure 13.15 Typical operating conditions for a load heat exchanger.

EFFECTIVENESS. The load heat exchanger effectiveness is calculated with a formula similar to that used for the collector-loop unit. The formula is:

$$E = \frac{T_4 - T_3}{T_1 - T_3}$$

$$\frac{110 - 55}{120 - 55}$$

$$= \frac{55}{65}$$

$$= 0.846$$

Using this formula and the preset operating conditions, this load heat exchanger would have an effectiveness of 0.846, or about 85-percent. A heat exchanger with this effectiveness would easily draw energy from storage and would not impose a severe penalty on the collection process.

MANUFACTURER'S DATA. To proceed with the heat exchanger design requires the use of manufacturer's data on specific heat exchangers. For this discussion, Halstead and Mitchell Bulletin C-350 has been utilized. If another brand of heat exchanger is chosen, that manufacturer's data should be used to insure accuracy.

First, the *Log Mean Temperature Difference* (LMD) for the heat exchanger must be calculated. This is a complex mathematical function used to describe the fluid and air temperatures. It depends on the heat-exchanger flow configuration, and it is needed because the exact temperature of any given point in the heat exchanger cannot be readily determined.

You will work with temperature changes (ΔT). Using the preset conditions and the manufacturer's data, LMD would be calculated as follows:

1. Calculate the smaller temperature change (ΔS). This is the heat exchanger's minimum temperature difference. In this case, the difference between the inlet water temperature (T_1) and the outlet air temperature (T_4).

$$\Delta S = T_1 - T_4 = 120°F - 110°F = 10°F$$

2. Calculate the larger temperature change (ΔL). This is the heat exchanger's maximum temperature difference. In this case, the difference between the outlet water temperature (T_2) and the inlet air temperature (T_3).

$$\Delta L = T_2 - T_3 = 65°F - 55°F = 10°F$$

3. Calculate the ratio of these temperature changes.

$$\frac{\Delta S}{\Delta L} = \frac{10°F}{10°F} = 1$$

4. Find the ratio of "D", the Log Mean Temperature Difference, to L. This ratio is listed in the manufacturer's data.

$$\frac{D}{\Delta L} = 1$$

5. Calculate the Log Mean Temperature Difference.

$$(D \div \Delta L)(\Delta L) = (1)(10) = 10 \text{ LMD}$$

With the log mean temperature difference determined, a set of coil characteristics under a given set of operating conditions should be selected. The Btu ouput of the heat-exchanger coil can then be determined.

Again, the manufacturer's data must be used. Figure 13.16 shows a set of coil characteristics and operating conditions for a typical load heat exchanger.

Coil dimensions	2 ft x 2 ft (4 sq ft)
Number of face tubes	16
Coil Circuiting	half serpentine
Number of circuits	8
Water flow per circuit	2 gal/min
Number of fins per inch	8 fins/in
Cubic feet of air supplied	1600 cu ft/min
Air velocity across face of coil	400 ft/min
Heat Transfer Coefficient (K)	145 Btu/sq ft/hr/°F/row
Water GPM correction factor	0.94
Pressure drop of water per pass	0.22 ft of water

Figure 13.16 A set of coil characteristics and operating conditions for a typical load heat exchanger.

$$145 \text{ Btu/sq ft/hr/°F/row}$$
$$\times \quad 10°F$$
$$\times \quad 4 \text{ sq ft}$$
$$\cdot \times \quad 1 \text{ row}$$
$$\times 0.94$$
$$\overline{5452 \text{ Btu/hr}}$$

$$8 \text{ circuits}$$
$$\times 2 \text{ gal/min/circuit}$$
$$\overline{16 \text{ gal/min}}$$

$$8 \text{ circuits}$$
$$\times 0.22 \text{ ft/pass}$$
$$\times \quad 2 \text{ passes/circuit}$$
$$\overline{3.5 \text{ ft/row}}$$

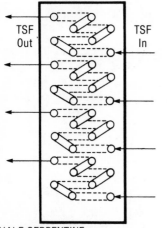

HALF SERPENTINE
Number of circuits is one-half the number of tubes across the coil face (or number of passes is twice the number of rows deep).

Figure 13.17 A four-row-deep, half-serpentine coil for a load heat exchanger.

Figure 13.17 shows a half-serpentine coil four rows deep. In this configuration, the number of circuits is one-half the number of tubes across the coil face, and the number of passes is twice the number of rows deep.

Figure 13.18 shows the face areas for standard-size coils in square feet. Figure 13.19 shows how to determine left-hand and right-hand coils.

To determine the Btu per hour produced by one row of tubes, the following formula is used:

(K)* (LMD) (coil area) (rows) (GPM corr.) = Btu/hr

Under the conditions set previously, the coil selected could produce 5452 Btu per hour from each row of tubes.

The total liquid flow to the heat exchanger is found by multiplying the number of circuits by the flow per circuit. Or, in this example, the total flow would be 16 gallons per minute.

The liquid pressure drop across the heat exchanger is found by multiplying the number of circuits by the pressure drop per pass by the number of passes per circuit. In this example, the total pressure drop per row of tubes would be 3.5 feet of water.

The air pressure drop for the heat exchanger is obtained from the manufacturer's data. It is a function of the number of coil rows and the air face velocity. Typical values for the air pressure drop in two sizes of heat exchangers are shown in Figures 13.20 and 13.21.

To determine the number of rows required in the heat exchanger the following formula is used:

$$\frac{(\text{Building hourly heat loss})(\text{Building design temperature})}{\text{Btu supplied by one row of exchanger}}$$

$$= \text{No. of rows}$$

*"K" is the heat-transfer coefficient for the particular heat exchanger. Found in manufacturer's data.

Fin Height Inches	Face Tubes High	Fin Length Inches																
		24	30	36	42	48	54	60	66	82	78	84	90	96	102	108	114	120
12	8	2.0	2.5	3.0	3.5	4.0	4.5	5.0	5.5	6.0	6.5	7.0	7.5	8.0	8.5	9.0	9.5	10.0
15	10	2.5	3.1	3.8	4.4	5.0	5.6	6.3	6.9	7.5	8.1	8.8	9.4	10.0	10.6	11.3	11.9	12.5
18	12	3.0	3.8	4.5	5.3	6.0	6.8	7.5	8.3	9.0	9.8	10.5	11.3	12.0	12.8	13.5	14.3	15.0
21	14	3.5	4.4	5.3	6.1	7.0	7.9	8.8	9.7	10.5	11.4	12.3	13.2	14.0	14.9	15.8	16.7	17.5
24	16	4.0	5.0	6.0	7.0	8.0	9.0	10.0	11.0	12.0	13.0	14.0	15.0	16.0	17.0	18.0	19.0	20.0
27	18	4.5	5.6	6.8	7.9	9.0	10.1	11.3	12.4	13.5	14.6	15.8	16.9	18.0	19.1	20.3	21.4	22.5
30	20	5.0	6.3	7.5	8.8	10.0	11.3	12.5	13.8	15.0	16.3	17.5	18.8	20.0	21.3	22.5	23.8	25.0
33	22	5.5	6.9	8.3	9.6	11.0	12.4	13.8	16.1	16.5	17.9	19.3	20.7	22.0	23.4	24.8	26.2	27.5
36	24	6.0	7.5	9.0	10.5	12.0	13.5	15.0	16.5	18.0	19.9	21.0	22.5	24.0	25.5	27.0	28.5	30.0

Figure 13.18 Face areas in square feet for standard-sized coils used in load heat exchangers.

For example: if the hourly heat loss is 300 Btu/hr/°F and the building design temperature is 65°F, the number of rows required is 3.57. A four-row heat exchanger must be chosen.

A four-row coil would have 64 tubes, 16 per row. There would be 8 circuits with 8 passes in a half-serpentine configuration as previously shown in Figure 13.17. The liquid pressure drop in the coil would become 14 feet of water. It is calculated by multiplying the pressure drop per row by the number of rows.

$$\frac{(300 \text{ Btu/hr/°F})(65°F)}{5452 \text{ Btu/hr/row}}$$

$$3.57 \text{ rows}$$

$$\begin{array}{r} 3.5 \text{ ft/row} \\ \times \quad 4 \text{ rows} \\ \hline 14 \text{ ft of water} \end{array}$$

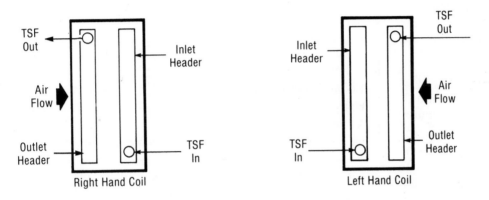

Figure 13.19 A method for determining left-hand and right-hand coils used in load heat exchangers.

Btu output per hr.	No. of rows	Liquid pressure drop, ft water	Air pressure drop, in water	No. of tubes
21,800	4	14.0	.150	64
27,260	5	17.5	.200	80
32,700	6	21.0	.240	96
38,160	7	24.5	.280	112

Figure 13.20 Typical values for air-pressure drop in 2 ft x 2 ft heat exchangers of various output capacities.

Btu Output per hr.	No. of rows	Liquid pressure drop, ft water	Air pressure drop, in water	No. of tubes
40,000	4	8	.150	64
50,000	5	10	.200	80
60,000	6	12	.240	96
70,000	7	14	.280	112

Figure 13.21 Typical values for air-pressure drop in 2 ft x 4 ft heat exchangers of various output capacities.

For your convenience, the typical specifications for two load heat exchangers have been determined as shown in Figure 13.22 and 13.23. The various entries were made using preset operating conditions, data from the Halstead and Mitchell Bulletin #C-350, and the calculations discussed in this section.

MAKING A DECISION

There are several very basic rules to follow in selecting efficient heat exchangers for the collector-to-storage loop and for the storage-to-load loop.

You should have decided that a counterflow heat exchanger is absolutely essential to prevent an efficiency loss in solar energy collection. Your final decision will involve heat exchangers with at least an 80-percent effectiveness. For the collector loop, a 90-percent effectiveness is recommended. Your specifications for the size of the heat exchanger will be determined by the load that the unit must carry. The manufacturer's data is essential for properly sizing a heat exchanger.

HEAT EXCHANGER SPECIFICATIONS
Design Criteria
Coil dimensions .... 2′ x 2′ (4 sq ft)
Number of face tubes/row .... 16 per row
Coil circuiting .... half serpentine
Number of circuits 8
Water flow per circuit .... 2 GPM
Fins per inch 8
Cubic ft of air supplied .... 1600 CFM
Air velocity across coil face .... 400 ft per minute
Heat transfer coefficient .... 145 Btu/sq ft/hr/°F/row
Water GPM correction factor 0.94
Pressure drop of water per pass .... 0.22 ft of water
Operating Conditions
T_1 = Water inlet temperature .... 120°F
T_2 = Water outlet temperature .... 65°F
T_3 = Air inlet temperature..................................... 55°F
T_4 = Air outlet temperature .... 110°F
Water flow rate .... 16 GPM
Air flow rate .... 1600 CFM
Air pressure drop.............. (varies with exchanger, see Figure 13.20)

Figure 13.22 Typical specifications for a 2 ft x 2 ft, liquid-to-air, load heat exchanger.

HEAT EXCHANGER SPECIFICATIONS
Design Criteria
Coil dimensions .... 2′ x 4′ (8 sq ft)
Number of face tubes per row .... 16 per row
Coil circuiting .... half serpentine
Number of circuits 8
Water flow per circuit .... 1.5 GPM
Fins per inch 8
Cubic feet of air supplied .... 3200 CFM
Air velocity across coil face .... 400 ft per minute
Heat transfer coefficient....................... 142 Btu/sq ft/hr/°F/row
Water GPM correction factor 0.88
Pressure drop of water per pass 0.13
Operating Conditions
T_1 = Water inlet temperature .... 120°F
T_2 = Water outlet temperature .... 65°F
T_3 = Air inlet temperature..................................... 55°F
T_4 = Air outlet temperature .... 110°F
Air flow rate .... 3200 CFM
Air pressure drop.............(varies with exchanger, see Figure 13.21)

Figure 13.23 Typical specifications for a 2 ft x 4 ft, liquid-to-air, load heat exchanger.

DECISION 14

Bank The Collected Energy

A building's hot water needs vary according to the occupant's lifestyle or working schedule. The hours of peak demand may fall at any time during the day or night. Usage may range from a few gallons to hundreds in a 24-hour period.

A building's space heating needs vary according to the weather. More or less heat may be required depending on the outside temperature, the building heat loss, and the desired comfort level. The hours of peak demand usually occur at night and during sunless periods. The heat required per hour may range from a few hundred Btu to many thousands.

The collectors in a solar energy system normally do not collect usable energy for more than six hours a day. And, when the sun is shining, they can usually collect more energy than the building needs to maintain comfortable temperatures and sufficient supplies of hot water. Because of this, an effective means of storing collected energy is an important part of the solar energy system. With storage capabilities, the system can provide heat and hot water as needed, night or day, regardless of the weather.

This section of The Solar Decision Book will help you to choose an effective means of solar storage. You will learn that:

- A solar hot-water tank must be of high quality, include some type of heat exchanger, and be well-insulated.

- Solar storage capabilities to meet space-heating needs involve rock-pebble beds for air-filled collectors and water tanks for liquid-filled collectors.

STORAGE FOR SOLAR WATER HEATING

The simplest storage device for solar water heating is a drum or pillow rooftop heater. This *storage-type water heater* was discussed briefly in Decision 5 of The Solar Decision Book. The heater may be a black plastic bag set on a level platform, a simple water drum mounted on the roof or on a tower, or it may be a tilted rectangular-shaped box which has reflectors and an insulated water compartment. In each case, the heater functions both as a solar energy collector and a warm-water storage unit. Since it must be located outside the building, heat loss at night or during cloudy weather is a major problem with a storage-type water heater.

The usual storage method for solar water heating is to use a water tank which is similar to a standard water heater. This tank however, will not have its own source of heat. In fact, for maximum effectiveness, it must not have a source of heat other than solar energy. It will have a heat exchanger, either built-in or mounted externally, to draw energy from the heat-transfer medium in the collector loop. It will be installed as a water preheater ahead of the building's auxiliary heater. The well or city water connection is made to the preheater tank.

When energy collection is sufficient, the solar preheater tank can supply all of the building's hot water. When energy collection is insufficient to meet hot-water needs, the solar preheater tank will supply warm water to the auxiliary heater for further heating. In this way, the solar preheater can usually minimize the fuel requirements for a backup water heater.

Solar preheater tanks for hot-water storage can be made of galvanized steel, glass-lined steel, stone-lined steel, copper, or high-temperature fiberglass. They are generally available in standard sizes of 40-, 65-, 80-, and 120-gallons. Regardless of the type or size, the preheater tank must be well-insulated to prevent heat loss. Also, a high-quality tank is recommended to insure long life. Average-quality tanks may not last the desired 20-year life of a good solar system.

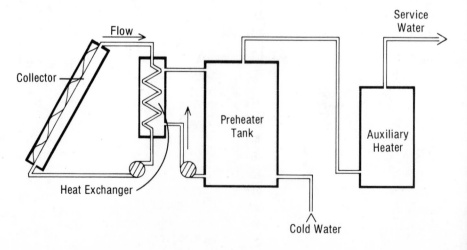

Figure 14.1 A water preheater tank with an external heat exchanger.

Figure 14.1 shows a solar preheater tank with an external heat exchanger. This is the most flexible storage system for solar water heating. Should the tank fail, only the tank needs to be replaced. The heat exchanger can remain in service. Properly designed, a solar water-heating system that uses a preheater tank with an external heat exchanger is very efficient.

For a preheater tank with a built-in heat exchanger, you have a choice of three types. The tank may have 1) a wrap-around or jacket-type heat exchanger, 2) an internal-coil heat exchanger, or 3) an internal-flue heat exchanger. Such preheater tanks are more expensive to replace than those with an external heat exchanger.

Figure 14.2 shows a solar preheater tank with a jacket-type heat exchanger. This is constructed like a tank within a tank. The heat-transfer fluid is circulated in the jacket that surrounds the interior water tank.

Two designs of this type of solar preheater are available. One design has a full jacket surrounding the water tank. The heat exchanger fluid flows down through this jacket. The other design has sets of parallel channels in which the heat-transfer fluid and tank water can flow without mixing. Both designs are efficient. Both incorporate the idea of a double-walled heat exchanger which is often required when the heat-transfer fluid is nonpotable. In each case, the heat exchanger should be operated in the counterflow mode. Usually, this means that the heated fluid from the collectors flows down, while the cold water from the tank or supply connection flows up.

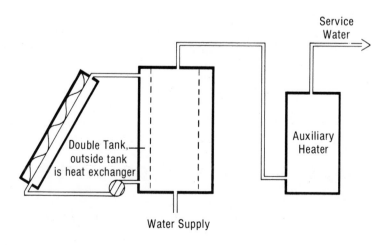

Figure 14.2 A water preheater tank with a jacket-type heat exchanger.

Figure 14.3 shows a solar preheater tank with an internal-coil heat exchanger. The large, finned copper coil is placed near the bottom of the tank. This "coil in tank" design is highly efficient as proven in numerous installations. The system is not double walled, and this may limit the choice of heat-transfer fluid. The presence of a larger copper coil in a steel tank is another limitation. The copper and steel interreact which causes corrosion and shortens the tank life. A stone-lined tank should be used to prevent early tank failure.

Figure 14.4 shows a solar preheater tank with internal flues acting as the heat exchanger. This type of tank is currently used in drain-down systems in which distilled water can be used as the heat-transfer fluid without fear of freezing. Because such systems use an open loop, pump horsepower requirements are quite large.

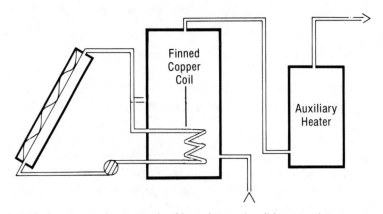

Figure 14.3 A water preheater tank with an internal-coil heat exchanger.

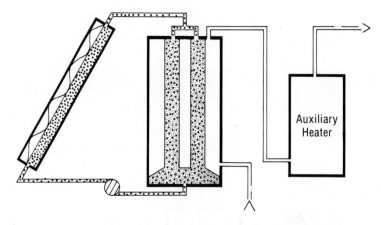

Figure 14.4 A water preheater tank with internal flues that act as the heat exchanger.

STORAGE FOR SOLAR SPACE HEATING

The simplest storage device for solar space heating is the building itself. This is true for both passive and active solar energy systems. For passive systems, the building can be designed or modified to collect energy during the day and to release that energy slowly during the night. The higher the thermal mass, the more effective the system. Properly insulated, the building can trap energy collected by passive means and can make maximum use of energy collected by active means.

Some active solar energy systems actually use the building alone for heat storage. These systems usually have air-filled collectors, and the heated air is piped directly into the building. With such systems however, the collectors can be used only when the building needs heat. On a cold day with the sun shining, this is fine. On a cloudy day or during the night, it is not. These systems have serious drawbacks in northern climates where weather conditions often require that the solar energy system provide stored heat around-the-clock or even for several days.

As such, a separate heat-storage unit is included in most active solar energy systems. On a warm day with the sun shining, energy can be stored for night-time or cloudy-day use.

Your Choices For Solar Storage

There are several options for solar storage, but the two most practical storage materials seem to be water and rocks. These two materials are both inexpensive and readily available.

The most common type of water storage system uses a large tank which can be located above or below ground, inside or outside the structure.

The most common type of rock storage system uses a huge bin or "bed" of stones and pebbles of a certain size and mixture. This bin is usually built below grade, next to or inside existing structures and as part of the basement in new structures.

Both types of heat storage systems require large areas. Properly designed however, either can be included in the solar energy system without significant loss of living area or productive area. Also, they can be installed without causing undue architectural problems.

Other methods of heat storage are being investigated. The goals of such research are reduced volume and increased storage capacity. Two materials drawing the most interest as possible heat-storage media are certain types of salts and paraffins. These are called *phase-changing materials,* or materials which can change from solid to liquid and back to solid. Certain salts and paraffins both change to liquid when they are heated. They change back to solids when they are cooled. As they melt into liquids, they absorb heat. As they cool to solids, they release that heat.

Phase-changing materials meet the requirements for small-volume heat storage. However they are not commercially feasible at this time. The costs of properly packaging these materials in some type of container that would work for solar storage are currently prohibitive. There are performance problems as well. The materials work only within a narrow temperature range, and they require frequent replacement.

These shortcomings of phase-changing materials — plus the lack of other suitable storage concepts — leaves water and rocks as the best solar storage choices at this time. Water and rocks should continue as the most popular storage materials for at least the next five years.

Selection Criteria

The storage system for solar space heating performs three major functions:

1. It absorbs heat from the collector heat-transfer media (liquid or air).
2. It stores this heat until it is needed.
3. It transfers heat to the space heating system on demand. (If so designed, the storage system also supplies energy for the water-heating system.)

The design of a particular solar energy system will usually dictate which type of storage material is used. Water-filled storage tanks are normally used with systems having liquid-filled collector loops. Rock-pebble beds are normally used with systems having air-filled collector loops. Of course, there are exceptions.

The cost and performance of each storage method should be considered. Water storage will usually be less expensive. Yet, owner preference, building codes, or the geographical area may make a rock-pebble bed the more attractive choice. In selecting a storage method, you should consider the type of container, whether or not heat exchangers will be used, pump and fan requirements, the system's operating temperature, and the insulation needed to prevent excessive heat loss.

The area available for solar storage should definitely be a consideration. Water storage requires less space, no matter how large or small the solar system. With liquid-filled systems, about 1.2 to 2.0 gallons of storage water are needed for each square foot of collector area. With air-filled solar systems, about 0.5 to 0.75 cubic feet of storage are needed for each square foot of collector area. About 7½ gallons of water will fit into one cubic foot of space.

So, for systems of identical size and capability, a rock-pebble bed will occupy 2½ to 3 times more space than a water-filled storage tank. This can be proved by comparing the heat-storage capacity of each material. The storage capacity varies according to the material's *specific heat,* or the number of Btu required to raise the temperature of one pound of the material one-degree Fahrenheit.

Water has a specific heat of one Btu per pound per degree F. It has a *density* , or weight per unit, of 62.4 pounds per cubic foot. The *heat capacity,* or amount of heat that can be stored in the material to raise the temperature one-degree F, is found by multiplying the specific heat by the density. Doing this, you will find that the heat capacity of water is 62.4 Btu per cubic foot for a 1°F temperature rise.

Stone has a specific heat of only 0.21 Btu/lb/°F. And, although solid stone has a density of 170 pounds per cubic foot, the air spaces or voids in a typical rock-pebble bed reduces its density to about 110 pounds per cubic foot. As a result, the heat capacity of a typical rock-pebble bed is only 23.1 Btu per cubic foot for a 1°F temperature rise.

Thus, for equal storage capacity, the rock-pebble bed would have to be sized 2.7 times larger than the water tank. The variation in voids between the rocks could raise or lower this figure. A good range, as mentioned earlier, would be 2½ to 3 times larger.

$$
\begin{array}{r}
1 \text{ Btu/Lb/°F} \\
\times\ 62.4 \text{ Lb/cu ft} \\
\hline
62.4 \text{ Btu/cu ft}
\end{array}
$$

$$
\begin{array}{r}
0.21 \text{ Btu/Lb/°F} \\
\times\ 110 \text{ Lb/cu ft} \\
\hline
23.1 \text{ Btu/cu ft}
\end{array}
$$

$$
\frac{62.4}{23.1} = 2.7
$$

Water-Filled Storage Tanks

Water tanks for solar storage can be designed in a variety of shapes and sizes. The tank materials can be selected to best fit the requirements of the system and the storage location. Structural requirements should be considered. Several precautions should be taken to insure proper siting, safety, and operation. The installed tank should be adequately insulated, engineered to withstand loading, fitted with correct-size heat exchangers, and easy to maintain. The costs can be reasonable and the performance excellent.

TYPES/MATERIALS. Water tanks for solar storage can be almost any size and shape you want. A huge reservoir of water can store heat for weeks and even months. However, the cost for such a tank might outweigh its value. Sizing the storage tank will usually call for a compromise between cost and storage capacity.

Several possible tank configurations are shown in Figure 14.5. These tank designs were set forth by Mr. Ellis E. Pickering in an NSF contract (NSF RA-N-75-095). They are shown here as a sampling of the tank designs possible with water storage for solar systems.

The welded-steel tank would be best for installation inside the building, near the heat-delivery system and sewers. It would be readily accessible for maintenance. The precast concrete vault-type and drainpipe tanks are excellent for underground storage when properly lined. The reinforced concrete block tank can be designed for either above-ground or below-ground installation. The designs would have to meet different loading requirements. Fiberglass tanks could be used for both above- and below-ground installations. In fact, a fiberglass septic tank could easily be outfitted for use as a solar storage tank. A wood-stave tank would necessarily be restricted to above-grade applications. An elastomeric (rubber) bag could be used as a pillow-type storage tank in crawl spaces. And, for very large storage capacities, a vertical tank in a drilled hole might be a good choice. The tank could be fabricated in place.

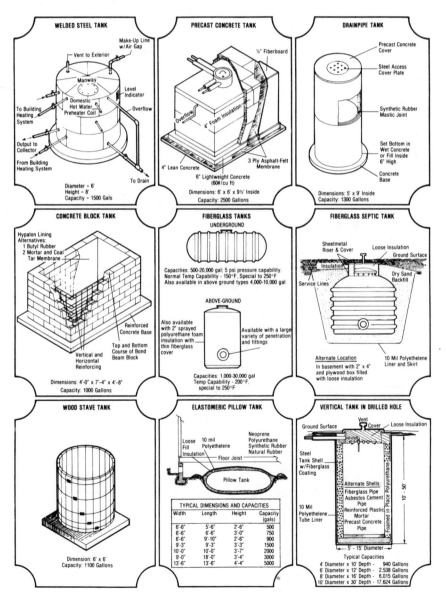

Figure 14.5 Several possible water storage tank configurations for solar systems.

14-7

Advantages	Disadvantages
Steel Shell	
1. Readily available 2. Light weight 3. Readily tapped 4. Relatively low cost 5. Simple fabrication 6. Available in bolted form 7. No capillary water seepage	1. Interior corrosion problems unless lined 2. Exterior corrosion problems in underground service 3. Access room for retrofit and replacement 4. Low resistance to underground loads without extra material
Aluminum shell	
1. Light weight 2. Readily tapped 3. Simple fabrication 4. No capillary water seepage	1. Interior corrosion problems unless lined 2. Exterior corrosion problems in underground service 3. Access room for retrofit and replacement 4. More difficult welding than steel 5. Higher cost 6. Low resistance to underground loads without extra material
Reinforced concrete	
1. Readily formed into any shape or size 2. Corrosion resistant 3. May be formed in place for retrofit situations 4. Greater resistance to underground loads 5. Relatively low cost 6. Mass may be used as a heat store 7. Readily available on a local basis	1. Heavy 2. Water seepage through cracks and via capillary water unless lined 3. Leakage at joints in precast form unless lined 4. Requires sophisticated design and workmanship 5. More difficult to tap
Reinforced plastics	
1. Light weight 2. Interior and exterior corrosion resistance 3. Water tightness 4. Readily tapped	1. Sophisticated design, fabrication, and test process 2. Lower temperature resistance 3. Low resistance to underground loads without extra material 4. Higher cost 5. Less availability than steel or concrete
Pipe sections (asbestos cement, fiberglass or lined steel in vertical orientation)	
1. Readily available 2. Requires less impact on building area 3. Readily adapts to retrofit situations 4. Corrosion resistant 5. Readily tapped	1. Foundation weight 2. May cost more than steel or concrete as presently produced 3. Low capacity in practical lengths unless vertically oriented
Wood	
1. Readily available 2. Light weight 3. Relatively low cost 4. Adaptable to retrofit situations with limited access 5. Corrosion resistant	1. Capillary water seepage unless lined 2. Above ground service only 3. More difficult to tap
Elastomeric fabrics	
1. Readily available 2. Adaptable to low height situations 3. Light weight 4. Corrosion resistant	1. More difficult to insulate 2. May have limited temperature capability unless fabricated with proper synthetic rubber 3. Limited applications, cannot be used underground

Figure 14.6 The advantages and disadvantages of various construction materials for solar storage tanks. (Reprinted courtesy of Solar Engineering Magazine.)

In an article for *Solar Engineering* magazine (Sept. '77), Mr. Pickering also compared the advantages and disadvantages of various storage tank materials. This comparison is shown in Figure 14.6.

STRUCTURAL CONSIDERATIONS. In buildings with full basements, tanks can be placed inside the structure with minor intrusion into the living or working space. Structures built over crawl spaces may represent a more difficult problem. With slab-on-grade structures, the tank will need to be mounted under the floor or outside. In all cases, tanks fitted into existing structures must have footings designed to carry their heavy load.

In no case, should the tank be constructed as part of the building's foundation or floor. The average basement floor — four inches of unreinforced concrete is completely inadequate to support the storage tank. A separate foundation or footing should be designed for the tank.

Depending on the system design, a 1000-gallon tank can handle the storage requirements for 500 to 800 square feet of collector. That's 2.0 gallons per square foot for the small collector array, and 1.25 gallons per square foot for the large collector array.

But 1000 gallons of water is heavy. it occupies 133.5 cubic feet and weighs 8330 pounds. More than four tons, not including the tank and its supporting hardware. You must consider this weight in calculating the footing or foundation for such a tank. Figure 14.7 shows three possible variations for a 1000-gallon rectangular storage tank. Figure 14.8 shows three possible variations for a 1000-gallon round storage tank. In both cases, rectangular or round, the tank's dimensions affect the load-bearing requirements. By decreasing the tank height and increasing the tank width and/or length, the load can be distributed over a greater area. Footing requirements would be reduced. Remember to include the tank weight in arriving at the gross weight which must be supported.

PRECAUTIONS. The solar storage tank must be structurally sound, sited and fitted with safety devices, and its water properly treated or conditioned.

Structural soundness calls for designs capable of withstanding normal as well as unusual loading. Whether full or empty, the tank must be engineered to withstand both dead and live loads, wind and snow loads, soil pressures, vehicular traffic if necessary, and earthquakes in certain areas. If the area's water table is high, the tank should be designed so that it will not float when empty. To meet loading requirements, internal bracing and baffling may be required. Such braces should not interfere with the proper functioning of the tank.

Proper siting is a necessary precaution for owner protection and maintenance. The tank should be located where the storage water can be pumped out or drained if necessary. It should be located where leaks can be repaired easily. And it should be located in such a manner that unexpected leaks will be found before they can damage the structure or its contents.

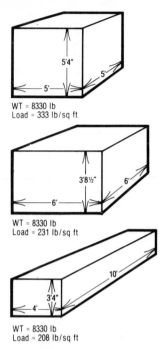

Figure 14.7 Three possible variations for a 1000-gallon rectangular storage tank. Dimensions affect load-bearing requirements.

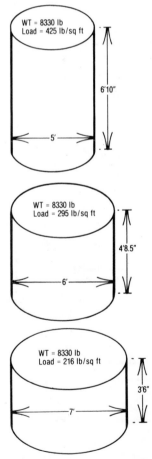

Figure 14.8 Three possible variations for a 1000-gallon round storage tank. Dimensions affect load bearing requirements.

In operation, the storage tank temperatures will range from a low of 45°F to a high of 200°F. The water expands at high temperatures and contracts at low temperatures. The storage tank must have room for expansion or have a separate expansion tank. Pressurized storage is not needed because the tank operates below water's boiling point. However, when the tank is part of a closed system, a safety valve should be included to vent any pressures that build up.

The storage water must be properly inhibited, demineralized, and neutral in pH to protect against corrosion and scale buildup in the piping, the tank, and the heat exchangers. This will also prevent the growth of algae, mold, and mildew.

INSTALLATION. Solar storage tanks must be durable and easy to maintain. This is possible only if premium materials are chosen, and the system is installed properly.

Whether indoors, subsurface, or outdoors, tanks must be insulated to retain the stored heat. Depending upon the tank location and end use, insulation requirements will vary.

During erection of the tanks, provision must be made for the required piping entrances and exits needed for instrumentation and water circulation.

Storage water should be regarded as nonpotable and labelled as such. There should be no connections between the domestic water system and the storage water. Any makeup water should be supplied by temporary hose or through a code-approved air gap.

Heat exchangers of an approved type should be used between storage water and service hot water. These heat exchangers should be located where they can be periodically checked for corrosion and malfunctions. Overflow devices, safety valves, and vents should terminate in a sanitary sewer or storm drain according to local codes and practices.

In residential systems, maintenance requirements should be minimal, designs should not be highly dependent on renewable water treatment, and the system should be engineered for gross neglect.

Rock-Pebble Bed Storage

Your options with rock-pebble beds are very few, compared to water-tank storage systems. Poured concrete, precast concrete, concrete block, and wood bins are your only choices. In the case of wood, the storage bin must not be below grade. In all cases, the storage bin should be lined.

Structural requirements are substantial compared to water-tank storage systems. This is due to the tremendous weights and volumes involved. For instance, a rock-pebble bed with the heat capacity of a 1000-gallon tank would occupy 360 cubic feet and weigh 39,600 pounds. Almost three times the volume (133.5 cu. ft) and almost five times the weight (8330 lb) of a comparable water-tank storage system.

Figure 14.9 shows five possible sizes for a rock-pebble bed which is equivalent in heat capacity to a 1000-gallon storage tank. By

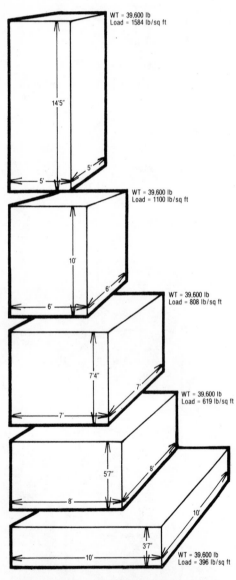

Figure 14.9 Five possible sizes for a rock-pebble bed which is equivalent to a 1000-gallon storage tank. Dimensions affect the load-bearing requirements.

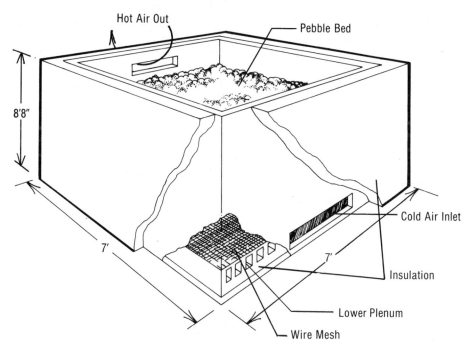

Figure 14.10 Design details of a typical rock-storage bed for an air-filled solar collector loop.

increasing the width and/or length and reducing the height, the load-bearing requirements are reduced. The heights shown do not include the air ducts of about 16-inches each which must be added to the top and bottom of the storage bin.

A typical rock-pebble bed could be constructed as shown in Figure 14.10. Such a storage system offers no known advantages over a water-tank storage system.

Storage System Insulation

Storage tank insulation prevents the loss of heat from the tank into its surroundings. Assuming that the tank is not used to heat living space by its surface radiation, insulation is dependent on the tank location and economic factors. To properly design insulation for a tank, a heat loss analysis must be carried out on the specific tank. For example, given a 5'x5'x5' cube of three-inch concrete containing 938 gallons of water and no insulation, the heat loss from the tank is 102 Btu/hr/°F.

If the tank is at 200°F and the surrounding air is 65°F, the heat loss from the tank becomes 13,770 Btu per hour, or 330,480 Btu per day.

One gallon of water weighs 8.33 pounds. 938 gallons weighs 7813 pounds. It takes one Btu per pound to raise the water temperature 1°F, so a loss of 7813 Btu will lower the tank temperature 1°F.

Thus, the tank will lose 1.76°F in temperature every hour or 42°F in a day.

$$
\begin{array}{r}
5\,\text{ft/side} \\
\times\ 5\,\text{ft/side} \\
\times\ 6\,\text{sides} \\
\hline
150\,\text{sq ft (surface)} \\
\times\ .68\ (\text{U-factor 3" concrete}) \\
\hline
102\,\text{Btu/hr/°F}
\end{array}
$$

$$
\begin{array}{r}
135°F\ (200-65) \\
\times\ 102\ \text{Btu/hr/°F} \\
\hline
13,770\,\text{Btu/hr} \\
\times\ \ 24\ \text{hr/day} \\
\hline
330,480\,\text{Btu/day}
\end{array}
$$

$$
\begin{array}{r}
8.33\,\text{Lb/gal} \\
\times\ 938\ \text{gal} \\
\hline
7,813\,\text{Lb} \\
\times\ \ 1\ \text{Btu/Lb/°F} \\
\hline
7,813\,\text{Btu/°F}
\end{array}
$$

$$
\frac{13,770}{7,813} = 1.76°F
$$

$$
\begin{array}{r}
1.76°F/\text{hr} \\
\times\ 24\ \text{hr/day} \\
\hline
42°F/\text{day}
\end{array}
$$

$$\begin{array}{r} 150\,sq\,ft \\ \times\ .05\ Btu/sq\,ft/hr/^{\circ}F \\ \hline 7.5\ Btu/hr/^{\circ}F \end{array}$$

$$\begin{array}{r} 135^{\circ}F \\ 7.5\ Btu/hr/^{\circ}F \\ \hline 1,013\ Btu/hr \end{array}$$

$$\frac{1,013}{7,813} = 0.13^{\circ}F$$

$$\begin{array}{r} 0.13^{\circ}F/hr \\ \times\ 24\ hr/day \\ \hline 3^{\circ}F/day \end{array}$$

$$\begin{array}{r} 7,813\ Btu/^{\circ}F \\ \times\ 3^{\circ}F/day \\ \hline 23,439\ Btu/day \end{array}$$

If R-20 insulation is placed around the tank, the heat loss becomes only 7.5 Btu per hour for a one-degree F loss.

With a 135°F temperature difference (200-65), this loss would amount to 1013 Btu per hour.

The tank would lose only 0.13°F per hour or 3°F per day.

This would be a reasonable loss of 23,439 Btu per day. It is only about seven percent of the heat loss from the uninsulated tank.

Such analysis is essential for designing tank insulation. A specification calling for losses in the vicinity of less than 3° to 5°F/day would appear reasonable. The choice of material for storage tank insulation is a function of economics, life, service conditions, and R-value. Generally:

- Service temperatures in the tank will be more than 45°F and less than 200°F.
- Service temperatures outside the tank will vary depending on location, above grade or below, inside or outside.
- The insulation must be protected against moisture, mechanical damage, fire, slumping or compacting, and loss of bond integrity to the tank.
- The R-value must remain constant over the life of the insulation.
- Insulation below the tank must support the required dead weight.

Fiberglass, foamed urethanes (overcoated for fire safety), isocyanurate, and glass fiberboard appear to be excellent tank insulations. The service temperature of polystyrene is too low (175°F), loose fill is prone to humidity pickup and compacting. This is especially true for mineral wool, perlite and vermiculite. Similar problems are seen with cellulosics.

MAKING A DECISION

In this section of The Solar Decision Book, you have learned about heat-storage systems for solar water-heating and solar space-heating. Storage for solar water heating is usually accomplished with a preheater tank which is quite similar to a standard water heater tank. Storage for solar space heating is accomplished with water tanks or rock-pebble beds. Liquid-filled collector loops call for water storage, while air-filled collector loops call for rock storage.

Your decision on solar storage will depend mostly on the type of solar energy system you prefer. However, the cost and performance of the solar storage methods should be studied.

DECISION 15

Include An Auxiliary Heater

Auxiliary Heater For Long-Sunless Periods

FOSSIL FUEL IS MORE ECONOMICAL THAN ELECTRICITY

The sun sends huge amounts of energy toward the earth. Each day, year-round. A solar system can trap quantities of that energy for water heating and space heating. And, under ideal conditions, that solar system can collect and store enough energy to provide all of a building's hot-water and heating needs.

But few solar systems, if any, operate under ideal conditions for 365 days a year. Solar systems are needed most in northern climes, where weather patterns are highly variable. The outside temperatures may range from a sizzling 95°F in the summertime to a brittle -20°F in the wintertime. The skies may be crystal clear, hazy, or heavily overcast.

As a result, most solar systems cannot be depended upon to provide 100-percent of the building's energy needs. Depending on the geographical area and the size of the system, about 45- to 70-percent is the average for economy reasons. For a higher percentage of energy collection, the solar system becomes far too costly to expect a good return on your investment. That's why an auxiliary heater is an important component in your energy planning.

Although it will serve only part-time duty, the auxiliary heater should be chosen with care. Some are more cost-efficient than others. The right decision can insure an economical and dependable backup energy source. This section of The Solar Decision Book will help you to make that decision. You will learn that:

- The "best choice" of auxiliary heat will vary. That choice may be dictated by economics, individual installation requirements, or personal preference.

- A heat pump can extend the solar system's capabilities for space heating, as well as provide cooling capabilities.

1 AUTOMATIC OPERATION

2 ECONOMICAL FUEL

3 COMMON HEAT DELIVERY WITH SOLAR

4 CARRY 100% HEAT LOAD

Figure 15.1 Four criteria for choosing an auxiliary heater.

SELECTION CRITERIA

An auxiliary heater must be included in almost all solar system installations. In existing buildings, this heater could be a conventional fossil-fuel furnace which is already in place. In structures under construction, the auxiliary heater could be as simple as an oversized water heater operated on fossil fuel or electricity.

In either case — existing structure or new construction — the selection criteria shown in Figure 15.1 apply. The auxiliary heater should:

- Operate automatically, as needed.
- Use the most economical fuel.
- Share a common heat-delivery system with the solar energy system.
- Be capable of carrying 100-percent of the building's heat load.

Automatic Operation

The need for automatic operation rules out heaters that are fueled with wood or coal. However, depending on personal preferences and the local availability, such fuels may be the best choice from a cost standpoint.

The more conventional fuels for automatic operation heaters are gas, fuel oil, and electricity. These fuels can be used in water heaters, boilers, and furnaces. Electricity can also be used for baseboard electrical resistance heating (ERH) and for heat pumps.

Fuel Economy

Of course, the auxiliary heater should not use up the savings generated by the solar system. This is not as absurd as it sounds. If you were to switch from 100-percent gas or oil heat to 50-percent solar and 50-percent electrical resistance heat, your energy costs would increase! Plus, you would not contribute to energy conservation. Fossil fuel is converted to electricity at only 30-percent efficiency. In contrast, a well-maintained furnace converts fossil fuel into useful heat at about 60- to 70-percent efficiency.

Figure 15.2 shows the projected 1979 costs for different auxiliary fuels. The cost of electrical resistance heating is extremely high. Gas and fuel oil can be reasonably used on a part-time basis. And both types of heat pumps are very cost-efficient.

Heat pumps function extremely well in areas of moderate climate. However, they cannot be expected to provide 100-percent of the heating load in very cold (below 20°F) climates. As such, the best

Electric resistance heating	$13.18/MM Btu
Gas or fuel oil (60% efficient)	7.10/MM Btu
Heat pump, air-to-air (COP) 2.5	5.28/MM Btu
Heat pump, liquid-to-air (COP 3.5)	3.90/MM Btu

Figure 15.2 Projected 1979 costs of different auxiliary fuels.

choice for economical auxiliary heat appears to be a fossil-fuel burning device backed by a solar-assisted heat pump.

Common Heat-Delivery System

In many cases, this requirement cannot be easily met. Where room units for electrical resistance heating are used, they will provide auxiliary heat. If hydronic baseboard radiators are used, some resizing will be required. The various options on the heat-delivery system are discussed in Decision 16 of The Solar Decision Book.

The Heating Load

This requirement must be considered based on the particular building and its geographical area. Building heat losses and seasonal weather patterns will dictate the size of the auxiliary heater. Generally, the heater should be sized to carry the entire heating load as if no solar system were installed. Weather conditions or system servicing may require the heater to do just that for extended periods of time.

THE MOST LIKELY CHOICES

Electrical Resistance Heating

Despite its high costs, electrical resistance heating makes sense in some cases. Homes built for electrical resistance heating generally have extremely low heat loss because of their construction. The fuel bill is high, but the system is in place and little or no provision has been made for a fossil-fuel heat-delivery system. Changing over to a fossil-fuel system alone would cut the utility bill almost in half. And, the installation cost would be much lower than for solar. For auxiliary heat in a solar installation, electrical resistance heating would be expensive. It would possibly ruin the economics of solar.

Owners of electrically heated structures are faced with a major decision. Stay with electricity, convert to fossil fuel, or convert to solar energy plus fossil fuel. A detailed economic analysis would be a logical first step.

Water Heaters

Domestic water heaters provide 30,000 to 40,000 Btu per hour from an input of 50,000 Btu of fossil fuel. This is for heaters with 30- to 65-gallon tanks. With a 500 Btu/hr/°F heat loss in a structure and a design temperature of 75°F, only 37,500 Btu per hour would be needed to keep the structure heated. A water heater would be a logical choice.

The life of a water heater, however, is limited. About five to eight years of normal service. If the heater is operated in a closed-loop system, the water could be treated. Such water would, of course, be nonpotable. Then, with such treated water and intermittent use, the heater could be expected to last much longer. Installation costs are minimal for such an auxiliary heater. Flue requirements are also quite inexpensive. Both gas- and oil-fired units are available. Auxiliary heat from the water heater appears to be a logical choice for retrofitting homes that currently have electrical resistance heating.

Boilers

Oil- or gas-fired boilers make excellent auxiliary heaters. They are more expensive than water heaters, but they have much longer life spans. Boilers are designed to operate in a 160° to 200°F temperature range. They would be overdesigned for the low-temperature heat-delivery systems used for solar. However, this should not cause any problems if the common delivery system is engineered for the higher temperatures.

Boiler efficiencies lie in the 50- to 70-percent range. Flue requirements are much more costly than for water heaters. Units with outputs from 50,000 to 210,000 Btu per hour are available as off-the-shelf equipment. Boilers as well as water heaters would be used to feed the liquid side of the solar fan coil in the heat-delivery system.

Forced-Air Furnaces

Forced-air furnaces also provide an excellent interface with a solar heat-delivery system. However, they do not integrate well with a decentralized room-type delivery system where no ductwork is available.

The basic furnace is generally less expensive than a boiler when it is combined with a central fan coil in the solar system. Efficiencies again lie in the 50- to 70-percent range. Flue requirements are similar to those of boilers. Normal off-the-shelf sizes range from 50,000 to 130,000 Btu per hour. Structures currently using forced-air heating are excellent candidates for solar energy systems.

Heat Pumps

AIR-TO-AIR HEAT PUMPS. The air-to-air heat pump functions extremely well as an auxiliary heater at temperatures down to 20°F. Below these temperatures, it suffers in efficiency and performance. When solar assisted by heat from a rock-pebble storage bed and air collectors, the heat pump adds much to the performance of the solar energy system.

Without such a solar assist, air-to-air heat pumps have limited utility in cold climates. Their use should be carefully checked with the local utility and pump manufacturer.

The heat pump also provides cooling during the summer. It thus has year-round utility. Heat pumps should be comparison-shopped. The purchaser should look at the cost, performance, service and expected life. Units differ considerably from manufacturer to manufacturer.

LIQUID-TO-AIR HEAT PUMPS. The liquid-to-air heat pump is an ideal auxiliary heater when coupled with liquid solar storage. It operates at very low cost. And it greatly enhances solar energy collection by drawing down the temperature of the solar storage water to as low as 45°F. Without question, the solar-assisted heat pump is most useful for auxiliary heat. It should be considered for all installations, except those with existing fossil fuel furnaces and no need for summer cooling.

STORAGE TANK TEMPERATURE RANGE	BTU IN STORAGE	HOURS OF SOLAR STORAGE @ TEMPERATURES OF		
		−10°	20°	40°
120 to 200°F	666,640	17.8	29.6	53.3
90 to 120°F	249,990	6.7	11.1	20.0
45 to 90°F	374,985	10.0	16.7	30.0
Total	1,291,615	34.5 hrs	57.4 hrs	103.3 hrs

Figure 15.3 Solar storage capacity at various temperatures.

STORAGE TANK TEMP °F	AVAILABLE Btu	COST/HR TO RUN	COST/MM Btu	FOSSIL FUEL COST/MM Btu
75	50,500	19.0¢	$3.70	$7.10
60	45,000	17.9¢	$3.90	$7.10
45	36,500	15.9¢	$4.30	$7.10
Fossil Fuel Cost = $7.10/MM Btu Electricity Cost = $13.18/MM Btu ($0.045/kwh)				

Figure 15.4 Heat pump "cost per Btu" compared to fossil fuels.

A heat pump takes low-temperature energy, concentrates it, and delivers that energy at higher temperatures. In a solar system, it can draw energy from solar storage and provide heat. The biggest advantage of using a heat pump, however, is that it draws energy from storage until the storage temperature reaches about 45°F. Without a heat pump, the storage temperature could be dropped to only about 80° to 90°F. At this point, usable heat could no longer be provided. The lower the storage temperature, the more efficient the collection process.

As an example, consider a storage tank filled with 1000 gallons of liquid. This amount of liquid can store 8333 Btu per degree F, with a maximum storage temperature of 200°F. Suppose the building heat loss is 500 Btu per hour per degree F. The heat required would be 37,500 Btu per hour at -10°F, 22,500 Btu per hour at 20°F, and 12,500 Btu per hour at 40°F. Then, the energy in solar storage would be as shown in Figure 15.3. By the use of a heat pump, the number of usable Btu is increased by almost 375 thousand. A 41-percent increase in storage capacity. And, at 40°F, 30 hours of useful heat.

Of course, heat pumps require expensive electrical energy for their compressors. Figure 15.4 compares the "cost per Btu" for a typical heat pump with that for fossil fuels. If the cost per Btu figures are averaged, this particular heat pump operates at about only 55-percent the cost of fossil fuels.

What happens in an extended period of no sun and subzero cold? There are two very practical alternatives. One is that city water can be pumped through the heat pump until the storage water comes back to a higher temperature. City water, and even well water, is normally at about 45° to 55°F and 83 to 166 Btu can be extracted from each gallon. Costs incurred would include heat pump operation and the cost of water or well pumping.

The other alternative would be to add an electric resistance heater to the heat pump. Certain types of heat pumps accept such heaters as accessories. Sizes vary, but some are capable of carrying the entire heating load. Although the operating cost would be high, this accessory might only be used a few days a year.

HEAT PUMPS FOR COOLING. The heat pump also can provide cooling. Good cooling efficiency is possible with storage temperatures up to 110°F. A more practical method is to obtain cooling by running city or well water through the heat pump. Or, the solar system can incorporate a cooling tower.

MAKING A DECISION

In this section of The Solar Decision Book, you have learned about choosing an auxiliary heater for a solar system. Fuel costs, installation requirements, and personal preferences enter into the decision. Heat pumps offer the most advantages while fossil-fuel burners are the most economical. Make the decision carefully. Your auxiliary heater may be called on to supply up to 50-percent of your annual energy needs.

DECISION 16

Deliver The Heat

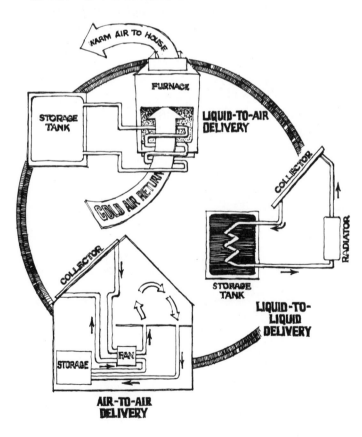

WARM AIR TO HOUSE

STORAGE TANK

FURNACE

LIQUID-TO-AIR DELIVERY

COLD AIR RETURN

COLLECTOR

COLLECTOR

RADIATOR

STORAGE TANK

LIQUID-TO-LIQUID DELIVERY

STORAGE

FAN

AIR-TO-AIR DELIVERY

The heat-delivery system is also known as the terminal system. The end of the line. This is where the collected solar energy is taken from storage and is put to work heating the structure.

Design of the terminal system is critical. A properly designed system will utilize solar storage water down to 80° to 90°F. And when a heat pump is included, down to 45° to 50°F. Improper design of the terminal system will result in limited energy storage and poor collector efficiency.

A collector loop cannot operate until the sun warms the heat-transfer medium to a temperature higher than that of the storage tank water. And the hotter the collectors get, the lower the efficiency at which they operate.

The design requirements for a solar heat-delivery system differ from those for fossil-fuel or electric-heat systems. Fossil fuels burn at more than 3000°F, and the heat is delivered at temperatures ranging from 140° to 200°F. Solar storage takes place at temperatures ranging from 90° to 200°F. And, the heat must be delivered at temperatures of 80° to 120°F.

This section of The Solar Decision Book will highlight the design requirements for a solar heat-delivery system. One that can draw usable heat at very low temperatures. And, one that can be integrated with whatever auxiliary heating means are employed. You will learn that:

- Solar storage must be utilized at low temperatures to maximize the collector efficiency.

- There are three ways to draw heat from solar storage.

- The heat-delivery design must heat the structure under all anticipated conditions.

- A heat pump can increase the usable storage capacity.

GENERAL DESIGN CONSIDERATIONS

The design of the terminal, or heat-delivery, system is very critical for effective use of the energy stored in the solar storage tank. The system should be designed so that usable heat can be drawn directly from solar storage at temperatures as low as 90°F. This will help insure maximum collector efficiency. The lower the solar storage temperature, the lower the temperature at which solar collection begins. Also, if the solar storage temperature is high, the collector efficiency drops. The collector loop cannot transfer as much energy to storage and, ultimately, to the heat-delivery system.

Figure 16.1 shows the collector efficiencies at various solar storage temperatures. The collector loop will not turn on until its heat-transfer medium reaches a temperature higher than that of solar storage. So, if the storage temperature is 180°F, the collector will not turn on until it reaches 185°F. This results in a very low collector efficiency of only 28-percent. And the energy that can be stored is only 56 Btu per hour per square foot of collector.

But, the collector efficiency improves dramatically as the solar storage temperature becomes lower. At a storage temperature of 80°F, the collectors turn on at 85°F, run at 60-percent efficiency, and collect 120 Btu per hour per square foot of collector. A much better picture of performance.

The amount of effective heat storage also depends on the lowest temperature at which the storage water can produce usable heat. Figure 16.2 compares solar storage capabilities at various tank temperatures when the storage turn-off temperature is 200°F. If solar heat can be delivered at 80°F instead of 140°F, the solar storage tank has twice the usable storage capacity. Adding a heat pump allows use of solar storage at temperatures down to 45°F. And the usable storage triples!

The heat pump thus increases the solar storage capacity to its practical limits. Water freezes at 32°F and boils at 212°F. The collectors can push the storage temperature to 200°F, while the heat pump can use stored heat from 80°F down to 44°F. So, the maximum range of usable solar storage is approximately 44° to 200°F.

MINIMUM SOLAR TANK TEMPERATURE, °F	COLLECTOR TURN-ON TEMPERATURE, °F	COLLECTOR OPERATING EFFICIENCY ® TURN-ON, PERCENT	ENERGY STORED Btu/HR/SQ/FT
180	185	28	56
140	145	40	80
100	105	54	108
80	85	60	120
45	50	70	140

CONDITIONS ASSUMED:
Double-glazed, selective-surface collector
Air temperature: 40°F ambient
I = 200 Btu/hr/sq/ft
$F_R \tau\alpha = 0.72$ $F_R U_L = 0.63$

Figure 16.1 Collector efficiencies at various solar storage temperatures.

MINIMUM SOLAR TANK TEMPERATURE, °F	MAXIMUM TEMPERATURE RISE IN STORAGE TANK, °F	AVAILABLE STORAGE, Btu
180	20	166,600
140	60	499,980
100	100	833,300
80	120	999,960
45	155	1,291,615
CONDITIONS ASSUMED: 200°F storage turn-off temperature 1000-gallon tank of water		

Figure 16.2 Solar storage capabilities at various tank temperatures.

TYPES OF HEAT-DELIVERY SYSTEMS

There are three types of heat-delivery systems that can draw heat from solar storage. These are:

- Liquid-to-air systems   • Liquid-to-liquid systems
- Air-to-air systems

A fourth type of system, air-to-liquid, is not practical because of heat exchanger inefficiencies. Liquid-to-liquid systems also have severe design limitations.

Liquid-To-Air Terminal Systems

The liquid-to-air heat-delivery system can take two forms. If the building is equipped with a hot-air circulating furnace, a liquid-to-air heat exchanger (fan coil) can be placed in the ductwork, as shown in Figure 16.3. The logical position for such a heat exchanger is in a plenum installed in the cold-air return of the existing furnace, on the suction side of the circulating blower. In this position, the heat exchanger acts as a preheater for return air before it passes through the furnace plenum. A heat-sensing element placed in this location will readily indicate to the fossil furnace whether it should or should

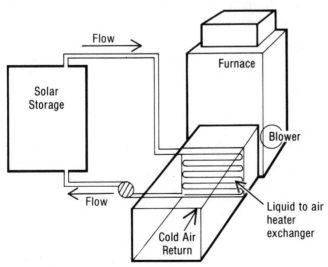

Figure 16.3 A liquid-to-air heat-delivery system with a centralized heat-exchanger in the furnace cold-air-return ductwork.

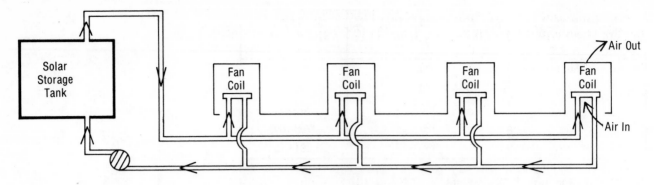

Figure 16.4 A liquid-to-air heat-delivery system with self-contained fan coils in individual rooms.

not supply auxiliary heat. If an air conditioning heat exchanger is installed in the auxiliary system, it is normally placed ahead of the furnace plenum or on a bypass plenum. Thus, the solar heat exchanger placed in this position will rarely interfere with the proper operation of the air conditioning unit.

If the building does not contain hot-air ductwork and solar heat delivery is to be via air, room-type liquid-to-air heat exchangers can be used. These units come in various sizes with self-contained fans or blowers.

As shown in Figure 16.4, the room-type fan coils can be fed individually by the solar storage system. This is usually a more practical approach for buildings without ductwork. More expense would be involved if ductwork were to be installed for a centralized heat exchanger.

These self-contained blower modules are readily available as standard plumbing and heating units at relatively low costs. Many have their own thermostats and, if desired, they can be purchased with auxiliary electric coils mounted in them. The operation expense for such coils however, is high.

Air-To-Air Terminal Systems

In solar systems which utilize air as the heat-transfer medium, only one type of heat-delivery system can be considered. The heat must be delivered into a rock-pebble storage bed and then into the house via hot-air ductwork. Such a system has only limited utility. Existing ductwork is rarely sized large enough for the low delivery temperatures. In new structures, the ductwork can be sized larger and such a heat-delivery system becomes much more feasible.

In current commercial designs for air-type systems, no heat exchanger is utilized between the load and solar storage. This is a serious drawback. Air-borne pollen, spores, fungi or bacteria could be carried from the building into the storage system. Storage conditions could be moist and warm. An ideal medium for harmful organic matter to take hold and multiply.

To prevent contamination of the rock-pebble storage bed, a device to sterilze the air or an air-to-air heat exchanger should be installed within the system. This is not currently a standard practice.

Air-to-air heat-delivery systems can be designed to operate efficiently down to storage temperatures of 80° to 90°F. Air-to-air heat pumps can be added to the design to allow operation at lower storage temperatures.

Liquid-To-Liquid Terminal Systems

Many buildings that utilize hot-water heating through hydronic baseboard radiation are candidates for solar retrofit. In general, hydronic baseboard radiators will not adequately act as efficient liquid-to-liquid heat exchangers. Most hydronic baseboard radiators are sized to provide adequate heat at delivery temperatures in the range of 200° - 220°F when the outdoor temperatures are lowest.

Figure 16.5 illustrates the problems that solar faces with baseboard radiators. The ability of the collectors to heat the storage water drops off as the outside temperature drops. At the same time, the water in the baseboard radiators must become hotter to heat the structure. At some point, around 20°F in this example, solar heat cannot effectively operate the baseboard radiators. Yet, that same solar heat is sufficient for 100-percent of the heating load if solar fan coils (liquid-to-air heat exchangers) are used.

In new structures, of course, additional radiators could be used. The increased radiation, with solar-heated water at only 120° to 140°F, would be sufficient to heat the structure. Fan coil systems could provide the same heat at storage temperatures as low as 100°F. This same capability could be provided by radiant-heat liquid coils embedded in the floor or ceiling. They would need to be sized for operation at 100°F. They are promising candidates for liquid-to-liquid heat-delivery systems.

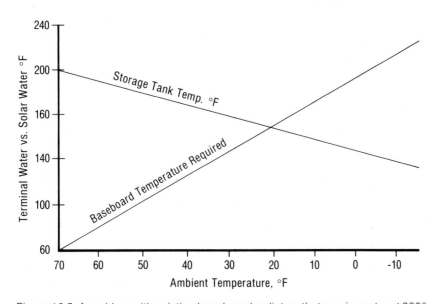

Figure 16.5 A problem with existing baseboard radiators that require water at 200°-220°F for effective heating. Solar storage cannot provide sufficient heat as the outside temperature drops.

TERMINAL DESIGN CONDITIONS

The lower the terminal design temperature employed, the larger the terminal system required. The volume of 140°F air needed to heat a structure is less than that of 90°F air. In retrofit situations, the ductwork is usually designed for 140°F air. Thus, the size of existing ductwork must be examined for suitability at lower delivery temperatures.

Also, the relationship between the solar storage temperature and the required terminal design temperature must be considered. The graph in Figure 16.6 shows the impact of this relationship.

Assume that the building is designed to be heated to 65°F from –10°F using 90°F solar storage water. At 65°F ambient, no heat is required while at –10°F, 90°F water is required. The heat required is directly proportional to the ambient temperature, and a straight 90°F design line can be drawn. This line shows that 10°F, 80°F water will provide 100-percent heat; at 40°F, 70°F water will provide 100-percent heat; and so on.

Tank storage capacity is also directly proportional to temperature change. A straight design line can be drawn from the top tank temperature to the design temperature. These two lines, when considered together, show that under any set of conditions existing within the design parameters, solar storage will satisfy the load.

When design lines are constructed for terminal design conditions of 140°F, 120°F, and 100°F, they intercept the tank storage capacity line. They show that auxiliary heat will be required below 12°F, 3°F, and –5°F with these respective terminal designs.

This particular exercise can be extremely useful when coupled with a knowledge of the weather conditions in a specific area.

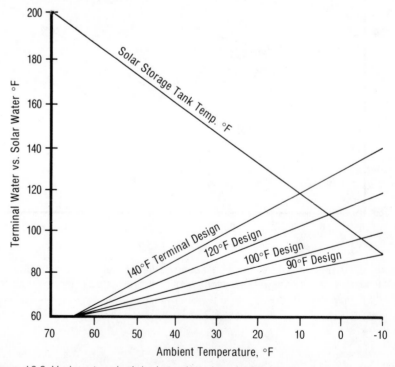

Figure 16.6 Various terminal designs plotted against solar storage temperatures.

HEAT PUMP DESIGN CONDITIONS

Figure 16.7 shows a heat-delivery system which will utilize solar storage down to 45°F. A heat pump is included to cover the heat requirements when the solar storage temperatures drop below the level usable by the 120°F terminal design. The structure can be heated to 65°F even at outside temperatures of -10°F.

With the 120°F terminal design, the heat pump is not required until the 15°F crossover point is reached. This crossover occurs when the storage water temperature is approximately 96°F, about the top operating temperature for the heat pump. The advantages of this combined design are:

• Heat-delivery sizing can conform better to existing ductwork in retrofitting applications

• Solar storage is utilized down to 45°F

• Solar collection efficiency is maximized

• Solar storage capabilities are maximized

Normally, the lowest ambient temperatures for a building structure are encountered at night. Thus, the heat pump tends to operate during the night, pulling the storage water down to its lowest possible point and insuring the maximum solar collection during the following day.

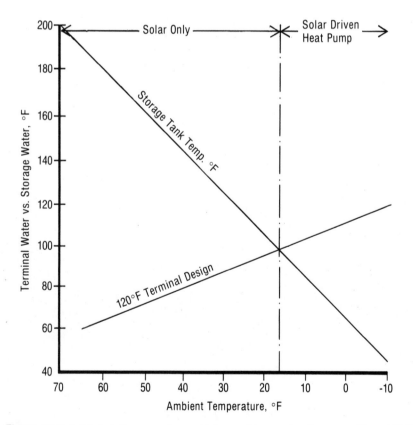

Figure 16.7 A heat-delivery system which combines a heat pump with a 120°F terminal design.

MAKING A DECISION

In this section of The Solar Decision Book, you have learned about heat-delivery systems, their design, their effect on collector efficiency and solar storage capabilities. The relationship between solar collection, storage, and terminal design is important for maximizing the effectiveness of your solar system.

Any decision on the heat-delivery system must include consideration of the existing terminal network, the existing mode of heating and cooling, and the interface between these and the solar system.

DECISION 17
Control The System

You cannot turn the sun on and off, and you cannot control its position in the sky. Nor can you control the outside temperature. And, while you can control the building heat loss to a certain extent, there is a limit to how much control you have over the building's energy needs. For these reasons, your solar energy system needs fairly sophisticated controls.

The controls for a solar energy system direct the system's activities, and make maximum use of the system's capabilities. They call for energy collection when the sun is shining. They call for heat delivery in precise response to the building's heating needs. And they call for cooling when the solar system has such capabilities.

The cost of such controls is a small percentage of the system costs. Without the appropriate controls, you would pay a dear price in lost system capabilities and performance. The right decision on controls insures effective solar system operation. This section of The Solar Decision Book will help you to make that decision. You will learn that:

- One set of controls is needed for solar collection.

- A second set of controls is needed for the heat-delivery system.

- A third set of controls is needed to satisfy cooling requirements.

OVERVIEW

Control systems are used on just about every electrical or mechanical device you use in your daily life. Some that quickly come to mind are a light switch, a TV adjustment knob, a car's accelerator, a motor speed controller, a radio channel selector, and an oven's temperature/time controls. Some controls are complex. For instance, an airplane's autopilot and a nuclear plant's computer-filled control room. But, many controls are simple.

Even the seemingly simple controls, however, are usually part of a much more complex control system. A light switch cannot turn a lamp on all by itself. It is only a small part of a control sytem which includes you and your controls as well as the power company and its controls.

Consider A Water Faucet...

The single lever faucet on many kitchen sinks is a real convenience. With the proper controls, it is a multifunctional valve having many capabilities. It can turn the water on or off. It can control the flow of water. And it can control the water temperature, from hot to cold or just pleasantly warm.

Some complex control mechanisms are required to make maximum use of this valve's capabilities. First, of course, sufficient supplies of both hot and cold water are needed. Then, a water-level measuring device and a water-temperature sensing device are needed. These devices must send their signals to a computer for analysis and action. And the computer must direct the activities of the valve's mechanical parts.

The water company controls the amount of water sent to the building. The building's water heater heats a portion of this water to a specified temperature. Your eyes see the level of water in the sink, while your fingers feel the water temperature. These two sensors — your eyes and fingers — then signal your brain. Upon analysis of the data, your brain directs your hand to move the lever up or down, to the right or to the left, or in a combination of directions.

Without this complex control system, the valve's capabilities could not be fully utilized. The valve cannot control itself.

The same is true for the controls in a solar heating and cooling system. A control system is needed to direct the system's activities and make maximum use of its capabilities.

Solar System Controls...

Solar system controls are more complicated than conventional heating system controls. They are called upon to make more decisions and to control more devices. The control system must analyze a number of incoming signals and make a number of important decisions. Are the collectors hotter than the storage tank? Will the tank accept more energy? Is there enough hot water? If not, should the auxiliary heater be fired? Does the building need heating or cooling? Where can the building economically obtain that energy? How should the heat pump be connected? . . . To the solar storage tank or to the cooling tower?

With modern solid-state electronic devices, a solar control system can be built to answer these questions. Easily and reliably. Such control systems are readily available.

CONTROLS FOR SOLAR COLLECTION

Water-Heater Collector Loop Controls

Figure 17.1 shows a typical coil-in-tank solar water heater. The function of the system is to heat the water in the tank by utilizing the energy which reaches the collectors from the sun.

To give the system that capability, a liquid is pumped around a closed loop that includes solar collectors and a heat exchanger in the water tank. When the collectors are hotter than the water in the tank, the pump turns on. The heat-transfer liquid is circulated in the loop. It carries energy from the collectors to the heat exchanger. At all other times, the pump remains off.

The control system contains sensors to read the temperature of the collectors and the temperature in the water tank. It must be capable of processing the data. In this way, the control system can measure the temperatures, compare them, and issue the correct instructions to the pump that circulates the heat-transfer liquid. The control system logic is shown in Figure 17.2.

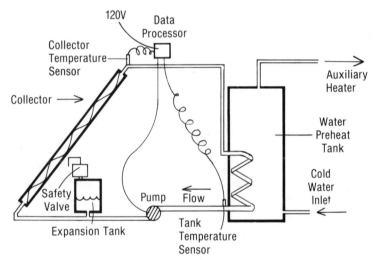

Figure 17.1 A typical coil-in-tank water heater with its controls.

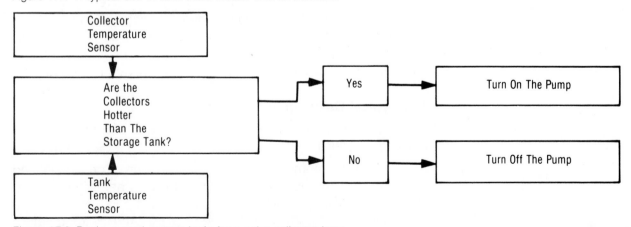

Figure 17.2 Basic control system logic for a solar collector loop.

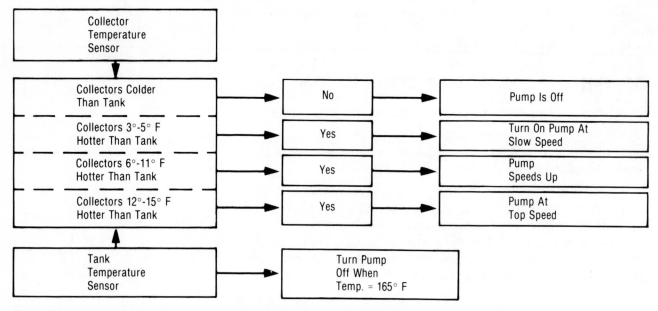

Figure 17.3 A logic diagram for a more sophisticated collector-loop control system.

To operate the system at high efficiency, however, a greater degree of control sophistication is required. This is obtained by running the pump faster or slower, depending upon the difference in temperature between the collectors and the tank. The logic for this type of control system is shown in Figure 17.3.

When the collector temperature is only three- to five-degrees Fahrenheit higher than the tank temperature, the pump turns on and runs at slow speed. As the temperature difference increases, the pump speeds up. When the difference reaches about 12° to 15°F, the pump will be running at top speed.

Such variable pump speeds are needed to maximize energy collection. On clear, sunny days, if the pump ran only at low speeds, the energy collection process would be inefficient. On cloudy days, if the pump ran only at high speeds, the collector temperature would quickly drop below the tank temperature. Also, the pump would continually cycle on and off, resulting in excessive pump wear and early failure.

In addition to maximizing energy collection, the control system also must have provision for protecting the water system. The collection process should be stopped when the water in the tank has reached the highest desired temperature. In a hot-water system, this temperature is normally about 160° to 165°F. A high-temperature limit switch is included on the controller to provide this capability.

The Typical Daily Operating Cycle

Figure 17.4 shows a typical daily operating cycle for the collection process in a solar system.

The control system is set to turn the pump on or off at specified temperature differences between the collectors and the tank. The temperature difference is labelled $\triangle T$. The temperature difference needed to turn the pump on is labelled $\triangle T_{on}$. And the temperature difference needed to turn the pump off is labelled $\triangle T_{off}$.

How these settings might typically work is shown in Figure 17.4. As the sun rises, the collector temperature rapidly rises above the tank temperature. The $\triangle T_{on}$ pump setting might be as shown. So, when the collector temperature reaches Point 1, the pump turns on. This circulates the heated collector liquid to the tank heat exchanger. Heat energy is pulled from the liquid and put into the tank water. This causes an initial drop in temperature of the collector liquid to Point 2. If the $\triangle T$ — or temperature difference between the collector liquid and tank water — is greater than the $\triangle T_{off}$ pump setting, the pump will continue to operate.

Even though the pump is running, the collector temperature will rise as the sun travels higher in the sky. This temperature will reach its highest point sometime in the afternoon depending on the sun's position and the outside temperature. The collector temperature will begin dropping however, as the sun travels lower in the sky.

At Point 3, the temperature difference between the collector liquid and tank water might be very little. It might equal $\triangle T_{off}$, or the setting that turns the pump off. If so, the tank temperature would start to fall off because the heated liquid is no longer being circulated to it. Also, the collector temperature would rise slightly because of the no-flow condition. Whatever solar energy is available would be absorbed into the collector liquid, but it would not be taken out at the tank heat exchanger. If this $\triangle T$ increases to Point 4, it would be less than $\triangle T_{on}$. So the pump would not turn on. It would remain off.

As the sun sets, the collector temperature would then rapidly fall off. It would become much lower than the tank temperature. And the pump would be off, not circulating the cooler liquid.

$\triangle T_{on}$ and $\triangle T_{off}$ depend on factory adjustments of the control system. One adjustment is called a *threshold setting*. It refers to the size of the temperature difference between the pump turn-on temperature and the pump turn-off temperature. The other adjustment is called a *hysteresis setting*. It is a time-delay circuit which prevents the pump from being cycled on or off immediately following a pump turn-off or turn-on event. Without this feature, the pump would cycle off and on at Points 1 and 4 causing unnecessary wear on the pump and controller.

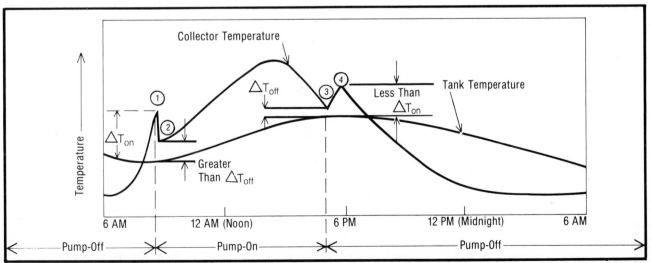

Figure 17.4 A typical daily operating cycle for the collection process in a solar system.

*Reprinted courtesy of Rho Sigma Inc.

The Controller Components

The type of control that provides the capabilities discussed is called a *differential thermostat*. It measures the difference between the collector and the tank temperature and issues the appropriate instructions to the pump.

Many other secondary features can be built into this basic control. A high-temperature limit switch, a relay for the storage pump to turn off and on, a relay for drain valves to open at freezing temperatures in water draindown systems, and a proportional speed controller are some possible secondary features for controls on specific solar energy systems.

Most differential thermostats are electronically operated. They use *thermistors* as the sensing devices to read temperatures. They use *microprocessors* to compare the sensor data and issue instructions to the pump. Electronic controls are cheaper and more reliable than mechanical, pneumatic, or hydraulic controls for the control job.

The thermistor is a device which changes its resistance with temperature. Figure 17.5 shows the specifications for a typical thermistor. Note that as the temperature rises, the resistance drops. By inserting this variable resistance in the control circuit of the microprocessor, the electronic action taken by the main circuit will change as the temperatures change.

°F	°C	RESIST. EQUIV.	°F	°C	RESIST. EQUIV.	°F	°C	RESIST. EQUIV.
32	0.0	32654/	106	41.1	5093.	180	82.2	1170.
34	1.1	30859.	108	42.2	4873.	182	83.3	1129.
36	2.2	29174.	110	43.3	4663.	184	84.4	1090.
38	3.3	27592.	112	44.4	4464.	186	85.6	1053.
40	4.4	26105.	114	45.6	4274.	188	86.7	1017.
42	5.6	24709.	116	46.7	4093.	190	87.8	982.
44	6.7	23395.	118	47.8	3921.	192	88.9	949.
46	7.8	22160.	120	48.9	3758.	194	90.0	917.
48	8.9	20998.	122	50.0	3602.	196	91.1	886.
50	10.0	19903.	124	51.1	3453.	198	92.2	857.
52	11.1	18873.	126	52.2	3312.	200	93.3	828.
54	12.2	17903.	128	53.3	3177.	202	94.4	801.
56	13.3	16988.	130	54.4	3048.	204	95.6	775.
58	14.4	16126.	132	55.6	2925.	206	96.7	749.
60	15.6	15313	134	56.7	2808.	208	97.8	725.
62	16.7	14546.	136	57.8	2697.	210	98.9	702.
64	17.8	13822.	138	58.9	2590.	212	100.0	679.
66	18.9	13139.	140	60.0	2488.	214	101.1	658.
68	20.0	12493.	142	61.1	2391.	216	102.2	637.
70	21.1	11883.	144	62.2	2298.	218	103.3	617.
72	22.2	11307.	146	63.3	2209.	220	104.4	597.
74	23.3	10762.	148	64.4	2124.	222	105.6	579.
76	24.4	10247.	150	65.6	2043.	224	106.7	561.
78	25.6	9760.	152	66.7	1966.	226	107.8	543.
80	26.7	9298.	154	67.8	1981.	228	108.9	527.
82	27.8	8862.	156	68.9	1820.	230	110.0	511.
84	28.9	8448.	158	70.0	1753.	232	111.1	495.
86	30.0	8056.	160	71.1	1688.	234	112.2	480.
88	31.1	7685.	162	72.2	1625.	236	113.3	456.
90	32.2	7333.	164	73.3	1566.	238	114.4	452.
92	33.3	6999.	166	74.4	1509.	240	115.6	438.
94	34.4	6683.	168	75.6	1454.	242	116.7	425.
96	35.6	6382.	170	76.7	1402.	244	117.8	413.
98	36.7	6097.	172	77.8	1351.	246	118.9	401.
100	37.8	5827.	174	78.9	1303.	248	120.0	389.
102	38.9	5570.	176	80.0	1257.	250	121.1	378.
104	40.0	5326.	178	81.1	1213.			

Accuracy of sensors is + .4° C over range of 0°—70° C. Maximum operating temperature is 220° C (428° F). Sensors having tighter tolerances are available.
*Reprinted courtesy of Rho Sigma Inc.

Figure 17.5 Temperature vs. resistance specifications for a typical thermistor.

The microprocessor is preprogrammed by the control manufacturer. The temperature sensors are located and protected by the installer. Once this is done properly, these differential thermostats will operate reliably for many years.

Space-Heating Collector Loop Controls

The same type of control system is used for the collector loop in space-heating systems. It is slightly different than that used for water-heating systems. The limit switch would be set at 190° to 200°F. Also, an on-off switch would be installed for the pump between the heat exchanger and the storage tank. A speed control is not needed on this storage pump motor.

CONTROLS FOR ENERGY DELIVERY

The control system for energy delivery to the building operates in a different manner than that for the collector loop. This control system has to make a different set of decisions.

In a space-heating and -cooling system, the temperature of the air in the structure must be raised or lowered at given times. A temperature-sensing device known as a *thermostat* is placed in the building. This thermostat is set by the building occupants to the desired room temperature. This is usually in the range of 55° to 80°F. When a temperature change is needed, the thermostat switch closes and calls for either hot or cold air.

In response to this call for action, the energy-delivery control system must turn on the proper energy source to satisfy the demand. The energy can come from a number of sources. Therefore, a second control must be provided to choose the proper source. The system is programmed to turn-on the cheapest available energy source at the time of demand.

In the example that will be discussed here, the heat sources ranked by cost are:

- 100-percent solar heat
- Solar heat assisted by heat pump
- Heat pump, operating from solar storage
- Auxiliary heater

The energy to meet a demand for cold air is provided by the heat pump. The pump automatically switches to its air conditioning mode.

The decision as to which heat source should be used is made by measuring the temperature of the water in the solar storage tank. In this example, the system has been designed as shown in Figure 17.6. When the temperature of the solar storage tank is above 120°F, the solar fan coil circuit is used. Between 90° and 120°F, the fan coil circuit and the heat pump are both operated. From 45° to 90°F, only the heat pump is used. And below 45°F, the solar system shuts down and the auxiliary heater is used.

Solar Storage Water Temperature	Active Heat Source(s) Used
Over 120°F	Solar Fan Coil
90 to 120°F	Solar Fan Coil and Heat Pump
45 to 90°F	Heat Pump
Below 45°F	Auxiliary Heater

Figure 17.6 Heat sources are selected according to storage water temperature.

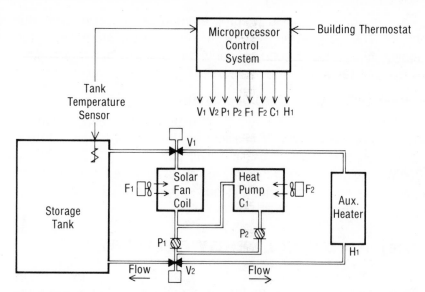

Figure 17.7 A typical energy-delivery system with controls. The cooling capability is not shown.

A schematic diagram of this sample system is shown in Figure 17.7. When solar storage is above 120°F, valves v_1 and v_2 are open to the solar storage tank, pump p_1 and fan f_1 are ready to operate. When the building thermostat calls for heat, p_1 and f_1 turn-on. Hot water is then circulated through the fan coil circuit. Building air is blown through the fan coil fins and returned to warm the building.

When the temperature of the solar storage water is between 90°F and 120°F, valves v_1 and v_2 are turned to solar storage. Pump p_2, fans f_1 and f_2, and the heat pump c_1 are ready to operate. When energy is demanded, the circuit is energized. Solar storage water is first circulated through the solar fan coil, then through the heat pump and back to the storage tank. Return air from the building is heated in both the fan coil and the heat pump, mixed in a common plenum, and returned to warm the building.

When the temperature of the solar storage water drops below 90°F, fan f_1 turns off and all the building air passes through the heat pump.

At a solar storage temperature of 45°F, valves v_1 and v_2 turn to the auxiliary heater. This heater is usually turned on when the solar storage temperature reaches 55°F to preheat the boiler water. Fan f_1 and pump p_1 are placed in the circuit. Then, upon building heat demand, hot water from the auxiliary heater is pumped through the solar fan coil to warm the circulating building.air.

When cold air is required to cool the building, the heat pump switches to its cooling mode and a source of cooling water is sent to it. This is done through valves v_3 and v_4 which are shown in Figure 17.8.

Figure 17.9 shows the various positions of the fans, pumps, valves, compressor, and ignition relays at each solar storage water temperature. This table serves as a start for control specification.

Quickly reviewing: the building energy-delivery system requires two sensing controls. One, the thermostat, is located in the building

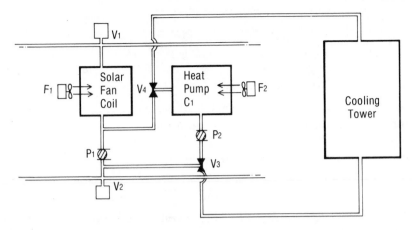

Figure 17.8 A typical schematic for a cooling capability in the solar system.

and calls for hot or cold air. It energizes the second control sytem. The sensor for the second system is located in the top of the solar storage tank. It sets up the proper energy-delivery circuit depending on the solar storage water temperature.

A thermistor sensing device which drives an electronic microprocessor is the recommended system. It senses the solar storage temperature and sets up the proper circuits for action. The building thermostat can be the standard HVAC mechanical control.

Heat-delivery systems will vary depending on the end use and the capabilities desired. Therefore, the controls are usually customized to the job. All of the control components are standard and readily available.

CONTROL		STORAGE TANK WATER TEMPERATURE				
	SYMBOL	OVER 120°F	90 to 120°F	45° to 90°F	UNDER 45°F	COOLING
Heat Delivery Valve	V_1	SS	SS	SS	AH	—
Heat Return Valve	V_2	SS	SS	SS	AH	—
Cooling Tower Valve	V_3	SS	SS	SS	SS	CT
Cooling Tower Valve	V_4	SS	SS	SS	SS	CT
Solar Fan Coil Pump	p_1	on	off	off	on	—
Heat Pump, Pump	p_2	off	on	on	off	on
Solar Fan Coil Fan	f_1	on	on	off	on	—
Heat Pump Fan	f_2	off	on	on	off	on
Heat Pump Compressor	c_1	off	on	on	off	on cooling
Auxiliary Boiler Heater	h_1	off	off	on (55°F)	on	—
SS = Solar Storage AH = Auxiliary Heater CT = Cooling Tower						

Figure 17.9 Control component settings for various storage temperatures.

SPECIFYING CONTROLS

In specifying controls you should tailor the control cost and complexity to your solar energy system. Generally, the more sophisticated the control devices, the more efficient the system.

Refer to the logic diagrams in this section. Refer also to your system design. The various sensors in the collector loop and the heat-delivery system provide *input* to the control system. These sensors are usually thermistors. They supply data in the form of varying resistance to a central control device.

If the central control device is a microprocessor, it contains a program of instructions. It also contains certain data within these instructions. The microprocessor continuously reads and executes these instructions, one after the other.

A typical instruction sequence might be this: Instruction #1 calls for input from sensor #1, which happens to be the storage tank sensor. Instruction #2 compares the value read from sensor #1 with a value stored within the microprocessor's memory. Instruction #3 makes a decision; if the value read from the sensor is greater than or equal to the stored value, the microprocessor is instructed to interrupt its program and jump to another program stored elsewhere in memory.

Instruction A of this secondary program orders the microprocessor to output a signal that turns off the pump in the collector loop. Instruction B orders a return to the main program.

If the comparison made by instruction #2 in the main program had shown the input value to be less than the stored value, instruction #3 would have ordered a continuation of the main program.

The logic design of the control unit, then, is one of input, comparison to its data base, and output.

Your specifications for controls must consider: the *input sensors*, number and placement; the control device(s) — if a microprocessor, the programming must be considered; and the *output devices* that control system functions.

A primary advantage in the use of microprocessor- based controls is the flexibility they afford. As a system is expanded, additional sensors and functions may be required. A microprocessor may be reprogrammed to accommodate the additional input and output requirements.

Sample specification forms for controls are shown in Decision 19 of The Solar Decision Book. Use Figure 19.18 for specifying collector-loop controls, Figure 19.19 for specifying heat-delivery controls.

MAKING A DECISION

In this section of The Solar Decision Book, you have learned about the control systems required to operate typical solar systems. You have learned that system capability requirements dictate the controls chosen, that collector-loop controls are different than energy-delivery controls, that electronic controls are preferred in most of the control applications. And you have also learned that the capabilities of a solar system cannot be fully utilized unless appropriate controls are part of the overall system design.

Your decision on controls is important. The wrong decision may leave the system performance to chance.

DECISION 18

Invest In The "Best"

WARM AIR

LIQUID-TO-AIR SPACE HEAT

COLD AIR

SILICONE LIQUID COLLECTOR LOOP

Today's solar energy systems are fully engineered. Minor performance improvements are expected, but no major technology changes are anticipated. While much has been learned in a few short years, fact being sorted from fiction, a variety of different systems are being installed.

Some of these systems will prove better than others. Some, unfortunately, will prove to be expensive mistakes. Because of the sizeable investment needed for a solar energy system, there's no longer room for mistakes. You want an effective, long-lasting system ... a system that will pay off in the years to come with peace of mind and with substantial energy cost savings.

The author has an opinion on what's "best". Some may not agree with that opinion. But, the recommendations made are for solar systems that offer proven performance. No experimentation. They are systems that will work and pay off in most any area of North America. And they are systems that utilize the components recommended throughout this book.

This section of The Solar Decision Book details the author's opinion. You will read about a solar water heating system. You will also read about a complete solar system for water heating, space heating, and space cooling. The systems discussed may help you make a decision on what's "best" for your solar investment dollar.

OVERVIEW

Some recommendations for solar water-heating systems and for complete solar energy systems are detailed on the following pages.

The recommended systems use a liquid for heat-transfer in the collector loop. Compared to systems using air as the heat-transfer medium, these liquid systems offer more flexibility for use on both new structures as well as existing structures.

The recommended systems use water for energy storage. Compared to systems using rock-bed storage, these systems are much smaller and easier to locate and install.

In the complete solar system, space heating is accomplished by blowing the structure air over a liquid-to-air heat exchanger. Unlike other heat delivery methods, such as air-to-air or liquid-to-liquid, this method can often utilize existing ductwork with little change. No need for resizing ducts or baseboard radiators. Also, by including a heat pump, solar-assisted heating is possible at low storage temperatures.

Space cooling is also accomplished by the liquid-to-air heat pump. Solar system cooling capabilities have not been fully explored. Some sytems use an absorption chiller, and the results are encouraging. A heat pump is recommended here because it increases the efficiency of the solar heating system, while providing good cooling capacity. It represents known and proven HVAC technology at low energy cost. As such, the heat pump is an attractive alternative to a separate and costly cooling system.

Together with these system recommendations, certain steps should be taken before installing any solar system. These were discussed in earlier sections of The Solar Decision Book. You should make the building an efficient heat trap. You should utilize maximum thermal mass in the structure. And you should make passive solar collection devices part of the structure design. Once these three steps are taken, the active solar system can be compact and highly efficient.

A SOLAR WATER-HEATING SYSTEM

Coil-In-Tank-Design

Figure 18.1 shows a solar energy system for heating water. This is the coil-in-tank approach for solar water heating. It can be used in all localities, except those in which the plumbing code requires a double-walled heat exchanger between the collector fluid and the service water. In such localities, a double-walled, counterflow heat exchanger is suggested. This type of heat exchanger is connected by appropriate piping to the service water tank.

The system operates as follows: SYLTHERM ™ 444 Heat-Transfer Liquid from Dow Corning is pumped to the collectors through a flow-control valve. It rises through the collectors, is heated by the sun, and flows down to the coil-in-tank heat exchanger. The heat-transfer fluid then gives up its heat to the service water, flows through the air

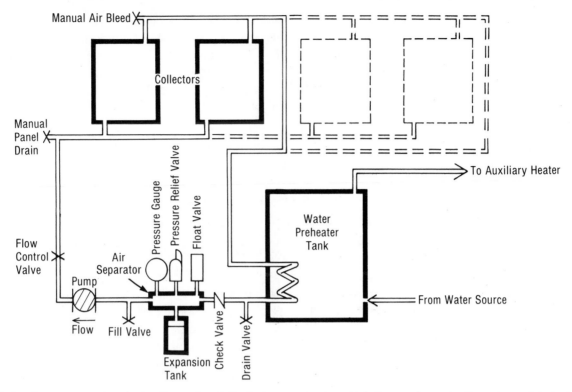

Figure 18.1 A solar energy system for heating water. Collected energy is placed into the service water through a coil-in-tank heat exchanger.

separator and a check valve to the pump, and is recirculated through the system.

Each piece of equipment in this recommended system has a purpose and should be included in each installation. The following discussion will familiarize you with the function of each piece of equipment.

VALVES. A flow-control valve is used to regulate the flow rate of the collector heat-transfer fluid. A thermometer is placed on either side of the tank coil. At close to solar noon on a clear day at average ambient temperature of the outside air, the valve is regulated to produce a 25° to 30°F temperature rise across the heat exchanger.

A manual air bleed valve and a manual panel drain valve are also used in the system. Both are normally closed. They are opened only to drain the collectors for maintenance or to relieve an unexpected air lock. Coin-operated valves are usually used.

A check valve in the system prevents the heat-transfer loop from thermosyphoning at night when the collectors are cold. It should be placed between a drain valve and a fill valve. The drain valve and fill valve can be standard shutoff valves and should contain provision for capping off after the collector loop is filled with heat-transfer fluid.

EXPANSION TANK. An expansion tank is required to relieve the pressure created when the heat-transfer fluid expands. This tank should be sized at 10-percent of the total fluid volume in the heat-transfer loop. A pressurized, diaphragm-type expansion tank is recommended. An air separator, air-float valve, and a 30-pound pressure relief valve should be included with the expansion tank.

PUMP. The circulator pump is critical. A canned wet-rotor pump or a magnetically driven pump without a mechanical shaft seal should be chosen. This is a closed loop, so a cast iron pump can be utilized. The pump can be located as shown or may be moved to the other side of the drain valve if desired. The pump should not be placed on the "hot" side of the heat exchanger.

PREHEATER TANK. The water preheater tank coil should be the largest coil offered by the manufacturer for the size of tank being employed. Because of the large amount of copper in the tank, glass-lined tanks will have short lives. Stone-lined tanks are recommended.

The preheater tank should contain a minimum of 1.25 gallons of water per square foot of collector area. Tank capacities of more than two gallons per square foot of collector are generally not required. For a 50-square-foot, two-collector system, this would place the minimum tank size at 65 gallons.

Auxiliary heat must not be placed in the preheater tank. This will severely limit the solar energy collected. City water or well water should be fed to the preheater tank, warmed by solar energy, and then used to feed the auxiliary heater. The auxiliary heater would be fired only when solar energy is not available.

PIPING AND CONNECTIONS. All piping should be hard-drawn copper, type L or better. Solder joints should be made with 95/5-tin/antimony solder or brazing. Screw joints should be made using Loctite® pipe dope with Teflon®. Soft copper tubing with compression fittings should be avoided. Some flared fittings have been used successfully.

No direct connections should be made between copper and aluminum parts. Connections made in this manner will be subject to exterior galvanic corrosion in damp weather. EPDM, Viton® or fluorosilicone rubber hoses may be used. Regular silicone rubber hose *cannot* be used with SYLTHERM ™ 444 Heat-Transfer Liquid. Special connectors such as Brazeway® connectors are available for use with some aluminum collectors that allow direct soldering or brazing.

COLLECTORS. Any well-manufactured, high-performance metal absorber collectors may be used with this system. Plastic collector panels should be avoided completely.

CONTROLS. The recommended system should be controlled with a differential thermostat and a proportional pump speed controller. The system should be set to turn on when the collectors are three-degrees F above the tank temperature. The pump should reach full speed at temperature difference of about 12°F. A high-temperature pump cutoff switch should be included to shut down the system when the tank water reaches about 160° to 165°F. The high-temperature sensor should be placed at the collector outlet and the low-temperature sensor should be placed at the heat exchanger coil outlet. The electrical system must be grounded for safety.

®Loctite is a registered trademark of Loctite Corporation.
®Viton and Teflon are registered trademarks of E.I. duPont de Nemours.
®Brazeway is a registered trademark of Brazeway, Inc.

Design With External Counterflow Heat Exchanger

Figure 18.2 shows a solar water-heating system which utilizes an external counterflow heat exchanger instead of an internal coil-in-tank heat exchanger. This heat exchanger can be either single- or double-walled, depending on the local plumbing code. Because of lower heat transfer across a double metal surface, a double-walled exchanger must be larger and, thus, will be more expensive.

PREHEATER TANK. With an external heat exchanger, glass- or stone-lined tanks are appropriate. If the tank reaches the end of its useful life, only the tank needs to be replaced. The heat exchanger can remain in service. This is not true for systems using coil-in-tank heat exchangers.

HEAT-EXCHANGER LOOP. The construction and operation of the collector loop when using an external counterflow heat exchanger is similar to that for the coil-in-tank system. However, there is a secondary heat-exchanger loop to the preheater tank.

In this secondary loop, cool water is drawn from the bottom of the preheater tank. It is circulated with a separate pump through the secondary side of the heat exchanger. It picks up heat and is returned to the top of the preheater tank.

PUMP. The secondary loop is an open loop. Therefore, a bronze or stainless steel pump must be used. The pump can be a canned wet rotor, magnetic or mechanical-seal shaft-driven type.

OTHER COMPONENTS. The collector-loop valves, expansion tank, and pump are the same as those recommended for the coil-in-tank design. Piping should be copper, type L or better. The pump is

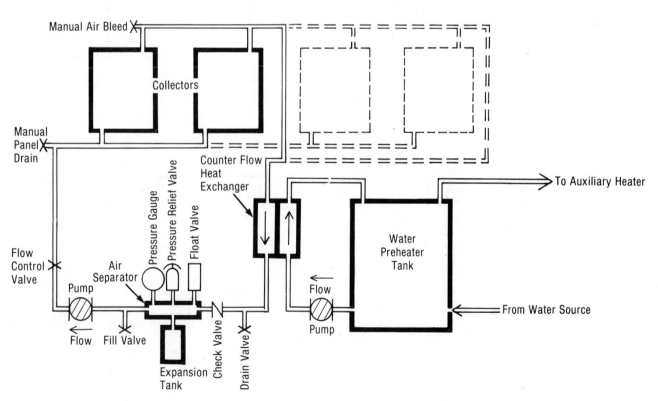

Figure 18.2 A solar water-heating system with an external counterflow heat exchanger.

activated by a second output on the differential thermostat. Proportional control is not used and the pump runs at a constant speed. The heat-exchanger must be well-insulated to prevent heat loss.

A COMPLETE SOLAR ENERGY SYSTEM

Figure 18.3 shows a complete solar energy system for heating water, heating the structure, and cooling the structure. With minor design variations because of plumbing code requirements, it can be used in all localities. The system offers good performance for new structures as well as for retrofitting existing structures.

Operation

The system operates as follows: SYLTHERM ™ 444 Heat-Transfer Liquid is used in the collector loop. Collector-loop operation is identical to that of the water-heater system using an external counterflow heat exchanger. A solar storage tank replaces the water preheater. It stores the collected energy until it is needed.

WATER HEATING. When the water preheater calls for heat, pump p_1 turns on to draw warm water from storage. The pump will not be turned on if the water in the solar storage tank is cooler than that in the preheater tank.

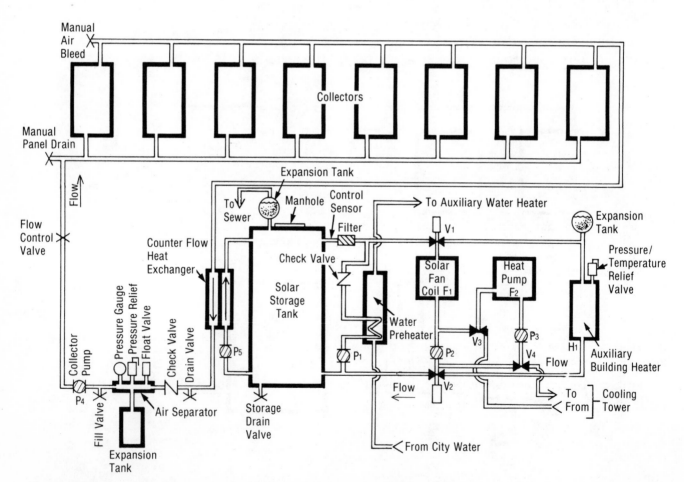

Figure 18.3 A complete solar energy system for water heating, space heating, and space cooling.

18-6

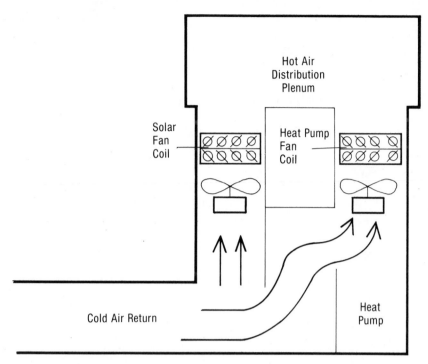

Figure 18.4 Heated air from the heat pump and from the fan coil is mixed in a common plenum.

SPACE HEATING. When the structure calls for heat, one of four actions takes place. If the storage tank water is warmer than 120°F, valves v_1 and v_2 turn to solar storage position, pump p_2 turns on, and fan f_1 turns on. Heated solar storage water then flows through the loop and the fan in the solar fan coil circulates building air to warm the building.

If the storage tank water temperature is below 120°F but above 90°F, valves v_1 and v_2 turn to solar storage, pump p_3 turns on, and fans f_1 and f_2 turn on along with the heat-pump compressor. The solar storage water now circulates through the solar fan coil to the heat exchanger in the heat pump and back to the solar storage tank. The air from the heat pump and the air from the solar fan coil mix in a common plenum as shown in Figure 18.4. This warm air is then circulated through the building.

If the storage tank water temperature is under 90°F but over 45°F, the same conditions exist. However, fan f_1 turns off and all of the building air circulates through the heat pump.

If the storage tank water temperature is under 45°F, valves v_1 and v_2 turn to the auxiliary heater. Pump p_2, fan f_1, and the heater h_1 turn on. Hot water at 140°F from the auxiliary heater is then circulated through the solar fan coil to provide heat for the building.

Valves v_3 and v_4 are manual valves which are always turned to solar storage except during the cooling season.

SPACE COOLING. When the structure calls for cooling, this solar system does not respond but remains inactive. At the beginning of the cooling season, v_3 and v_4 should be manually turned to the cooling tower position. When the air conditioning thermostat calls for cooling, the heat pump automatically shifts to its cooling mode. Pump

p_3 turns on, as do fan f_2 and the heat pump compressor. Cold air is then supplied to the building. Water is circulated through the cooling tower to keep the air conditioner (heat pump) supplied with cool water.

A word about the cooling tower: Quite often it is not required. City, well, or pond water can be circulated through the heat exchanger in the heat pump. Any source of clean, noncorrosive, cool water may be utilized when available. Heavily chlorinated water, such as swimming pool water, should not be used. They only exception is if the heat pump manufacturer specifically states that the heat exchanger in the heat pump is designed to cope with the corrosive effects of such water.

Components

At first glance, this complete solar energy system sounds complicated. This is not the case. The system is very easily controlled for automatic operation. This becomes obvious after examining the control system logic discussed later in this section.

Each piece of equipment in this design, like in the water-heating system, has a specific purpose and should be included in each installation. The following discussion will familiarize you with the function of each piece of equipment.

COLLECTOR LOOP. The collector loop is an external counter-flow heat-exchanger loop utilizing a single-wall heat exchanger. Its design and operation are similar to that of the water-heating system previously discussed. However, the secondary loop goes to the solar storage tank, rather than to the water preheater tank. Also, the high-temperature pump cutoff point is raised from 160-165°F to 195-200°F.

STORAGE TANK. The solar storage tank is a nonpressurized tank which may be built of any of the materials outlined in Decision 14. The storage tank will be thermally cycled from 45°F to 200°F. It must be built and lined with this thermal cycle in mind. The storage tank should be sized to hold 1.5 to 2.0 gallons of storage water per square foot of collector. The water preheater capacity should be counted as part of the total storage-system capacity.

The tank must have a tightly gasketed cleanout manhole, large enough for a serviceman to enter. The drain valve should lead to a storm drain or sewer as required by local codes, or provision should be made for complete pumpout if necessary.

EXPANSION TANK/OVERFLOW PIPE. If any part of the heat-delivery system is higher than the top of the solar storage tank, then an expansion tank should be used. It should be positioned higher than the highest point in the heat-delivery system. This is required to maintain a positive pump head. The expansion tank should be sized at about 10-percent of the solar storage tank capacity.

An overflow pipe to a storm drain or sewer is necessary. If an expansion tank is required, the overflow pipe should be located at the top of the expansion tank. Otherwise, it should be located at the top of the solar storage tank.

STORAGE WATER. Solar storage water is nonpotable water, unsuitable for drinking or service use. It must be conditioned to maintain tank and component life. Therefore, no connection between the solar storage tank and city or well water should be made, except through a code-approved air gap.

The proper conditioning of the storage water is very important. Unfortunately, the water treatment cannot be generalized. It depends on the type of water and the materials of tank construction. The reader should contact local sources for recommendations or obtain a copy of *The Betz Handbook of Industrial Water Conditioning* which is available from Betz Laboratories Inc., Trevose, Pa. 19047.

PIPING AND VALVES. The delivery main for solar storage water is connected to an outlet placed close to the top of the tank. After the main leaves the tank, it should first run through a line filter to remove any particles which build up in the storage and delivery system. The delivery main terminates in a bronze three-way valve, v_1, which is operated by a solenoid. This valve can connect either solar storage heat or auxiliary heat to the solar fan coil. The control solenoid is wired in parallel with a second valve, v_2. This valve is in the return main and it serves the same function as v_1. These valves should be open to the solar storage water when they are nonenergized. The solar storage water return main is connected to an outlet near the bottom of the tank.

Because of the high cutoff temperatures, all piping used in the complete solar heat-delivery system must be copper, type L or better. Plastic piping cannot be tolerated.

CIRCUITS. There are four separate circuits connected across the delivery/return mains: the *water preheater circuit,* the *solar fan-coil circuit*, the *solar fan-coil/heat-pump circuit,* and the *auxiliary heater circuit.*

The *water preheater circuit* contains a stone-lined coil-in-tank water preheater, a check valve, and a small circulating pump. The loop is controlled by a differential thermostat. This thermostat turns on the circulating pump when the storage tank water temperature exceeds the preheater tank water temperature by three to five degrees F. The check valve prevents thermosyphoning. The high-temperature sensor for the thermostat is mounted on the delivery main close to the solar storage tank. The low-temperature sensor is mounted at the water preheater tank outlet to the circulating pump. The pump may be any of three types previously mentioned and must be bronze or stainless steel.

If the code demands a double-walled heat exchanger between the water preheater and solar storage, then the system should be changed to conform to Figure 18.5 or Figure 18.6. In Figure 18.5, the coil-in-tank preheater is removed from the delivery/return mains and connected to a tankless coil positioned inside the top of the solar storage tank. The two separate coils provide the double wall. An

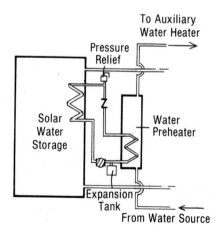

Figure 18.5 A water preheater that combines a tankless coil and a coil-in-tank design to meet code requirements for a double-wall heat exchanger.

expansion tank and a pressure-relief valve must be added. In Figure 18.6, an external counterflow heat exchanger is used to provide the double wall.

The *solar fan-coil circuit* contains: v_1, a three-way valve connecting either solar-storage heat or auxiliary heat to the fan coil; a bronze or stainless steel circulating pump, p_2, to circulate the fluid; and v_2, a three-way valve connecting the return main.

The *solar fan-coil/heat-pump circuit* contains the solar fan coil and the liquid-to-air heat pump connected in series. This circuit is shown separately in Figure 18.7 for clarity. The circuit includes valve v_1, the solar fan coil, valve v_3, the heat-exchanger coil that lies within the heat pump, a bronze or stainless steel circulating pump p_3, valve v_4, and a Tee in the line between pump p_2 and valve v_2. Valves v_3 and v_4 are turned to the heating circuit in the winter months, and must be manually changed to the cooling-tower circuit for the cooling season. Automatic valves are not required, but they could be used if desired.

The heat pump is connected in series with the solar fan coil. The heat pump has a high temperature cutoff of about 100°F supply water, but it must be used to help meet the heat demand when the temperature of solar storage water drops below 120°F. To provide water to the heat pump at the proper temperature, the solar fan coil and the heat pump are operated together in the temperature range of 90° to 120°F solar storage water. The solar storage water temperature drops to a useable heat pump temperature because it circulates through the fan coil before feeding the heat pump heat exchanger. The heat pump should not be connected in parallel across the mains. Water by-pass through pump p_2 will be minor when pump p_3 is running. A valve is not required at this location.

The *auxiliary heating circuit* consists of an auxiliary water heater/boiler, an expansion tank, a pressure/temperature relief valve, and mains to connect to v_1 and v_2, pump p_2, and the solar fan coil. The heater is fired when the solar storage water temperature reaches about 55°F. This insures that the heater will reach its operating temperature of 120° to 140°F, before it needs to be used. The heater must be ready to produce useable heat when the solar storage water temperature drops to 45°F.

The expansion tank should be sized at 10- to 12-percent of the liquid capacity of the loop, measured from v_1 through the heater to v_2. The temperature/pressure relief valve should operate in the 165°F/30-40 lb. range. A high-temperature cutoff switch (150°F) and a low-water-level cutoff switch should be included in the firing circuit.

The *auxiliary heater* is detailed in Decision 15. For heating loads up to 30,000 Btu per hour, a standard water heater may be employed. It will only be used occasionally and should have a long operating life.

Controls

COLLECTOR LOOP CONTROLS. The collector loop control system is similar to the water-heater control system. The one exception is that the high-temperature switch is set to cut off the pump in the

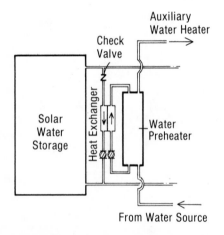

Figure 18.6 A water preheater that uses an external counterflow heat exchanger to meet code requirements for double-wall heat exchanger.

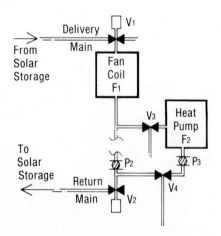

Figure 18.7 The solar fan-coil/heat-pump circuit.

collector loop when the storage water temperature reaches approximately 195 to 200°F.

HEAT-DELIVERY CONTROLS. A single sensor mounted in the top of the solar storage tank handles the settings required for the heat-delivery system pumps, valves, and fans. Depending upon the heat available in the storage tank, it sets up the various system components in an on/off position as required. For example: At storage temperatures above 120°F, the solar fan-coil loop should be operated. This requires turning on both the pump p_2 and the fan f_1. It also requires that the heat pump loop remain off. Water will be taken from solar storage under this condition, thus valves v_1 and v_2 are turned to the solar storage position. The system is now ready to operate, but is not turned on. "System turn-on" will take place when the structure demands heat. "Turn-on" is signalled by a thermostat which reads the building temperature and closes the circuit to turn on the system when needed. This thermostat would be located within the building structure.

When the temperature in the solar storage tank drops to below 120°F (but over 90°F), the circuit turns off pump p_2 and turns on the heat pump fan coil f_2 and pump p_3. Fan coil f_1 continues to run.

At storage temperatures of about 90°F, the solar fan coil cuts out and the heat pump is utilized to heat the building. In anticipation of a possible need for auxiliary heat, the ignition source of the auxiliary heater is armed. When the storage temperature drops to 55°F, the heater is fired. At a storage temperature of 45°, the entire solar system and the heat pump system is shut down. Valves v_1 and v_2 are switched to the auxiliary loop, and heat is supplied from the auxiliary heater.

If at any time during this sequence of events, the building no longer requires heat, the entire system shuts down.

The water preheater pump p_1 is run by a differential thermostat. This thermostat turns on the pump whenever the preheater tank temperature is lower than the storage tank temperature. A 45°F cutoff switch can be part of the main control, but it usually is not needed.

In the cooling season, the cooling tower valves v_3 and v_4 can be manually repositioned to the cooling loop. Then, the heat pump can be operated in the cooling mode from its internal control system. Should heat be required at night, it can be obtained from the solar fan coil without the use of the heat pump.

CONTROL	STORAGE TANK WATER TEMPERATURE					
	SYMBOL	OVER 120°F	90 to 120°F	45° to 90°F	UNDER 45°F	COOLING
Heat Delivery Valve	V_1	SS	SS	SS	AH	—
Heat Return Valve	V_2	SS	SS	SS	AH	—
Cooling Tower Valve	V_3	SS	SS	SS	SS	CT
Cooling Tower Valve	V_4	SS	SS	SS	SS	CT
Solar Fan Coil Pump	p_2	on	off	off	on	—
Heat Pump, Pump	p_3	off	on	on	off	on
Solar Fan Coil Fan	f_1	on	on	off	on	—
Heat Pump Fan	f_2	off	on	on	off	on
Heat Pump Compressor	c_1	off	on	on	off	on cooling
Auxiliary Boiler Heater	h_1	off	off	on (55°F)	on	—

SS = Solar Storage
AH = Auxiliary Heater
CT = Cooling Tower

Figure 18.8 Control logic for the energy-delivery loop.

Figure 18.8 shows the control logic settings for the energy-delivery loop. The area of 90° to 120° is handled by a combination of the solar fan coil and the heat pump. This is necessary because of the need to supply air at temperatures above 120°F. And, because of the need to reduce the temperature of the water to the heat pump to meet the pump's requirements. The air is mixed in the plenum to provide the proper temperature for heating and comfort.

MAKING A DECISION

You have just studied a solar water heating system and a complete solar system. These systems use SYLTHERM™ 444 Heat Transfer Liquid in the collector loop and water for solar storage. The building heat is provided by circulating structure air over a liquid-to-air heat exchanger. Solar storage is fully utilized down to 45°F at a very low heating cost by designing a heat pump into the system. The same heat pump also provides air conditioning during the summer months. Back-up auxiliary heating is provided by a water heater or boiler.

These systems, when designed to the criteria outlined in The Solar Decision Book, are long-lasting systems. With proper maintenance, they should perform effectively for at least 20 to 25 years. They can be placed in either new or existing buildings. In existing buildings, some auxiliary heater changes may be needed to make the best use of your energy dollar.

If your decision is to move ahead and install an active solar system, you can install these systems with the confidence that your solar investment will pay off.

DECISION 19

Determine The System Size

SOLAR HOME SPECIFICATIONS

COMPUTER ANALYSIS

Count the hours of daylight. Determine the amount of solar radiation for each hour. Subtract the radiation lost during the rainy and cloudy hours. Make these calculations for each day of the year. Then, add up the figures for a total. That's the heat energy available for use in your solar system.

Next, determine the hourly heat loss for the building. Multiply this loss by the difference between the outdoor temperature and the desired indoor temperature. Make these calculations for each day of the year and, again, add up the figures for a total. That's the energy needed to heat your structure.

Once you have the energy available and the energy needed, you can start sizing your solar collectors. To arrive at the correct size however, requires more than 17,000 separate calculations. No doubt, unless this Herculean mathematical task is done for you, your chances of purchasing a solar energy system are small. The decision on system size would be most difficult, if not nearly impossible.

Fortunately, though, the system-size decision can be an easy one. This section of The Solar Decision Book will start you in the right direction toward making that decision. You will learn that:

- Sizing solar systems is a relatively easy process if the proper information is available.

- The most reliable estimate of a solar system's capability comes from computer simulation programs.

- Once the heat loss and the city is known, the required collector size can be determined in a matter of minutes.

- Once the collector size is determined, the system's components can be sized in a few hours.

BEFORE YOU START...

Previous sections of The Solar Decision Book have prepared you for estimating the system size. First, you learned about the need for energy and its rising costs. Then, you examined your options for energy conservation and alternate energy sources. You scrutinized solar-system performance, the soundness of the solar investment, the equipment available and selection criteria for solar components. You also studied the author's recommendations regarding the best systems for your energy dollar.

All of this information can now be used to size the necessary components for your solar system. For specific information on a component, you may want to re-read certain pages within the appropriate decision on the component. Before you start sizing the system and specifying components, however, review some of your preliminary decisions. You should have already decided that:

- The collector site is large enough and is oriented within a good solar window.

- The structure or its near surroundings can accommodate the solar storage tank and other solar equipment.

- The solar heat-delivery system can be satisfactorily integrated with the structure.

- Energy conservation measures can cut heat losses, and that such measures can be accomplished before or during the installation of the solar system.

- Passive solar collection devices can be utilized where practical.

- Investment in the solar system is attractive from a real-estate viewpoint and it adds to the property value.

- Adjacent property owners will not be building structures or planting trees which will interfere with the solar window at some future date.

- The solar system falls within local building codes and its effect on property taxes is known.

A TOOL FOR SYSTEM SIZING

A solar energy system can be designed and sized for any geographical area of the country. With the proper procedure, such design and sizing can result in very predictable performance. The system owner can rest assured that the expected performance will be achieved day after day, year after year.

There are many design variables, and a mountain of calculations. Special computer programs, however, have been developed to aid in solar system design and sizing. These programs can digest the input on weather, location, energy requirements, and other data. They can sort the variables and measure the effects of one set versus another. And they can produce the recommendations needed to achieve the desired results.

The Computer Simulation Program

Several computer design programs are in use in the solar energy industry.

The computer simulation program in The Solar Decision Book was developed by the University of Wisconsin solar laboratories. It is known as the *F-Chart*. "F" equals the fraction of the heating load supplied by solar energy. This is usually expressed as %F or the percent of the total heating load carried by solar. Percent F is determined by solving a mathematical model containing: the degree days, the sunshine factors, the ambient temperatures, the building heat loss, the amount of hot water required, the collector orientation and the design parameters of the system.

The easiest way to use F-Chart is to "presolve" the model for given system configurations in the specific geographical location, against given heat loads. This information can then be placed on a chart showing %F plotted against square feet of collector. Figure 19.1 shows a sample chart for a water-heater system. Figure 19.2 shows a sample chart for a combination space-heating and water-heating system.

Appendix C contains a set of tables from which you can draw an F-Chart for your area or location. Data is given for 96 cities across North America. The instructions for constructing the F-Charts are also given.

If 50-percent solar heat is desired, read across the chart from 50-percent F to the proper heat loss curve. Then, read down to the number of square feet of collector needed.

The F-Chart does not predict what the solar system will produce in daily heat. But it does predict the average performance of a system under average weather conditions. Over a number of years, the F-Chart will be very accurate.

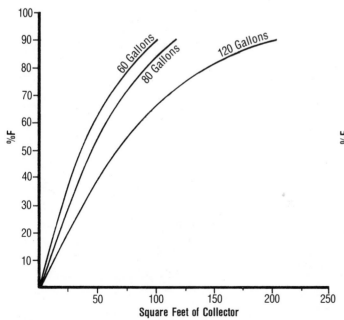

Figure 19.1 A sample F-chart for a solar water-heating system.

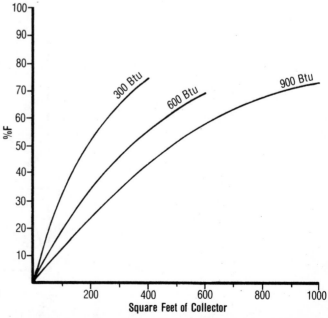

Figure 19.2 A sample F-chart for a solar system with space-heating and water-heating capabilities.

The effect of the solar-assisted heat pump cannot be shown using an F-Chart. The heat pump has two major impacts on the system performance. First, it increases the efficiency of the solar collectors by lowering the temperature of the solar storage tank. Second, it lowers the cost of auxiliary fuel because of its high efficency. Thus, with the system design using a heat pump as shown in Decision 18, the F-Charts in the appendix will turn out very conservative.

OPTIMUM SAVINGS VERSUS PERCENT SOLAR. The F-Chart computer simulation program not only does a thermal analysis. It also does a cash flow analysis of the solar savings for the anticipated life of the system. It compares the system investment and running costs with the costs of using conventional fuels and it computes the solar savings.

The optimum savings for a given set of conditions will come at a specific percent-F. These savings are a function of the system cost versus the cost of auxiliary fuel which is inflated at a chosen annual increase.

A typical F-Chart cash flow analysis for a solar system is shown in Figure 19.3. The analysis shows that the optimum solar savings occur between 55- and 73-percent F. Water-heating systems generally provide maximum savings when the system is designed between 45- and 70-percent F. Space-heating systems generally provide optimum savings when the system is designed between 45- and 65-percent F.

Cash flow analyses are not charted in The Solar Decision Book. The large number of variables in such analyses would require the development of many charts to satisfy even a small segment of readers.

CONVENTIONAL FUEL COST CALCULATIONS. How much will it cost to heat your building and your hot water over the next 20 years? While no one can give you an exact answer, a reasonable

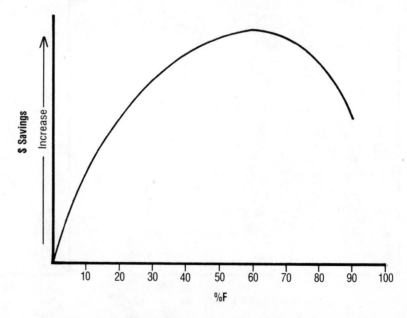

Figure 19.3 A typical F-chart cash flow analysis for a solar system.

ESTIMATED ANNUAL ENERGY COSTS IN 1979				
Gallons water used/day	MM Btu used* per yr.	Electricity @ 5¢ per KWH	Oil @ 54¢/Gal	Gas @ 40.5¢/CCF
20	5.2	$ 76	$ 37	$ 35
40	10.3	151	74	70
60	15.5	227	111	105
80	20.7	303	149	140
100	25.8	378	185	174
120	31.0	454	223	209
140	36.2	503	260	244
160	41.4	607	297	279
180	46.5	681	334	314
200	51.7	757	371	349

*Assuming entrance water @ 55° F and service water @ 140° F.

FUTURE ENERGY COSTS AT 11-PERCENT INFLATION RATE

Cost in 1979 (from table)	$ _____ 1979
Cost in 1984 (1979 x 1.69)	$ _____ 1984
Cost in 1989 (1979 x 2.84)	$ _____ 1989
Cost in 1994 (1979 x 4.78)	$ _____ 1994
Cost in 1999 (1979 x 8.06)	$ _____ 1999

Figure 19.4 A form for estimating future costs of heating water with conventional fuels.

CALCULATING 1979 HEATING COSTS

1. Building Heat Loss .... _____ Btu/hr/°F
2. Number of Degree Days/Year .... _____ DD/yr
3. Btu Required Per Year [(#1) x (#2) x 24] .... _____ Btu/yr
4. Estimated Cost of Fuel/MM Btu in 1979
   Electric = $14.65
   Oil   = $ 7.18
   Gas   = $ 6.75
5. Estimated Cost of Heating in 1979 .... _____ Dollars
   (#3) (#4) ÷ 1,000,000

Future Energy Costs at 11% Inflation Rate

Cost in 1979 (from step 5 above)	$ _____ 1979
Cost in 1984 (1979 x 1.69)	$ _____ 1984
Cost in 1989 (1979 x 2.84)	$ _____ 1989
Cost in 1994 (1979 x 4.78)	$ _____ 1994
Cost in 1999 (1979 x 8.06)	$ _____ 1999

Figure 19.5 A form for estimating future costs of heating space with conventional fuels.

estimate can be made if certain fuel costs and inflation rates are assumed. Figure 19.4 shows how to make these calculations for heating water. Figure 19.5 shows how to estimate space-heating costs. For both sets of calculations, projected 1979 fuel costs and an annual inflation rate of 11-percent are used.

SIZING THE SYSTEM
Solar Water-Heating Systems

ENERGY REQUIREMENTS. To determine the amount of energy needed to heat your water, you need three pieces of data:

- hot-water supply temperature

- cold-water supply temperature

- number of gallons of hot water needed daily

To meet FHA Minimum Property Standards, the hot-water supply temperature must be at least 140°F. The incoming cold-water supply temperature can vary from 45° to 75°F depending on the geographic location and the season of the year. Data is generally available from your water company. Without such data, a year-round average temperature of 55°F can be used. Daily hot water usage is about 20 gallons per person per day in residences. Small commercial buildings, which do not use process water, will have an equivalent or lower usage.

If the hot water supply temperature is reduced to 120°F, solar collection will be slightly more efficient. However, the usage figure should be raised to 25 gallons per person per day. The lower temperature hot water will require less mixing with cold water. The flow of hot water would thus be greater.

SIZING PROCEDURE. Figure 19.6 shows a sizing chart for solar water-heating systems. This sizing chart is intended for use with the water-heating systems outlined in Decision 18 and the solar performance data (F-Charts) shown in Appendix C.

The F-Charts in Appendix C are calculated using double-glazed, selective-surface collectors. Why were these chosen? Could other collectors be used successfully? The author chose double-glazed, selective-surface collectors because they are the highest efficiency flat-plate collectors available. Single-glazed, selective-surface collectors or double-glazed, nonselective-surface collectors could have been substituted. The data for developing F-Charts would have been different. You may elect to use one of the other collectors. If you do, the percent-F versus square feet of collector will differ from that developed in Appendix C.

To use the sizing chart in Figure 19.6, proceed as follows:

- Fill in the desired daily hot water load. (1)

- Choose the nearest weather station to the location. (4)

- Prepare an F-Chart for that weather station using Appendix C.

- Decide on the percent-F you would like from the system. (5)

- Using the weather-station chart in Appendix C, determine the number of square feet needed in the collector array to give you the desired percent-F. (6)

- Multiply the collector area by 0.039 to obtain the flow rate of the heat-transfer liquid in the collector loop. (8)

- Check the type of heat exchanger being used. (9)

- Multiply the collector area by 225 to determine the maximum amount of heat that can be transferred to the heat exchanger. (10)

ITEM	VALUE	UNITS	REFERENCE
1. Daily Hot Water Load		Gal/day	Decision 19
2. Hot Water Service Temperature	140	°F	Decision 19
3. Cold Water Supply Temperature	55	°F	Decision 19
4. Closest Weather Station			Appendix C
5. Percent Solar Desired		%F	Appendix C
6. Size of Collector Array		Sq ft	Appendix C
7. Collector Heat Transfer Liquid	SYLTHERM™ 444		Decision 11
8. Collector Flow Rate (0.039) x (#6 above) =		GPM	Decision 12

9. Heat Exchanger Type
 	
    Coil-In-Tank . . . . _____
    Double Wall Counterflow . . . . . . _____
    Single Wall Counterflow . . . . . . _____
			Decision 13
			
			Decision 18

10. Maximum Energy From Collectors (225) (#6 above) =		Btu/hr	Decision 10
11. Storage Tank Flow Rate*		GPM	Specified by Manufacturer
12. Pump Head in Collector Loop		Ft water	Decision 12
13. Pump Head in Storage Loop*		Ft water	Decision 12
14. Water Preheater Tank Size (See #6 above)		Gallons	Decision 19 Use nearest size in range of 1.5 to 2.0 gal/ft²
15. Amount of Heat-Transfer Liquid		Gallons	Decision 11
16. Expansion Tank (0.10) (#15) =		Gallons	Decision 19

*Not used with coil-in-tank designs.

Figure 19.6 A sizing chart for solar water-heating systems.

- Using the manufacturer's literature, choose a heat exchanger that offers an effectiveness of 90-percent or higher. You will need the information from steps 8, 9, and 10 to select this heat exchanger.

- The manufacturer's literature will give you the rate of flow required in the storage loop. Place this data in the chart at step 11. This step is not needed when using coil-in-tank designs. Instead, use the collector flow rate from step 8.

- Determine the pump head (friction losses in feet of water) in the collector loop. Use the procedure outlined in Decision 12. For systems with coil-in-tank heat exchangers, also place this figure in the chart at step 13.

- Determine the pump head in the storage loop for counterflow heat exchangers. (13)

- Detemine the size of the water preheater tank by multiplying the collector area by 1.75. The sizing charts will be accurate for tank sizes of 1.50 to 2.00 gallons per square foot of collector. Modify your answer to fit the nearest size of commercial water tank in that range. (14)

- Determine the volume of heat-transfer fluid required. (15)

- Multiply the volume of heat-transfer fluid by 10-percent to determine the required size of the expansion tank. (16)

If these steps are followed and completed properly, you will have sized a solar water-heating system. The components will be matched and the desired performance can be achieved.

Solar Space-Heating Systems

ENERGY REQUIREMENTS. To determine the amount of energy needed to heat your building, you need two pieces of data:

- hourly heat loss (Btu/hr/°F)
- building design temperature (°F)

The hourly heat loss is determined by running a heat loss analysis as outlined in Appendix A. The building design temperature is the lowest outside air temperature at which you wish to heat the building to 65°F.

From these two pieces of data, you can calculate the *building design load* as follows:

(hourly heat loss) (65°F - building design temperature) = Hourly Building Design Load

SIZING PROCEDURE. Figure 19.7 shows a sizing chart for the collector loop in a solar system for space-heating and water-heating. This sizing chart is intended for use with the complete heating system shown in Decision 18 and the solar performance data (F-Charts) shown in Appendix C. The same criteria for collector selection as discussed on page 19-6 apply here.

ITEM	VALUE	UNITS	REFERENCE
1. Building Heat Loss		Btu/hr/°F	Appendix A
2. Building Design Temperature		°F	Decision 19
3. Building Design Load		Btu/hr	Decision 19
4. Daily Hot Water Load	80	Gallon	Decision 19
5. Hot Water Service Temperature	140	°F	Decision 19
6. Cold Water Supply Temperature	55	°F	Decision 19
7. Closest Weather Station			Appendix C
8. Percent Solar Desired		%F	Appendix C
9. Size of Collector Array		Sq ft	Appendix C
10. Collector Heat-Transfer Liquid	SYLTHERM™ 444		Decision 11
11. Collector Flow Rate (0.039) (#9) =		GPM	Decision 12
12. Heat Exchanger Type	counterflow s.w.		Decision 18
13. Maximum Heat From Collectors (225) (#9) =		Btu/hr	Decision 10
14. Storage Tank Flow Rate		GPM	Specified by manufacturer
15. Pump Head in Collector Loop		Ft water	Decision 12
16. Pump Head in Storage Loop		Ft water	Decision 12
17. Water Preheater Tank Size	120	Gallon	Decision 19
18. Solar Storage Tank Size (1.75) (#9) - 120 =		Gallon	Decision 19
19. Amount of Heat Transfer Liquid		Gallon	Decision 11
20. Expansion Tank Size (0.10) (#19) =		Gallon	Decision 19

Figure 19.7 A sizing chart for the collector loop in a solar system for space-heating and water-heating.

To use the sizing chart for the collector loop (Figure 19.7), proceed as follows:

- Fill in the building heat loss in Btu/hr/°F as calculated using Appendix A. (1)
- Fill in the building design temperature. (2)
- Calculate the building design load. (3)
- The daily hot water load and the service and supply temperatures were precalculated in Appendix C. For up to 100 gallons per day, make no changes. For 120 gallons per day, add one collector to the array.
- Choose the weather station closest to the location.
- Prepare an F-chart for that weather station using Appendix C.
- Decide on the percent-F you would like from the system. (8)
- Using the weather-station chart, determine the collector area needed to give you the desired percent-F. (9)
- Multiply the collector area by 0.039 to obtain the flow rate of the heat-transfer fluid in the collector loop. (11)
- Multiply the collector area by 225 to obtain the maximum amount of heat that can be transferred to the heat exchanger.
- Using the manufacturer's literature, choose a single-wall counter-flow heat exchanger that has an effectiveness of 90-percent or higher. You will need the data from steps 11 and 13 to make this selection.

ITEM	VALUE	UNITS	REFERENCE
1. Water Preheater Flow Rate	5	GPM	Decision 12
2. Preheater Loop Pump Head P_1		Ft water	Decision 12
3. Building Design Load		Btu/hr	Decision 19
4. Fan Coil Inlet Water T_1	120	°F	Decision 13
5. Fan Coil Outlet Water T_2	65	°F	Decision 13
6. Fan Coil Inlet Air T_3	55	°F	Decision 13
7. Fan Coil Outlet Air T_4	110	°F	Decision 13
8. % Effectiveness, Fan Coil	85	% E	Decision 13
9. Fan Coil Output, Must = #3 or Greater		Btu/hr	These figures are calculated from the manufacturer's literature. Examples are shown in Decision 13.
10. Air Flow Rate, Fan Coil		CFM	
11. Water Flow Rate, Fan Coil		GPM	
12. Coil Face Velocity, Air		FPM	
13. Coil Face Dimensions (h x l)	X	inches	
14. Pressure Drop, Water side		Ft water	
15. Pressure Drop, Air Side		In water	
16. Pump Flow Rate P_2 = (#11)		GPM	Same as in step #11
17. Pump Head Loss P_2		Ft water	Decision 12
18. Inlet Water Temperature, Heat Pump	45 – 65	°F	Decision 18
19. Pump Flow Rate, Heat Pump, P_3		GPM	Specified by manufacturer
20. Pump Pressure Drop, P_3		Ft water	Decision 12
21. Heat Pump Output, 45°F Water		Btu/hr	Decision 18
22. Auxiliary Heater Water Output Temperature	130	°F	Decision 18
23. Auxiliary Heater Output		Btu/hr	Decision 18

Figure 19.8 A sizing chart for the heat-delivery loop in a solar system for space-heating and water-heating.

- The manufacturer's literature will also give you the rate of flow required in the storage loop. Insert this figure in the chart at step 14.
- Determine the collector loop pump head (friction losses in feet of water) using the procedures outlined in Decision 12. (15)
- Determine the pump head in the storage loop. (16)
- Multiply the collector area by 1.75 gallons to determine the solar storage tank size. Subtract the size of the water preheater tank and insert the result in step 18. The sizing charts will be accurate for tank sizes 1.50 to 2.00 gallons per square foot of collector. If necessary, modify the results within that range to fit the available space for the storage tank.
- Calculate the amount of heat-transfer fluid required. (19)
- Multiply the amount of heat-transfer fluid by 10-percent to determine the size of the expansion tank. (20)

This completes the sizing of the collector loop and the solar storage tank. All components will be matched and the performance known if the procedure outlined is followed.

To use the sizing chart for the heat-delivery loop (Figure 19.8), use the following procedure:

- Calculate the preheater loop pump head. This is pump, p_1, in Figure 18.3 in Decision 18. (2)
- Insert the building design load from Figure 19.7. (3)
- Using the manufacturer's literature, determine the proper solar fan coil size and operating conditions. A complete discussion of this procedure is given in Decision 13.
  Note: The fan coil output must be equal to or greater than the building design load. Also, the air velocity through the coil (10) must provide the proper face velocity in feet per minute. (12)
- Insert the pump flow rate determined from the manufacturer's literature. (11) This is pump, p_2, in Figure 18.3 in Decision 18.
- Calculate the head loss for pump p_2. Use the entire loop to and from the solar storage tank as shown on page 18-6 as the solar fan coil circuit. (17)
- Using the heat pump manufacturer's literature, determine the proper flow rate through the heat exchanger in the heat pump. (19)
- Calculate the head loss for pump, p_3. Use the entire loop to and from the solar storage tank as shown on page 18-10 as the solar fan coil/heat pump circuit.
  Note: Ignore pump p_2 and be certain to calculate the pressure drop across the solar fan coil at the *new* flow rate needed to run the heat pump. (20)
- Choose a heat pump with an output equal to or greater than the building design load using 45°F water. (21)
  Note: Check to be certain that this heat pump is also large enough to cool the structure during the air conditioning season.
- Choose an auxiliary heater which has an output equal to or greater than the building design load. (23)

This completes the sizing of the heat-delivery loop for a solar system. The components will be matched and the performance known if the procedure outlined is followed.

SPECIFYING THE EQUIPMENT

With the system now sized and the various components matched for the proper performance, the proper specifications for each piece of equipment should be written. Figures 19.9 through 19.20 show sample specification forms for the major pieces of equipment in solar systems. Properly completed, these sheets can aid job pricing and equipment purchasing.

Collector Manufacturer	
Model Number	
Number of Covers	2
$F_R \tau \alpha$	0.74±5%
$F_R U_L$	0.67±5%
ASHRAE 93-77 Tested	Yes
Testing Laboratory	
Warrantee Period	
Stagnation Tested at	
Maximum Recommended Tube Velocity	
Operating Temperature Range	−30°F. To 200°F.
Pressure Drop at Maximum Velocity	
Estimated Collector Life	20 Years Min.
Glazing Materials	
Gasketing Materials	
Insulation Materials	
Absorber Plate Material	Metal
Absorber Plate Coaring	Selective
Heat Transfer Fluid Approved For	SYLTHERM®444
Gross Collector Module Size	
Physical Size: Width _____ Length _____ Height _____	
Net Aperture Size	
Suggested Retail Cost per sq. ft.	

Figure 19.9 A sample specification form for solar collectors.

Heat Exchanger Manufacturer .... _____

Model Number .... _____

Flow Configuration .... Counterflow

Double or Single Wall Construction .... _____ *

Heat Transfer Medium, Primary .... Liquid, SYLTHERM®444

Heat Transfer Medium, Secondary.. Liquid; Water

Warrantee .... _____

Estimated Life... 20 Years Min.

Construction Metals .... _____

Physical Size: .... Width _____ Length_____ Height _____

Operating Conditions, Collector side

   Flow Rate, GPM .... _____ *

   Maximum Heat Supplied, Btu/hr .... _____ *

   % Effectiveness Desired .... 90% Minimum

   Pressure Drop @ Flow Rate .... _____ *

   Max/Min Operating Temperature .... 45 To 200°F.

   Operating Mid-range .... 120 To 160°F.

   Collector Inlet Temp. Rise (CRF) .... 3.3°F. (0.11)

Operating Conditions, Storage side

   Flow Rate, GPM .... _____ *

   Max/Min Operating Temperature .... 45 To 200°F.

   Operating Mid-range .... 120 To 160°F.

   Pressure Drop at Flow Rate.. _____ *

Suggested Retail Cost.. _____

*Available from the system sizing charts.

Figure 19.10 A sample specification form for collector-loop heat exchangers.

Pump Manufacturer .... _____

Model Number .... _____

Motor Coupling... Wet Rotor Or Magnetic

Mechanical Seal .... No

Warrantee .... _____

Estimated Life... 20 Year Minimum

Pump Body and Impeller Material .... Cast Iron Or Better

Pump Gasketing Materials .... 200 To 225°F. Rubber

Pump Curves Available .... Yes, SYLTHERM®444

Operating Motor Voltage .... 110v. 60 Hertz (USA)

Starting Amperage .... _____

Can Motor be Speed Controlled .... Yes

Flange Connections .... O-Ring Sealed

Operating Conditions

   Flow Rate, GPM .... _____ *

   Pressure Drop, Ft of Water .... _____ *

   Closed or Open System .... Closed

   Max/Min Operating Temperatures .... 45 To 200°F.

   Operating Mid-range .... 105 To 145°F.

   Fluid Pumping... SYLTHERM®444

Suggested Retail Cost.. _____

*Available from the system sizing charts.

Figure 19.11 A sample specification form for collector-loop pumps.

```
Pump Manufacturer ..............................................._____
Model Number ..................................................._____
Motor Coupling..................................................External Direct Is Okay
Mechanical Seal ................................................Acceptable
Warrantee ......................................................_____
Estimated Life..................................................20 Year Minimum
Pump Body and Impeller Material ...............................Bronze Or Stainless
Pump Gasketing Materials ......................................200 To 225°F, Rubber
Pump Curves Available .........................................Yes, Water
Operating Motor Voltage .......................................110v, 60 Hertz (USA)
Starting Amperage ............................................._____
Can Motor be Speed Controlled ................................Not Required
Flange Connections ............................................O Rings Or Flat Gaskets
Operating Conditions
   Flow Rate, GPM ............................................_____ *
   Pressure Drop, Ft. of Water ..............................._____ *
   Closed or Open System .....................................Open
   Max/Min Operating Temperatures ...........................45 To 200°F.
   Operating Mid-range .......................................105 To 145°F.
   Fluid Pumping.............................................Water
Suggested Retail Cost ........................................._____
```

*Available from the system sizing charts.

Figure 19.12 A sample specification form for storage-loop pumps.

```
Pump Manufacturer ..............................................._____
Model Number ..................................................._____
Motor Coupling..................................................External Direct Is Okay
Mechanical Seal ................................................Acceptable
Warrantee ......................................................_____
Estimated Life..................................................20 Year Minimum
Pump Body and Impeller Material ...............................Bronze Or Stainless
Pump Gasketing Materials ......................................180 To 200°F., Rubber
Pump Curves Available .........................................Yes, Water
Operating Motor Voltage .......................................110v 60 Hertz (USA)
Starting Amperage ............................................._____
Can Motor be Speed Controlled ................................Not Required
Flange Connections ............................................O Ring Or Flat Gasket
Operating Conditions
   Flow Rate, GPM ............................................_____ *
   Pressure Drop, Ft. of Water ..............................._____ *
   Closed or Open System .....................................Open
   Max/Min Operating Temperatures ...........................45 To 180°F.
   Operating Mid-range .......................................70 To 110°F.
   Fluid Pumping.............................................Water
Suggested Retail Cost ........................................._____
```

*Available from the system sizing charts.

Figure 19.13 A sample specification form for delivery-loop pumps.

Tank Manufacturer .... _____

Model Number .... _____

Storage Capactiy .... _____ *

Tank Body Material .... Steel

Tank Lining .... Stone

Tank Insulation .... R-10 Minimum

Plumbing Options .... _____

Tank Jacket .... _____

Sacrificial Anode .... Yes

Physical Size: .... Height _____ Diameter _____

Auxiliary Heater .... No

Internal Heat Exchanger .... Yes, Copper Coil

Maximum Working Pressure .... _____

Weight, Empty .... _____

Warrantee .... _____

Estimated Life .... 10 Year Minimum

Operating Conditions

    Heat Exchanger Flow Rate .... _____ *

    Heat Exchanger Pressure Drop .... _____ *

    Heat Exchanger % Effectiveness Desired 90%

    Temperature Drop Across Exchanger .... 30°F, Solar Noon, Clear Sky

    Hourly Heat Input .... _____ *

    Max/Min Operating Temperatures .... 45 To 165°F.

    Operating Mid-range .... 85 To 125°F.

Heat Exchanger Fluid .... SYLTHERM® 444

Suggested Retail Cost .... _____

*Available from the system sizing charts.

Figure 19.14 A sample specification form for coil-in-tank water preheater tanks.

Tank Manufacturer .... _____

Model Number .... _____

Storage Capacity .... _____ *

Tank Body Material .... Steel

Tank Lining .... Glass or Stone

Tank Insulation .... R-10 Minimum

Plumbing Options .... _____

Tank Jacket .... _____

Sacrificial Anode .... Yes

Physical Size: .... Height _____ Diameter _____

Auxiliary Heater .... No

Internal Heat Exchanger .... No

Maximum Working Pressure .... _____

Weight, Empty .... _____

Warrantee .... _____

Estimated Life .... 6 to 10 Years

Operating Conditions

    Max/Min Operating Temperatures .... 45 To 165°F.

    Operating Mid-range .... 85 To 125°F.

Suggested Retail Cost .... _____

*Available from the system sizing charts.

Figure 19.15 A sample specification form for water preheater tanks with an external heat exchanger.

Heat Exchanger Manufacturer ....
Model Number ....
Flow Configuration .... Counterflow
Heat Transfer Medium, Tubes .... water
Heat Transfer Medium, Fins .... Air
Warrantee ....
Estimated Life.. 20 Year Minimum
Construction Metals ....
Coil Dimensions: .... Length_____ Height _____ ✳
Number of Face Tubes Per Row ....
Coil Circuiting ....
Number of Circuits ....
Water Flow Per Circuit ....
Water Flow Per Circuit ....
Fins Per Inch ....
Air Velocity Across Coil Face .... ✳
Heat Transfer Coefficient ....
Water GPM Correction Factor ....
Pressure Drop of Water Per Pass ....
Number of Tube Rows ....
Btu Output Per Hour ....
Operating Conditions
    Water Inlet Temperature.. ✳
    Water Outlet Temperature .... ✳
    Air Inlet Temperature .... ✳
    Air Outlet Temperature .... ✳
    Percent Effectiveness .... ✳
    Water Flow Rate .... ✳
    Air Flow Rate .... ✳
    Liquid Pressure Drop.. ✳
    Air Pressure Drop ....
Suggested Retail Cost ....

Figure 19.16 A sample specification form for heat-delivery fan coils.　　　*Available from the system sizing charts.

Tank Manufacturer or Designer ....
Model or Job Number ....
Max/Min Thermal Cycle .... 45 To 200°F.
Storage Medium.. water
Freezing Precautions Needed .... Yes
Conditioning, Storage Medium ....
Tank Lining ....
Closed or Open System .... Open
Maximum Working Pressure ....
Materials of Construction ....
Physical Dimensions: .... Width _____ Length_____ Height _____
Tank Capacity .... ✳
Drain Valve .... Yes
Expansion Tank ....
Gasketed Manhole .... Yes
Plumbing Options Required ....
Live Load Limits ....
Dead Load .... Empty _____ Full _____
Tank Insulation .... R-20. Minimum
Suggested Retail Cost ....

Figure 19.17 A sample specification form for solar storage tanks.　　　*Available from the system sizing charts.

Manufacturer ....

Model Number ....

Power Imput .... *110v 60 Hertz (USA)*

Differential Thermostat .... *Yes*

Sensor Type .... *Thermistor*

Available Control Functions

    Collector Pump Switch .... *Yes*

    Collector Pump Speed Control .... *Yes*

    Storage Pump Switch .... ✱

    Storage Pump Speed Control .... *No*

    High Limit Cutoff .... *Yes @   °F.*

    Low Limit Cutoff .... *Yes @ 45°F.*

    Flow Starts @ Temp. Differential of .... *3 to 5°F.*

    Max. Flow @ Temp. Differential of .... *12 to 15°F.*

    Anti-freeze Drain Circuit .... *No*

NEMA/UL Approved .... *Yes*

Sensor Model Number ....

Ground Provisions .... *Yes*

Plug-in or Hard-Wire ....

Warrantee ....

Estimated Life ....

Suggested Retail Cost ....

*Available from the system sizing charts.

Figure 19.18 A sample specification form for solar collector controls.

```
Manufacturer ............................................_____
Model Number ..........................................._____
Power Imput .............................................  110v 60 Hertz (USA)
Differential Thermostat ..................................       No
Sensor Type .............................................    Thermistor
Available Control Functions
    Building Thermostat On/Off Switch .................._____  Yes
    Water Preheater Pump Relay .........................._____  Yes
    Solar Fan Coil Pump Relay ..........................._____  Yes
    Heat Pump Loop Pump Relay ..........................._____  Yes
    Auxiliary Heater Pump Relay .........................._____  No
    Solar Fan Coil Fan Relay ............................_____  Yes
    Heat Pump Fan Relay ................................._____
    Heat Pump Compressor Relay ........................._____  Yes
    Three-way Valve Relay ..............................._____  Yes
    Cooling Tower Valve Relays .........................._____  No
    Auxiliary Boiler Ignition Relay ....................._____  NO
    High Limit Cutoff Relay ............................._____  Yes @      °F.
    Low Limit Cutoff Relay .............................._____  No @       °F.
    Solar Heat Control Band ............................_____  Over 120°F.
    Solar Plus Heat Pump Control Band ..................._____  90 To 120°F.
    Heat Pump Control Band .............................._____  45 To 90°F.
    Auxiliary Heater Control Band ......................._____  Below 45°F.
All Relays to be Controllable to Any Control Band ......._____  Yes
NEMA/UL Approved ......................................_____  Yes
Sensor Model Number ..................................._____
Ground Provisions ......................................_____  Yes
Warrantee ..............................................._____
Estimated Life..........................................._____
Suggested Retail Cost...................................._____
Control System Logic Diagram ..........................._____
```

Figure 19.19 A sample specification form for heat-delivery controls.

```
Heat Pump Manufacturer ..................................................._____
Model Number ............................................................_____
Type Pump ...............................................................___Liquid-To-Air_____
Rated Heat Output in Btu Per Hour ......................................._____ *
Rated Cooling Output in Btu Per Hour ...................................._____ *
Rated Heat COP/EER ....................................................._____
Rated Cooling COP/EER .................................................._____
Auxiliary Electric Heaters .............................................._____
Air Filters ............................................................._____
Electrostatic Air Cleaner .............................................._____
Operating Voltage ......................................................._____
Operating Amperage ....................................................._____
Condensor Coil Operating Range ........................................___45 To 100°F._____
Condensor Coil Flow Rate, Water ........................................_____
Air Flow Rate in CFM ..................................................._____
Physical Dimensions: ......................Width _____ Length_____ Height_____
Weight ................................................................._____
Warrantee .............................................................._____
Estimated Design Life .................................................._____
Operating Conditions-Heat Mode
  Water Inlet Temperature ............................................___45 To 90°F._____
  Air Inlet Temperature .............................................___50 To 60°F._____
Operating Conditions-Cooling Mode
  Water Inlet Temperature ............................................_____
  Air Inlet Temperature .............................................._____
Suggested Retail Price ................................................._____
```

*Available from the system sizing charts.

Figure 19.20 A sample specification form for heat pumps.

MAKING A DECISION

In this section of The Solar Decision Book, you have learned how to size a solar system and how to specify the equipment required for that system. The system used as the basis for sizing was discussed in Decision 18. In the author's opinion, this type of system represents the best "state of the art" solar energy system. One that can be designed and sized to give you predictable performance for years.

As you can see, sizing solar systems is relatively easy when the proper information is available. This information can be provided by a computer simulation program which takes into account all the known variables.

You should now be able to decide that *you* can size a good solar system.

DECISION 20

Price The Job

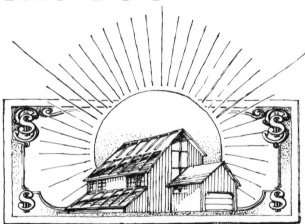

What will you pay for the major components of your solar system? What other materials will be needed? Does the building structure require modifications? How many hours of labor will be needed to install the system?

These are the most important questions that require answers to price the job. However, the answers will not show all of the costs in a solar energy system. The solar system contractor must also include education, transportation, business overhead, engineering and consulting fees, subcontractor costs, system warranty and maintenance costs, start-up costs, and profit.

All of the obvious costs as well as the not-so-obvious costs should be included in pricing the job. This will help insure a realistic job price. The building owner will receive good value for the investment. And the contractor will receive a fair profit for the services provided.

Pricing a solar energy system is not as difficult as you may think. This section of The Solar Decision Book will help you to develop a step-by-step pricing method. You will learn that:

- Getting ready to install a solar energy system requires an investment in both time and money. This investment must be considered in pricing the job.

- Depending on the type of job, the services of an engineering consultant may be required.

- The building may require structural modifications.

- Materials costs as well as labor costs can be itemized.

- Costs for subcontracted services, overhead, and various allowances can also be itemized.

GENERAL CONSIDERATIONS

Owner Installation Versus Contractor Installation

Can the building owner install the solar energy system? The answer is "yes". However, it is a qualified yes. The building owner can install a solar energy system. But the owner must have the proper mechanical skills. The owner must be willing to make the necessary educational investment. The owner must be willing to utilize engineering consultant services as needed. And, the owner must be willing to purchase the necessary tools and equipment.

However, as the contractor, the owner assumes any and all risks involved in purchasing and installing the solar equipment. Errors in judgement or construction may turn into costly mistakes.

Most building owners will elect to hire a qualified contractor. The investment in time and money for a good system often necessitates this decision. As such, this section of The Solar Decision Book is written for the professional mechanical contractor. Much of the information, however, can be used as a pricing guide for the do-it-yourselfer.

The Basics Of Job Pricing

Pricing a solar energy system should include all materials, labor, subcontractor fees, engineering consultant fees, agreed-upon warrantees and maintenance, start-up costs, call-back services, contingency fund, overhead, and profit.

The first time contractor must include some of the cost of manufacturer's technical service, standards development, possible installation school, instruction manuals, and learning new mechanical skills. Becoming a qualified solar contractor involves time and money. Such an investment should be recovered by including a portion of the costs in the first few solar installations. These are reasonable costs.

Large or complex solar systems may require detailed structural calculations for collector racks and storage tanks. Such calculations should be done by a qualified professional engineer who is familiar with these types of structural requirements. Professional engineers are usually state-licensed and a list of names can readily be obtained.

Building alterations may be required to reduce infiltration, lower transmission losses, and prepare the structure to receive the solar collectors. These alterations may not be part of the solar system installation. They may not be the responsibility of the solar contractor. However, such alterations must be accomplished before going ahead with the job.

The job pricing method which follows refers to pricing the type of systems discussed in Decision 18 and sized in Decision 19. The method is specific to those systems. Should the system be changed, the pricing steps should be reviewed so that all costs are covered in arriving at a job price.

In the following sections, a variety of forms are given to help you use a step-by-step method of estimating costs and for pricing the job. Specific forms are given for the following costs:

- Education and engineering services
- Building modifications
- Materials for the collector loop
- Labor for collector loop installation
- Materials for the storage system
- Labor for storage system installation
- Materials for the heat-delivery loop
- Labor for the heat-delivery loop installation
- Subcontracted services
- Overhead and miscellaneous expenses
- The total job

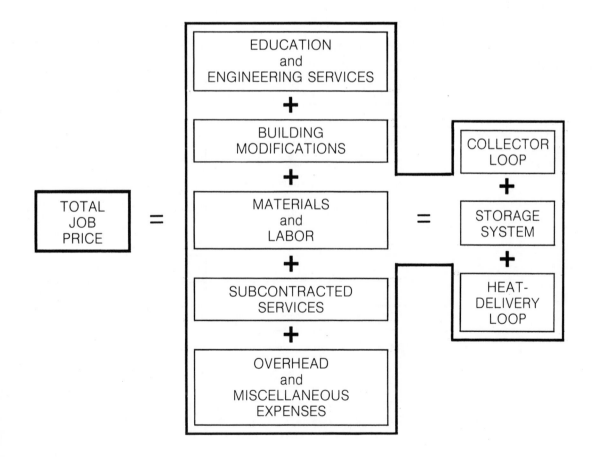

Education and Engineering Costs

A sample form for estimating education and engineering costs is shown in Figure 20.1. Spaces are given for estimated costs as well as the quoted prices. Job price minus estimated cost equals the gross estimated profit. By splitting out the estimated profit on each item, you can plan the proper markup for that material or service.

This form covers your costs for reference books, attendance at solar installer schools, travel and expenses for manufacturer technical services or consultation. These costs are part of your investment in becoming a knowledgeable solar contractor. They should be recovered during the first year of work.

The form also covers your costs, if any, for contracting with a design consultant or professional engineer. These services may or may not be required depending on the particular job. If they are required, the costs should be included in the job price.

EDUCATION & ENGINEERING SERVICES		
Education Items	**Cost Estimate**	**Job Price**
The Solar Decision Book		
ASHRAE Handbook of Fundamentals ...		
ANSI A 58.1 (1972) Building Code Requirements for Minimum Design Loads		
FHA: Intermediate Minimum Property Stds. Supplement, Solar Heating and Domestic Hot Water Systems		
ARI Std 410: Forced Air Cooling and Air Heating Coils		
NFPA 90A: (1976) Stds for the Installation of Air Conditioning and Ventilating Systems		
NFPA 90B: Stds for the Installation of Warm Air Heating and Air Conditioning Systems		
Other: _____		
_____		
Solar Installers School		
Manufacturers Technical Service		
Subtotal:		
Engineering Items		
Solar Design Consultant		
Engineering Services		
• Collector Mounting Foundations		
• Solar Storage Tank		
Other: _____		
_____		
Subtotal:		
Total:		

Figure 20.1 A sample form for estimating education and engineering costs.

BUILDING MODIFICATIONS		
Item	Cost Estimate	Job Price
Collector Array Mounting Foundations		
• Design and Engineering	_____	_____
• Drawing and Specifications	_____	_____
• Materials	_____	_____
• Site Preparation	_____	_____
• Labor	_____	_____
• Clean-up and Inspection	_____	_____
Subtotal:	_____	_____
Building Modifications to Lower Infiltration		
• Inspection and Recommendations . . .	_____	_____
• Analysis and Quotations	_____	_____
• Materials	_____	_____
• Labor	_____	_____
• Clean-up and Inspection	_____	_____
Subtotal:	_____	_____
Building Modifications to Lower Transmission		
• Inspection and Recommendations . . .	_____	_____
• Analysis and Quotations	_____	_____
• Materials	_____	_____
• Labor	_____	_____
• Clean-up and Inspection	_____	_____
Subtotal:	_____	_____
Other Required Building Modifications		
_____	_____	_____
_____	_____	_____
_____	_____	_____
_____	_____	_____
_____	_____	_____
Subtotal:	_____	_____
Total:	_____	_____

Figure 20.2 A sample form for estimating building modification costs.

Building Modification Costs

A sample form for estimating building modification costs is shown in Figure 20.2.

This form covers costs for collector array mounting foundations. It also covers costs for building modifications to lower infiltration losses or transmission losses. These costs may or may not be the responbility of the solar contractor. When they are, a job price needs to be calculated and included in the final solar system price. Include the cost of supervising and inspecting the subcontractor's work, if you are responsible for such work.

The Collector Loop Costs

The costs for the solar collector loop are best estimated in two stages. First, estimate the cost of materials. Second, estimate the cost of installation labor.

COLLECTOR LOOP MATERIALS. A sample form for estimating the costs of collector loop materials is shown in Figure 20.3. This form is designed for use with any of the three systems discussed in Decision 18. The various parts of the three collector loops are itemized. Also, piping, fittings, and several optional parts are included. Spaces are given for part model numbers, the cost estimate, and the job price. In using this form, remember that:

- A separate form will be used for labor costs.
- The collector mounting brackets may or may not be part of the collector price. This should be taken into consideration in purchasing the collectors.
- There is no external heat exchanger with the coil-in-tank system. Instead, include the tank complete with its internal heat exchanger coil.

COLLECTOR LOOP INSTALLATION LABOR. A sample form for estimating the costs of collector loop installation labor is shown in Figure 20.4. The individual tasks are itemized to simplify the labor cost estimate. On this form, you will:

- Estimate the number of hours required to perform each installation task.
- Multiply the time estimate by the hourly rate to determine the total direct cost.
- Add the cost of insurance, taxes, and employee benefits.
- Add the profit desired from the labor.

20-6

COLLECTOR LOOP MATERIALS			
Materials, By Item	Model	Cost Estimate	Job Price
Collector Mounting Brackets ..	_____	_____	_____
Solar Collectors	_____	_____	_____
Heat Exchanger	_____	_____	_____
Collector Pump	_____	_____	_____
Controller...................	_____	_____	_____
Check Valve	_____	_____	_____
Air Separator	_____	_____	_____
Fill Valve	_____	_____	_____
Flow Control Valve	_____	_____	_____
Manual Air Bleed Valve	_____	_____	_____
Manual Collector Drain Valve ..	_____	_____	_____
Float Valve	_____	_____	_____
Pressure Relief Valve	_____	_____	_____
Pressure Gauge	_____	_____	_____
Heat Transfer Fluid	SYLTHERM® 444	_____	_____
Manifold Piping	_____	_____	_____
Manifold Connectors	_____	_____	_____
Collector Loop Piping	_____	_____	_____
Tees	_____	_____	_____
Elbows	_____	_____	_____
45° Elbows	_____	_____	_____
Miscellaneous Fittings	_____	_____	_____
Loctite Pipe Dope with Teflon ..	592	_____	_____
Flow Meter (optional)	_____	_____	_____
Thermometer Wells (optional)..	_____	_____	_____
Thermometers (optional)	_____	_____	_____
Miscellaneous			
For Coil-in-tank, Add Tank Here and Delete Heat Exchanger Above			
Insulation for Pipe & Components			
_____			
_____			
Total:	_____	_____	_____

Figure 20.3 A sample form for estimating the costs of collector loop materials.

Items that should be included in insurance and taxes are: workman's compensation, FICA (employer's share), unemployment taxes (federal and state), union dues, and inspection fees.

Items that should be included in the employee benefits package would normally include: health and life insurance, paid vacations, holiday and sickness allowances, bonus and pension plans, and any other employee benefits.

Any subcontractor's cost, such as a crane, should be transferred to the Subcontractor's Estimating Form, Figure 20.9. Such a cost should not be included in the total for the labor estimate.

COLLECTOR LOOP INSTALLATION				
Labor Item	No. Men	Hours	Labor Rate	Total Cost
Transport collectors to job site	_____	_____	_____	_____
Install collector mounting system	_____	_____	_____	_____
Hoist Collectors	_____	_____	_____	_____
(Subcontract Crane $ _____ Transfer to subcontractors form)				
Connect Collectors to Mountings	_____	_____	_____	_____
Fabricate the Manifolds	_____	_____	_____	_____
Pipe Collectors to Manifolds	_____	_____	_____	_____
Pipe Collector Loop to Service Room	_____	_____	_____	_____
Install Heat Exchanger (or coil-in-tank)	_____	_____	_____	_____
Install Pump	_____	_____	_____	_____
Pipe Collector Loop in Service Room	_____	_____	_____	_____
Install Controller	_____	_____	_____	_____
Inspect & Check Piping Loop Against Working Drawings and Specs	_____	_____	_____	_____
Air Pressure Test Collector Loop	_____	_____	_____	_____
Leak Repair Allowance	_____	_____	_____	_____
			Subtotal:	_____
Fill Collector Loop	_____	_____	_____	_____
Start-up & Check-out of Loop	_____	_____	_____	_____
Set Loop Flow Rate (clear sky, noon)	_____	_____	_____	_____
Insulate Loop Piping and Components	_____	_____	_____	_____
Label & Indentify Loop Parts	_____	_____	_____	_____
Type Instruction/Service Manual	_____	_____	_____	_____
Paint & Clean-up	_____	_____	_____	_____
			Subtotal:	_____
Insurances and Taxes				_____
Employee Benefits				_____
			Subtotal:	_____
			Profit:	_____
			Total:	_____

Figure 20.4 A sample form for estimating the costs of collector loop installation labor.

The Storage System Costs

The costs for the solar storage system are best estimated in two stages — materials, then labor.

A sample form for estimating the costs of storage system materials is shown in Figure 20.5. This form can be used for the storage loop in a complete system, as well as for the storage loop in a water-heater system with an external heat exchanger.

A sample form for estimating the costs of storage system installation labor is shown in Figure 20.6. This form includes the same insurance and benefit provisions as on the form for estimating collector loop labor costs.

STORAGE SYSTEM MATERIALS			
Materials, By Item	Model	Cost Estimate	Job Price
Solar Storage Tank			
Solar Storage Tank Pump*			
Solar Storage Expansion Tank			
Drain Valve*			
Piping*			
Tees*			
Elbows*			
45° Elbows*			
Miscellaneous Fittings*			
Water Treatment Chemicals			
Water Test Kit			
Sight Glass (optional)			
Sensor Well (optional)			
Relief Valve*			
Insulation for Pipes and Components*			

*Use these items only for jobs that have a water heater with an external heat exchanger.

Figure 20.5 A sample form for estimating the costs of storage system materials.

STORAGE SYSTEM INSTALLATION				
Labor Item	No. Men	Hours	Labor Rate	Total Cost
Install Solar Storage Tank; or......................	_____	_____	_____	_____
Water Preheater Tank*............................	_____	_____	_____	_____
Install Expansion Tank...........................	_____	_____	_____	_____
Install Pump*...................................	_____	_____	_____	_____
Pipe Loop*......................................	_____	_____	_____	_____
Connect to Auxiliary Heater/ City Water* (water preheater only)	_____	_____	_____	_____
Insepct and Check Piping Loop Against Working Drawings & Specs	_____	_____	_____	_____
			Subtotal:	_____
Fill Storage Tank*...............................	_____	_____	_____	_____
Treat Storage Water	_____	_____	_____	_____
Start-up & Check-out Loop*	_____	_____	_____	_____
Leak Repair Allowance*..........................	_____	_____	_____	_____
Insulate Loop Piping & Components*	_____	_____	_____	_____
Label & Identify Loop Parts*.....................	_____	_____	_____	_____
Paint and Clean-up*	_____	_____	_____	_____
			Subtotal:	_____
Insurance and Taxes...				_____
Employee Benefits				_____
			Subtotal:	_____
Profit on Labor .... Profit:				_____
			Total: (add 3 subtotals and profit)	_____

*Use these items only for jobs that have a water heater with an external heat exchanger.

Figure 20.6 A sample form for estimating the costs of storage system installation labor.

The Heat-Delivery Loop Costs

Again, the costs for materials and labor are estimated separately. In many cases, the materials selected may affect the labor costs for installation.

Figure 20.7 shows a sample form for estimating the costs of heat-delivery loop materials. And Figure 20.8 shows a sample form for estimating the costs of heat-delivery loop installation labor.

HEAT DELIVERY LOOP MATERIALS			
Materials, By Item	**Model**	**Cost Estimate**	**Job Price**
Filter, Heat Delivery Manifold	_____	_____	_____
3-Way Valve, Heat Delivery Manifold	_____	_____	_____
3-Way Valve, Heat Return Manifold	_____	_____	_____
Solar Fan Coil	_____	_____	_____
Heat Pump	_____	_____	_____
Water Preheat Tank	_____	_____	_____
Auxiliary Building Heater	_____	_____	_____
Coil Chamber and Plenum	_____	_____	_____
Blower, Solar Fan Coil	_____	_____	_____
Expansion Tank	_____	_____	_____
Pressure/Temperature Relief Valve	_____	_____	_____
Pump, Water Preheater	_____	_____	_____
Pump, Solar Fan Coil	_____	_____	_____
Pump, Heat Pump	_____	_____	_____
2-Manual 3-Way Valves	_____	_____	_____
Check Valve	_____	_____	_____
Differential Controller, Preheater Tank	_____	_____	_____
Controller, Heat Delivery System	_____	_____	_____
Cooling Tower (optional)	_____	_____	_____
Heat Delivery Loop Piping	_____	_____	_____
Tees	_____	_____	_____
Elbows	_____	_____	_____
45° Elbows	_____	_____	_____
Miscellaneous Fittings	_____	_____	_____
Insulation for Pipes and Components	_____	_____	_____
		Total:	_____

Figure 20.7 A sample form for estimating the costs of materials for the heat-delivery loop.

HEAT DELIVERY LOOP INSTALLATION				
Labor Items	No. Men	Hours	Labor Rate	Total Cost
Transport Components to Job Site	_____	_____	_____	_____
Install Water Preheater	_____	_____	_____	_____
Install Solar Coil Chamber	_____	_____	_____	_____
Install Solar Fan Coil Blower	_____	_____	_____	_____
Install Solar Fan Coil	_____	_____	_____	_____
Install Heat Pump	_____	_____	_____	_____
Install Ductwork to Cold Return	_____	_____	_____	_____
Install Auxiliary Building Heater	_____	_____	_____	_____
Install Expansion Tank	_____	_____	_____	_____
Install Cooling Tower (optional)	_____	_____	_____	_____
Pipe Delivery/Return Manifolds	_____	_____	_____	_____
Pipe Water Preheater	_____	_____	_____	_____
Pipe Solar Fan Coil	_____	_____	_____	_____
Pipe Heat Pump	_____	_____	_____	_____
Pipe Auxiliary Heater	_____	_____	_____	_____
Pipe Cooling Tower (optional)	_____	_____	_____	_____
Install Water Preheater Controller	_____	_____	_____	_____
Install Heat Delivery Controller.................	_____	_____	_____	_____
Inspect and Check Piping Loop Against Working Drawings & Specs	_____	_____	_____	_____
Subtotal:				_____
Fill System Loops	_____	_____	_____	_____
Start-up and Check-out Loops	_____	_____	_____	_____
Leak Repair Allowance........................	_____	_____	_____	_____
Insulate Piping & Components	_____	_____	_____	_____
Label & Identify Loop Parts....................	_____	_____	_____	_____
Type Instruction/Service Manual	_____	_____	_____	_____
Paint and Clean-up	_____	_____	_____	_____
Subtotal:				_____
Insurance and Taxes..				_____
Employee Benefits				_____
Subtotal:				_____
Profit:				_____
Total:				_____

Figure 20.8 A sample form for estimating the costs of installation labor for the heat-delivery loop.

Costs Of Subcontracted Services

A sample form for estimating the costs of any subcontracted sevices is shown in Figure 20.9. This form makes allowance for estimating and pricing machinery rental and work performed by other trades.

Overhead And Miscellaneous Expenses

A sample form for estimating the costs of your overhead and miscellaneous expenses is shown in Figure 20.10. This is where you add your expense of being in business to the price quotation. Your office, your shop, your tools, your supervision should be included in the job price. So should such costs as those for vandalism, drawings, legal fees, performance bonds, warrantees, and maintenance contracts.

SUBCONTRACTED SERVICES		
Item	Cost Estimate	Job Price
Crane, for Collector Hoisting	_____	_____
Excavating, for Footings, Foundations, Tank	_____	_____
Electrical Wiring of Components and Controls	_____	_____
Sheet Metal, Heat Distribution to House	_____	_____
Masonry, for Stacks, Tanks, Walls	_____	_____
Insulating, for Components and Piping	_____	_____
Roofing, Repair and Renewal	_____	_____
Inspection/Permit Fees	_____	_____
	_____	_____
	_____	_____
	_____	_____
	_____	_____
	Total:	_____

Figure 20.9 A sample form for estimating the costs of subcontracted services.

OVERHEAD, EXPENSES		
Item	Cost Estimate	Job Price
Shop Overhead	_____	_____
Office Overhead	_____	_____
Tool Allowance	_____	_____
Transportation Allowance	_____	_____
Supervision Allowance	_____	_____
Loss and Liability Insurance	_____	_____
Breakage and Vandalism	_____	_____
Working Drawings and Specifications	_____	_____
Contracts and Legal Fees	_____	_____
Contingency Allowance	_____	_____
Performance Bonds	_____	_____
System Warrantee and Maintenance Allowance	_____	_____
	_____	_____
	_____	_____
	Total:	_____

Figure 20.10 A sample form for estimating the costs of overhead and miscellaneous expenses.

JOB PRICE	
Education and Engineering Services (20.1)	$_____
Building Modifications (20.2)	$_____
Collector Loop Materials (20.3)	$_____
Collector Loop Labor (20.4)	$_____
Storage Loop Materials (20.5)	$_____
Storage Loop Labor (20.6)	$_____
Heat Delivery Loop Materials (20.7)	$_____
Heat Delivery Loop Labor (20.8)	$_____
Subcontracted Services (20.9)	$_____
Overhead and Allowances (20.10)	$_____
Total Job Quotation:	$_____

Figure 20.11 A sample form for estimating the total job price. Ten subtotals are used in preparing the job quotation.

The Job Quotation

Now, a realistic price is easy to calculate. Simply, total the various prices on each of the forms shown in Figure 20.1 through Figure 20.10. You can use the sample form shown in Figure 20.11.

Just ten easy steps to a price you can live with. One that covers obvious costs as well as not-so-obvious costs. And one that will insure value for the owner's investment and a fair return for the contractor's materials and labor.

MAKING A DECISION

In this section of The Solar Decision Book, you have learned about a step-by-step method for estimating the cost and quoting a price of a solar energy system. This is not the only method that can be used. A variety of contractor quotation programs exist. None of them are perfect and never will be as long as labor, weather, and dozens of suppliers are involved.

In this method of estimating and pricing, you have made allowance for any education needed to get ready to install solar systems. You have covered the costs of a consultant or engineer on a big installation. You are aware that structural work and costs may be required before proceeding with the solar installation.

You have also learned that the cost estimate is best approached by splitting out the labor, materials, and outside services. By doing so, the profit opportunity can be maximized. These costs and profits are best calculated in the sequence in which the material is used or the labor performed. This will allow you to know exactly where costs may be running high or low.

The decision to bid the job belongs to you. If you do, this pricing method will help you to determine a fair price for both you and the customer.

DECISION 21

Install The System

A solar energy system that collapses in the first windstorm or under a blanket of snow is not a good investment. Neither is one that shifts and sags after the first year's operation. Such problems are, of course, catastrophic. They underscore the importance of proper system installation.

Even minor faults in system installation can become nagging owner headaches. Problems such as storage tank seepage, poor insulation, leaking pipe joints, inadequate owner's instructions, unforseen safety hazards, and components inaccessible for servicing can be very costly to correct.

As the owner of a solar heating system, you should be concerned with whether the installer has left behind a system which is safe, efficient, reliable, and presents no health hazards. While building codes provide a measure of protection, they represent minimum standards. They do not address the system's efficiency. And they do not require that the installer educate you on how the system works or how it should be maintained.

Skilled installers will understand these problems. In addition, they will possess the correct mechanical skills needed for proper solar installation. These skills are generally available from HVAC contractors or from specialized solar contractors.

Some installation requirements and mechanical skills are critical. This section of The Solar Decision Book covers these. Special attention is given to particularly troublesome areas of installation.

SYSTEM LOADING REQUIREMENTS

Structural requirements for small buildings are detailed in *Building Code Requirements For Minimum Design Loads In Buildings And Other Structures,* ANSI A 58.1 (1972). Additional information can be gathered from:

- FHA, Minimum Property Standards
- The Uniform Building Code
- Local or model building codes

All structural loading should be in compliance with these and other applicable standards. The structural loads of major importance in the installation of solar equipment are dead loads, live loads, wind loads, snow loads, seismic loads, hail loads, dynamic loads and thermal cycling. The solar system components must be engineered and installed correctly to withstand such loading. Particular care should be given to the collectors and the storage tanks.

Dead Loads

The dead load of the solar system must be carefully calculated. The structure and/or any footings and foundations must be properly sized to carry the load safely. Remember, however, that the liquids used for heat transfer and for solar storage should be included for calculations of total weight, but not when calculating the effect of uplifting or overturning forces. For these calculations, the equipment weight should be calculated dry. Empty tanks and collectors do not resist uplift in the same manner as do full ones.

Live Loads

If the collectors are part of the roofing system, they must be engineered to support service personnel as well as environmental loads such as snow or ice. If the collectors are mounted on top of the roofing system, this is not necessary. FHA suggests that the integral roof system be engineered to withstand a concentrated load of 250 pounds distributed over a four-square-inch area where maintenance may be required.

Storage tank tops should be engineered in the same manner to insure the safety of service personnel. If the tank is located where vehicles may drive over, the top must be strengthened to withstand such traffic. The water in solar storage tanks can reach temperatures of 200°F, a serious hazard should an accident occur.

Wind Loads

The wind loads that collectors must withstand depend on the type of installation. When the collectors are part of the roof (integral), the wind-load resistance can be engineered into the roof. However, most collectors are mounted on top of the roof — either flush with the roof or at an angle to the roof. Or, the collectors are rack-mounted — either on the roof, on a sidewall, or on the ground.

Each case must be treated in a different manner. Flush-roof-mounted collectors should be engineered to withstand the same wind loads that the roof does. Collectors angled away from the roof or mounted on open racks must resist any uplift loads from wind striking the rear of the collector. These collectors should be engineered to withstand winds gusting to 130 miles per hour. Steady wind pressures do not usually cause failure. Sudden gusts that apply uneven and large forces are more likely to cause problems.

Collectors can weigh from 75- to 250-pounds each. If ripped from the roof, the collectors could do considerable damage to the structure and its occupants. The collectors should be fastened securely through the roof as shown in Figure 21.1. Threaded bolts should be used, rather than relying on lagging into the roof structure itself.

Collectors mounted on racks which are not part of the roof structure require particular care. The collectors must be properly mounted on the racks. Also, the racks themselves must be properly designed and fastened.

The same situation exists for wall-mounted collectors. Care should be taken to distribute the forces over a wide area. The mounting surface should be securely fastened across the wall. The collectors should not be secured with single point mounts.

With exterior racks, the resistance to sideways movement also becomes very important. Proper angle bracing is needed to resist sideways pressure and to prevent collapse.

Ground-mounted racks are subject to live downward loads, sideways loads, and uplift loads. All of the preceding information pertains to ground mounts. In addition, the ability of footings or foundations to prevent overturning is important. Devices such as wedge-shaped footings as in Figure 21.2 may be used. Frost heaving or thaw-induced sinking must be guarded against. The dead and live loads must be distributed to prevent these problems. Ground mounts should also be curbed where vehicles could accidentally contact them.

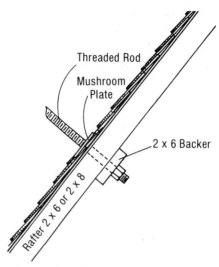

Figure 21.1 Roof-mounted collectors should be fastened securely.

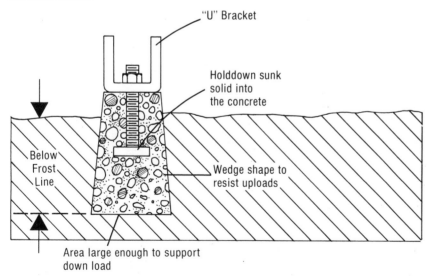

Figure 21.2 Typical wedge-shaped footing for ground-mounted collector rack.

Snow Loads

Snow can accumulate on, around, and under the collectors. For certain collector configurations, snow drifting and/or ice buildup can cause particular hazards. These conditions impose added live loads on the collectors as well as the structure. Saw-tooth arrays are especially prone to creating heavy roof loads from snow and ice. Such seasonal loading must be taken into account when engineering the system.

Also, some attention should be given other seasonal hazards. Care must be taken to prevent water backup under shingles and facia boards. Damage from snow slides or accumulated ice must be prevented or minimized.

Seismic Loads

In certain sections of the country, the design must be able to withstand earthquakes. The *Uniform Building Code* published by the International Conference Of Building Officials, Whittier, California deals with this subject. In such areas, flexible connectors are used to allow for movement between the mechanical and electrical components.

Hail Loads

Most of the United States has one or more hailstorms a year. The exceptions are the eastern seaboard and a narrow band running from Yuma, Arizona, to Reno, Nevada. Conditions are particularly severe in the plains states. The solar collectors must be engineered to withstand local hail conditions. The probability of hail in a given locality can be obtained from the local weather station.

Dynamic Loads

Fixed flat-plate collectors are usually not subject to dynamic loads. However, movable collectors such as the "tracking" type are. They should be properly engineered to withstand dynamic loads.

Thermal Cycling

The entire solar system is subject to thermal forces which cause it to expand and contract. This thermal cycling takes place continuously, day after day. It is one of the more common causes of system failure. Thermal cycling reaches its zenith at the collector under no-flow conditions. During no-flow, the collector absorber plates can reach temperatures of 400° to 450°F. This thermal stress can cause sagging of glazings, buckling of absorber plates, mechanical rupture of connectors and piping, and physical degradation of the system. The collector must be designed and installed to withstand such stress. Collector manufacturers engineer and test collectors against these types of failures. The installer should become familiar with the forces at work and stay within the thermal limitations of the equipment.

Collector Cover Loads

Some special consideration must be given to the loads on collector cover glazings. Unvented collectors can build up pressures that rupture the seal on the cover glazing. Additionally, high winds can create suction loading by decreasing the pressure across the glazing. These two conditions, coupled with thermal expansion, require that the glazing be properly secured to the collector housing.

MASONRY CONSIDERATIONS

Concrete and masonry may play an important role in the installation of a solar system. These are high-thermal-mass materials which may be utilized extensively to make the structure a better heat trap. They may also be needed to insure proper performance from fireplaces and furnaces, to aid installation of ground-mounted collector racks, or to simply construct the solar storage tank.

Chimneys

In existing structures, the erection of solar collectors may raise the roof line. This may cause wind turbulence which affects the draft of chimneys and furnace stacks. Such chimneys and stacks may require added height.

The prevailing winds should also be studied to determine what happens to stack gases and particulate matter such as soot. These can settle on the glazing of the collectors. Steps must be taken to prevent this. Otherwise, glazing buildup will cause a deterioration of system performance.

Footings and Foundations

When installing heavy equipment such as storage tanks and ground-mounted collector racks, the soil loading and the composition of the footings and foundations must be carefully engineered. Reinforcing mesh and bar is generally called for in the case of extensive loading. Hold-downs and mounting hardware must be securely sunk and held within the footing or foundation. Such hardware must be protected against longterm corrosion. Concrete mixtures must be carefully prepared, poured, and protected against freezing and too-rapid drying. All retaining forms must be removed before backfilling. Otherwise, the buried forms will rot and cause voids around the footings.

Tank Walls And Covers

Storage tank walls, whether above or below ground, are subjected to large lateral forces. Below-ground tanks should be engineered to withstand soil pressures, hydrostatic loads, flotation, vehicular wheel loads and human traffic. Above-ground tanks should be engineered to withstand internal weights and pressures from their contents. Structural steel reinforcing is generally called for in both poured concrete and concrete block tanks. In all cases, assume that the covers will need to support live loads. They must be carefully reinforced according to good engineering practice.

THERMAL AND MOISTURE PROTECTION

Solar systems are exposed to harsh environments. Also, they must withstand attack from within. Two very common causes of failure are inadequate sealing against moisture and inadequate protection against temperature extremes.

Moisture Protection

Water seeping into the solar storage tank contaminates the storage liquid. Such contamination can cause buildup of corrosion in system components. This can also reduce the system's energy storage capabilities. Water seeping into collectors contaminates the heat-transfer liquid. The result may be corrosion and loss of collection efficiency.

Faulty installation of the system is the usual cause of water seepage into components. The seepage may go beyond the system itself, though. It may enter the building's structural components and its insulation. Poorly protected insulation rapidly accumulates moisture and loses its R value.

Solar storage tanks must be waterproofed and protected on both their exteriors and interiors to prevent moisture seepage. A positive moisture barrier between the tank and the insulation and over the exterior of the insulation is imperative. The barrier must be engineered to withstand the rigors of the particular installation. Concrete tanks should have interior linings or coatings. Steel tanks should be carefully coated to prevent rust and corrosion. Fiberglass tanks generally do not need coatings or linings unless called for by the manufacturer. These tanks, however, have some thermal limitations. The manufacturer's recommendations should be carefully followed.

Moisture seepage into the collectors is unacceptable and must be completely avoided. Such seepage can condense on the glazing and scatter the solar radiation. It can also penetrate the back and sidewall insulation, lowering its R value and increasing the energy losses from the collector.

To prevent seepage into collectors, a primary weatherseal is needed at the glazing and the collector must be angled properly to insure water runoff. Temperatures on the glazing range from below zero to more than 300°F. So, primary weather sealants with high- and low-temperature properties should be chosen. The sealant must have good adhesion, high elongation and compressibility, and not harden or become brittle with time and exposure.

Roof-mounted collectors and their related parts necessitate making openings into the structure. Such openings must be properly sealed and closed with the appropriate mastics and sealing compounds. Otherwise, leakage into the structure will result. Thermal expansion and contraction must be allowed for around components such as piping.

Thermal Protection

The insulating of components such as tanks and collectors has been covered in various sections of The Solar Decision Book. To prevent the loss of heat throughout the system, insulation is needed on pipes, ducts, heat exchangers, and other system equipment as called for by the particular installation.

There are a number of considerations for providing this thermal protection. First, insulations adequate to provide the required thermal protection must be chosen. Second, the general properties of the insulation must be carefully considered. Exposed plastic foam, non-fire-retarded cellulosic fill, kraft-asphaltic vapor barrier, and other flammable insulations must be shielded from the interior of the building by fire barriers. Proper blocking must be installed to provide air spaces around electrical equipment, wiring, and lighting fixtures when loose fill is used. Third, the operating temperatures of the equipment must be taken into consideration. Fourth, the resistance of the insulating material to moisture and humidity cycling must be considered.

PIPE UP THE SOLAR SYSTEM

HVAC contractors will encounter very few problems with solar system piping, if the same general procedures used with Freon systems are followed. Plumbing contractors who work only with water will need to practice the proper techniques for making high-temperature, hard-soldered joints. The techniques used by the plumbing industry are not adequate for the demands of the solar collector loop installation. This may sound like a harsh statement. However, the use of standard plumbing techniques in joint fabrication has accounted for more solar system failures than any other single cause.

Recommended Pipe Joints

Three types of joints are used in the fabrication of the solar collector loop: threaded, flared, and hard soldered. In every case, hard-soldered joints are preferred. Threaded joints must be made of similar materials, wherever possible. This insures that the same co-efficient of expansion exists between the piping and the fitting. Fittings should be examined carefully for out-of-round and poor thread cutting.

The joint compound is all important. Loctite® pipe dope with Teflon® (Part No. 592) is the recommended joint compound. No substitutions should be made unless specifically recommended by the component manufacturer. The joint must be completed before the compound sets up.

If soft annealed copper tubing is being used, flared fittings can be considered. Compression fittings should not be used. Flared joints must be very carefully made. The tube must be cut to the proper length, all burrs must be removed, the coupling slipped over the end of the tube, and the end then precisely flared in a flaring block. Following this, the flare should be carefully inspected for any cracks, burrs, or imperfections. It should then be carefully hand assembled to the fitting ready for final tightening. IMPORTANT: The tubing should not be allowed to turn on the flared fitting face.

Solder Joints

Making good solder joints is extremely important. The general technique is worth reviewing.

In the fabrication of soldered joints, a satisfactory joint begins with selection of the proper flux and solder. The flux should be a non-aggressive material free of chlorides and highly acidic or alkaline materials. A water-based flux is generally more satisfactory than an animal-fat-based flux. *Under no circumstances, should a 50/50 tin/lead solder be used. Such a material is not satisfactory for the collector loop temperature ranges.* The minimum satisfactory soldering material is 95/5 tin/antimony solder A brazing alloy melting at or above 1000°F would be excellent.

There are 12 simple steps to make a good solder joint. These are shown in Figure 21.3, and are as follows:

1. Measure the length of tube.
2. Cut the tube square.
3. Ream the cut end.
4. Clean the tube end.
5. Clean the fitting socket.
6. Apply flux to the tube end.
7. Apply flux to the fitting socket.
8. Assemble the joint.
9. Remove the excessive flux.
10. Apply heat.
11. Apply solder.
12. Allow the joint to cool.

These steps are basically simple, but they make the difference between good and poor joints. They normally take less time to do than to describe. For good results, none should be omitted.

CUTTING. The tube must be cut to the exact length with a squre cut. Tube cutters should generally be used for sizes up to one-inch. Alternate methods for larger pipes are abrasive saws or hack saws. With these methods, the joint must be filed square following cutting.

REAMING. Either the tube cutter or the abrasive saw will leave small burrs on the end of the tubing. These must be removed to prevent localized turbulence which will result in excessive corrosion. Often, particularly with soft-annealed tubing, the tube will be out of round and must be brought to true dimension and roundness with a sizing plug and ring.

CLEANING. The surfaces to be joined must be completely clean and free from oil, grease, and heavy oxide. The end of the tube must be cleaned for a distance slightly more than is required to enter the socket of the fitting. Fine crocus cloth (00), cleaning pads, or special wire brushes may be used. Rub hard enough to remove the surface

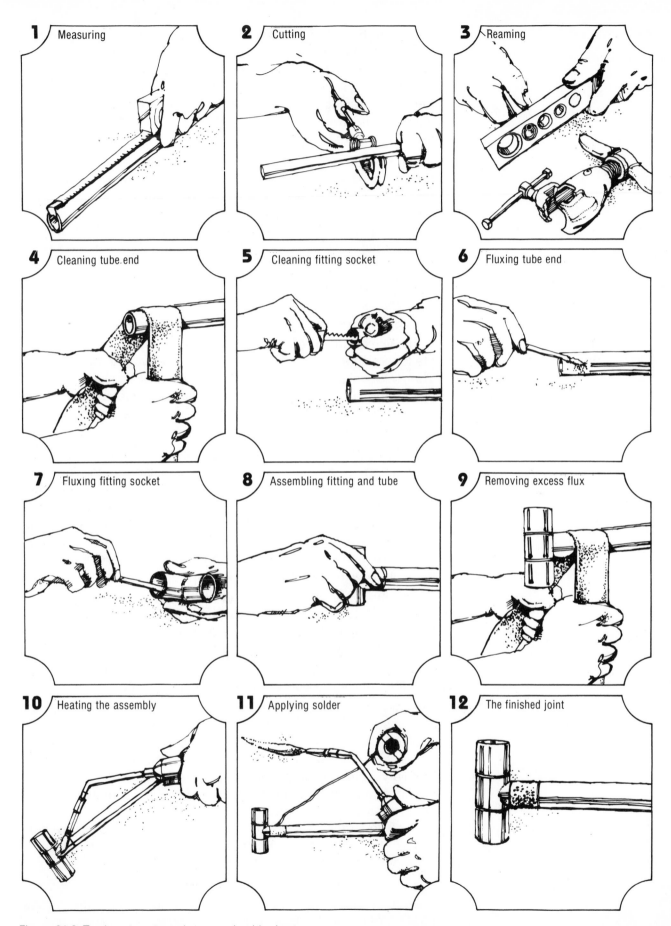

1 Measuring

2 Cutting

3 Reaming

4 Cleaning tube end

5 Cleaning fitting socket

6 Fluxing tube end

7 Fluxing fitting socket

8 Assembling fitting and tube

9 Removing excess flux

10 Heating the assembly

11 Applying solder

12 The finished joint

Figure 21.3 Twelve steps to make a good solder joint.

film or soil, but not hard enough to remove metal. Take extreme care so that particles of material do not fall into the tube or the fitting. The socket of the fitting should be similarly cleaned observing the same precautions. Tubes and fittings are made to close tolerances. Abrasive cleaning should not remove significant amounts of metal. If too much metal is removed during cleaning, the capillary space may become so large that a poor joint will result.

FLUXING. As soon as possible after cleaning, the surfaces to be joined should be covered with a thin film of flux. Fluxes must be mildly corrosive and generally contain zinc and ammonia chlorides. At all cost, avoid highly aggressive fluxes and tallow bases. Stay with only mildly aggressive fluxes in water-based compounds. Apply the flux with a small brush or a clean rag. Be careful not to insert the flux into the fitting to the point where it remains in the loop.

NOTE: For safety, avoid using fingers. Flux accidentally carried to the eyes can be very harmful.

ASSEMBLING. Assemble a joint by inserting the tube into the fitting. Make sure the tube is firmly against the end of the socket. Give the tube a small twist to help spread the flux over the two surfaces. Then remove any excess flux from the outside of the pipe. The joint is now ready for soldering. Soldering should take place within one or two hours of fluxing. The flux assembly should never be left overnight before soldering.

APPLY HEAT AND SOLDER. Heat is usually applied with a propane, butane, air-acetylene or an oxy-acetylene torch. The flame is played on the fitting and moved to heat as large an area as possible. The flame must not be pointed into the socket. This will overheat and burn the flux, destroying its effectiveness. Once the flux has been burned, solder will not enter the joint. The joint must be opened, recleaned, and refluxed. Overheating is apt to cause joints to crack, particularly with cast fittings, and must be avoided.

You can tell whether the joint is hot enough by bringing the solder in contact with the tube with the flame removed. If the solder does not melt, more heat should be applied. With a correctly heated joint, the action will draw solder over the entire joint. Pretinning is not necessary and is not recommended. It will interfere to some extent with the capillary action of drawing the solder into the joint.

Soldered joints depend on capillary action to draw free-flowing molten solder into the narrow clearance between the fitting and the tube. The flux acts as a cleaning and wetting agent. It permits uniform spreading of the molten solder over the surfaces to be soldered. Capillary action is most effective when the spaces between the surfaces to be jointed is between 0.002 and 0.005 inches. While a certain amount of looseness of fit can be tolerated, this will cause difficulty with large-size fittings. Particularly, when the joints are horizontal. Oversized fittings and horizontal joints usually result in too large of a gap at the top and a resultant leak.

Good support and alignment contribute to good joints. Wherever possible, joints should be made as subassemblies in the vertical position before installation. Wherever copper pipe is to be joined to copper valves and other materials, the manufacturer's instructions should be carefully followed. These usually include keeping the valve in the full-open position before applying heat and applying heat to the tube only.

COOLING. The joint must cool naturally for some time. This is particularly true if cast fittings are used. Too-rapid cooling cracks fittings and contributes to poor solder joints. Do not test solder joints by placing them in water or placing water in them. If the joints have been made as described there should be no leaks and final air testing of the collector loop will reveal this.

Brazed Joints

Brazed filler metals, sometimes referred to as "hard solders" or "silver solder", call for much different techniques than for standard solders. Contractors doing brazing should consult with brazing manufacturers.

Technical Assistance

The Copper Development Association Incorporated has published a book called *The Copper/Brass/Bronze Product Handbook* for copper tubing used in plumbing, heating, air conditioning and refrigeration. This book is generally available from your local plumbing or heating supply house. If not, you can obtain a copy of this book by writing the Copper Development Association at one of the following addresses:

Eastern Regional Office
Copper Development Association Incorporated
1011 High Ridge Road
Stamford, CT 06905

Western Regional Office
Copper Development Association Incorporated
22925 South Arlington Avenue
Torrance, CA 90510

Nothing is more frustrating than to build a solar collector loop and then find that less-than-perfect soldering or brazing is causing leaks. The system must then be drained and cleaned and the leaks repaired. A very costly experience for the contractor. Thus, the reader is advised to manufacture sample joints at the bench and saw them apart to insure that the particular procedure used is doing the job.

TIPS ABOUT THE COLLECTOR LOOP

In all cases, the recommendations of the manufacturer should be followed for installing the solar collectors. Proper installation, testing, and filling are required to insure efficient energy collection. System performance and maintenance may very well depend on the procedures used.

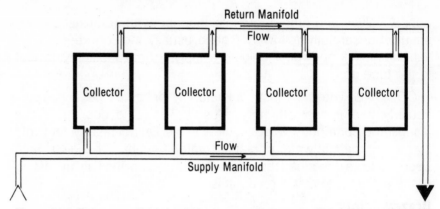

Figure 21.4 Return manifold should be connected from the last collector fed by the supply manifold.

Connecting Collectors To Manifolds

When solar collectors are installed in a large array, they are generally installed in parallel and fed from a manifold. This manifold can either be an integral part of the collector or a separate component. Both ingoing and outgoing manifolds are employed.

When the manifold is part of the collector, the manufacturer has generally computed and allowed for thermal expansion and contraction between manifold and collector. With external manifolds, this often becomes the responsibility of the installing contractor. Manufacturer instructions may or may not be included.

External manifolds take many forms. They may or may not be prefabricated. With external manifolds, the installer should use flexible piping between the collector and the manifold to allow for expansion and contraction. For good flow distribution, the return manifold should be connected to the return loop from the last collector fed. This is shown in Figure 21.4.

Flexible connectors can take many forms. These range from high-temperature rubber tubing to bellows-type, copper-flex tubing. If there is any question, the panel manufacturer and the heat-transfer-fluid manufacturer should be contacted for specific recommendations. If hard-soldered connectors are used, dissimilar metals such as aluminum and copper should not be joined. Galvanic corrosion will quickly destroy the joint.

Testing The Completed Collector Loop

The collector loops discussed in The Solar Decision Book are not engineered for water. Nor are certain other designs for collector loops. In many cases, the metals employed can be severely corroded by contact with water. As such, the collector loop should never be water tested. Exceptions, of course, would be water-based collector systems and those systems for which the manufacturer specifically recommends water testing. All other types of collector loops should be tested with air before filling.

The general procedure for testing is to charge the loop with air at a pressure 15-percent below the value of the system's pressure-relief valve. Generally, 25-pounds-per-square-inch is adequate. The loop should be pressurized for 24 hours. No loss of air pressure over that period of time can be tolerated. If any loss occurs, a leak is indicated. The leak must be located and repaired before filling the system.

Freon- or nitrogen-testing procedures are also common. These procedures allow the use of a sniffer to determine leak locations. This is particularly useful in large, complex systems where many joints must be inspected. You should not, however, pressure-test a system which is not designed to be pressurized. Nor should you over-pressurize a system beyond its design capabilities.

Filling The Collector Loop

The recommended systems in The Solar Decision Book are designed for filling with heat-transfer fluid from the service room. Filling from the top of the collector array is unnecessary. Figure 21.5 shows a typical filling hookup. Filling is accomplished as follows:

- With the collector pump off (it is not designed for dry operation), start the auxiliary pump. As soon as the loop is filled, the return line will stop bubbling.

- When the loop is filled, turn off the drain valve and continue to pump until the loop pressure builds to approximately 80-percent of the rating of the pressure-relief valve. This will usually be about 22 to 24 psi. Higher pressures are not recommended.

- Close the fill valve and stop the auxiliary pump.

- Turn on the system circulating pump.

During the first few days of operation any air left in the system will be bled from the automatic air eliminator. At the end of that period, the system pressure should be reduced to about 15 psi. This is accomplished by cracking the drain valve to bleed excess pressure from the system. If an air lock is encountered during or after filling, the manual-bleed valve on the collectors can be used to purge the system. Observation of the flow meter, if one is included in the system, will reveal the presence of air in the fluid.

THE FINISHING TOUCH...

When the contractor leaves the job, the structure owner must be left with a system in which the components are clearly labelled. The operating procedures and maintenance recommendations must be fully identified. The safety and/or health hazards must be defined and, where necessary, prominently displayed. The components must be accessible and serviceable by qualified HVAC service personnel.

Labelling The System

Figure 21.6 shows an example of how a pipe in the solar collector loop might be labelled. Other components in the system could be

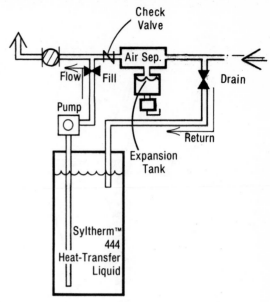

Figure 21.5 A typical hookup for filling the collector loop with heat-transfer fluid.

Figure 21.6 An example of how a pipe in the solar collector loop might be labelled.

Figure 21.7 Examples of possible owner's manuals.

labelled in a similar manner. Standard labels or labelling techniques have not been developed as yet. However, as a guide, the following information could be included:

- The component name and part number.
- The function of the component in the system.
- The operating pressures and temperatures.
- The direction of flow.
- The contents.
- Safety or health hazards.
- Trouble symptoms.
- Maintenance schedules.
- Service notes.

Writing An Owner's Manual

The owner's manual can take several forms. It can be as simple as a dozen or so typewritten sheets or as comprehensive as a notebook with detailed literature on each component in the system. With more and more standardization in the types of solar systems being installed, the owner's manual may easily become a personalized booklet issued by the contracting firm to support its system. Figure 21.7 shows some examples of possible owner's manuals.

An owner's manual is not only important to the system owner. The contractor benefits because such a manual will most likely discourage unnecessary system tampering and, possibly, reduce the number of callbacks for unnecessary inspection or service. A knowledgeable owner will often detect minor problems before they become serious.

The information that goes into an owner's manual is up to the contractor. However, such a manual may soon become a standard requirement in the solar industry. As a guide, the following information could be included:

- Installation instructions
- Start-up instructions
- Operating instructions
- Maintenance instructions
- Safety precautions
- Warrantee information
- Component manufacturers' names and addresses
- Sources for repair parts
- System schematics, complete with operational descriptions

Defining Safety And Health Hazards

The installed solar energy system should pose no undue hazards to the building's occupants or to service personnel. As a general rule, components must be installed in a manner which precludes falling, tripping, or bumping by anyone working or living with the system. In addition, adequate protection against fire, burns, leakage, corrosion should be provided.

Most important, any and all potential safety or health hazards should be clearly defined. Each hazard should be pointed out in the owner's manual. Where possible, certain hazards should be noted on the component labels or as separate caution labels in key areas of the system.

Examples of possible hazards which should be considered include:

- Fire, from combustible liquids or solids.
- Burns, from heated pipes and tanks.
- Ruptures in pipes, from excessive temperature or pressure.
- Growths, from mold, mildew, fungi or bacteria.
- Contamination, from the mixing of potable water with heat-transfer liquid.
- Infestation, from vermin or rodents.
- Building materials decay, from moisture leakage or corrosive action.

Servicing The System

The solar system and its components must be serviceable by trained service personnel. Such service should be possible with the installer/owner manual and a minimum amount of special tools. All maintenance and repairs should be possible without the need to dismantle a major part of the system. As such, all components requiring service or maintenance should be readily accessible.

MAKING A DECISION

In this section of The Solar Decision Book, you have learned about some of the more important installation requirements for solar systems. You have read about the general construction procedures utilized, the loading requirements for system components, the need to consider concrete and masonry in the installation, some tips for thermal and moisture protection of system components. You have also learned about the importance of good solder joints and the procedures for connecting, testing, and filling the collector loop.

A highly skilled mechanical contractor, backed by good structural engineering or architectural sources, is required for a major installation. When the skilled installer leaves, a complete manual should be in the hands of the building owner. The manual should detail the system operation and maintenance requirements. And the system should be serviceable by qualified HVAC personnel.

Making the decision to become a skilled installer of solar systems involves obtaining and understanding the basic structural requirements of the system. It also involves obtaining and/or writing the correct operating and maintenance procedures for the owner. Coupled with good mechanical skills, such knowledge will pay off with properly installed systems. The type that will require infrequent servicing. And the type that will stand up over the years as good investments for their owners.

APPENDICES

Page

Calculating Structure Heat Losses

The principles of building heat loss were discussed in Decision 2 of The Solar Decision Book. You learned that heat is lost from or enters into a building by two principal methods: transmission and infiltration.

Transmission is defined as the movement of energy through a solid such as a floor, wall or ceiling. The rate of that movement depends on the composition of the solid and the temperature differential between the two sides of the solid.

Infiltration is defined as the movement of air through openings in the structure. The rate of air flow depends on the size of the openings and the velocity of the air movement.

A building's hourly energy losses by transmission and infiltration can be determined. If a one-degree F temperature differential exists between the inside and the outside of the building, the heat loss can be described in Btu/hr/°F.

Once the heat loss in Btu/hr/°F is known, you can calculate the building's heat losses based on the average temperatures for the area in which the building is located. To make this calculation, a generally available figure known as a degree day is used. A degree day is the temperature difference between 65°F and the average temperature of the day. For example: On a given day the high temperature is 40°F and the low temperature is 20°F. The average temperature is then 30°F. The day contains 35 degree days.

The building's heat loss for the day is calculated as follows: The Btu/hr/°F is multiplied by 24 hours and the number of degree days. Suppose the Btu/hr/°F loss is 300 Btu. The building's daily heat loss would then be 252,000 Btu. For most locations, the number of degree days per month or year is usually available from the weather bureau. Publications such as the ASHRAE Handbook of Fundamentals list the degree days for major cities. By using the degree day figures, you can calculate your building's heating load, on a monthly or yearly basis.

$$\begin{array}{r} 40° \\ + 20° \\ \hline 60° \\ \div 2 \\ \hline 30° \text{ average} \end{array}$$

$$\begin{array}{r} 65° \\ -30° \\ \hline 35° \text{ days} \end{array}$$

$$\begin{array}{r} 300 \text{ Btu/hr/°F} \\ \times 35° \text{ days} \\ \times 24 \text{ hrs/day} \\ \hline 252,000 \text{ Btu} \end{array}$$

Determining Transmission Losses

Transmission losses can be determined when you know the rate at which heat moves through the walls, ceilings, and floors. This rate is very easy to calculate by using R and U values. Any type of insulation has an R-rating or resistance to transmission. For instance, three inches of certain insulation may be rated as R=10. This indicates its resistance to heat flow. R-ratings are additive. Six inches of the same insulation would have a rating of R=20.

R-ratings for common building constructions are well known and are often expressed as the U-factor. The U-factor is the reciprocal of R, or 1 divided by R. So, if R=10, then U would equal 0.1. If R=20, U=0.05.

"R" and "U" are expressed in units of Btu/sq ft/hr/°F. A surface with U=0.05 is losing heat at the rate of 0.05 Btu/sq ft/hr/°F. Thus, if the surface area is 250 square feet and the temperature differential is 10°F on a U=0.05 wall, the heat loss would be 125 Btu per hour. The transmission heat loss for that wall on a day having 35 degree-days would be 10,500 Btu.

$$U = \frac{1}{R}$$

$$\frac{1}{10} = 0.1$$

$$\frac{1}{20} = 0.05$$

$$\begin{array}{r} 250 \text{ sq ft} \\ \times 10°F \\ \times 0.05 \text{ Btu/sq ft/hr/°F} \\ \hline 125 \text{ Btu/hr} \end{array}$$

$$\begin{array}{r} 0.05 \text{ Btu/sq ft/hr/°F} \\ \times 250 \text{ sq ft} \\ \times 24 \text{ hr/day} \\ \times 35° \text{ days} \\ \hline 10,500 \text{ Btu} \end{array}$$

Determining Infiltration Losses

Infiltration in today's structures is most easily calculated in terms of *air changes per hour.* "Air changes per hour" describes the number of times each hour that the air in the structure is exchanged with outside air. Most structures are now designed to have from 0.7 to 1 air change per hour. In older structures, these air changes may be greater.

For solar heat loss calculations, one air change per hour is generally used. Energy of 0.018 Btu is needed to heat one cubic foot of air one degree F. Suppose that the structure contains 10,000 cubic feet of air, has one air change per hour, and a 10°F temperature differential exists between the inside and outside air. The hourly infiltration loss would be 1800 Btu per hour. In the same example, the infiltration loss for a day having 35 degree-days would be 151,200 Btu.

The Total Structure Heat Loss

Adding all transmission and infiltration losses gives the total structure heat loss. This can be expressed in Btu/hr/°F or in total daily heat loss per degree day, Btu/day/°F. In The Solar Decision Book, the heat loss is expressed as Btu/hr/°F.

WALLS. Transmission losses through solid walls, those without windows and doors, are easily calculated using the total wall area. However, most walls contain windows and doors. In heat loss calculations, the losses through windows and doors must be calculated separate from those through solid walls. Different types of walls, windows, and doors have different U-factors.

CEILINGS. Transmission losses through ceilings are calculated much the same as those through walls. Openings in the ceiling are treated like doors and windows. The area is subtracted from the gross ceiling area. For a ceiling between two heated floors of a structure, no heat losses are calculated.

CONCRETE SLABS ON GRADE. Transmission losses are not calculated for the area of concrete slabs. Instead, transmission losses through the perimeter of the exposed edge are calculated.

BASEMENT WALLS BELOW GRADE. Basement walls below grade are given a U-factor of U=0.06. Above the frost line, the outside temperature is used to calculate the temperature differential. Below the frost line, the temperature used is 45°F, or a differential of 20°F.

BASEMENT FLOORS. Transmission losses through basement floors are calculated to be one Btu/hr/square foot, regardless of the outside temperature.

U-FACTORS. The U-factors for various types of wall construction, ceilings, windows, doors, and concrete slabs are shown in the table, *Heat Transmission: Materials of Construction.*

$$\begin{array}{r} 0.018 \text{ Btu/cu ft/}°F \\ \times\ 10,000 \text{ cu ft/hr} \\ \times\ 10\ °F \\ \hline 1800 \text{ Btu/hr} \end{array}$$

$$\begin{array}{r} 0.018 \text{ Btu/cu ft/}°F \\ \times\ 10,000 \text{ cu ft/hr} \\ \times\ 24 \text{ hr/day} \\ \times\ 35° \text{ days} \\ \hline 151,200 \text{ Btu} \end{array}$$

HEAT TRANSMISSION: MATERIALS OF CONSTRUCTION

EXTERIOR WALLS	AVERAGE U-FACTORS, Insulated as shown			
	None	1"	2"	4"
Standard 2x4 construction sheathed in wood or insulating board, covered with wood siding, shingles, brick and sheetrocked or plastered	.22	.12	.09	.07
12" concrete blocks	.49	.14	—	—
8" poured concrete walls	.70	.16	—	—

INTERIOR CEILINGS	AVERAGE U-FACTORS, Insulated between rafters as shown					
	None	1"	2"	3"	4"	6"
Ceiling applied directly to wood rafters with wood sheathing covered by asphalt or cedar shingles	.64	.19	.12	.09	.077	.05

	AVERAGE U-FACTORS, Insulated between joists as shown					
	None	1"	2"	3"	4"	6"
Horizontal ceiling under a pitched roof with no flooring on the ceiling. Rafters covered by wood sheathing and asphalt or cedar shingles	.32	.15	.10	.09	.077	.05

There is no heat loss in ceilings between heated floors. For ceilings over insulated crawl spaces, use ½ of the U value shown. For ceilings over vented or unheated crawl spaces, use the indicated U value. For ceilings over unheated basements, use 1/3 of the indicated U value.

CONCRETE SLAB ON-GRADE FLOORS	AVERAGE U-FACTORS, per lineal foot		
	None	1" x 12"	1" x 24"
	0.81	0.46	0.21

WINDOWS	AVERAGE U-FACTORS
Single Glazing	1.31
With Storm Window	0.61
Thermopane	0.45

DOORS	
3/4" Wood	0.69
1 5/8" Wood	0.46
1 5/8" Wood with Storm Door	0.32

HEAT LOSS CALCULATIONS

This appendix in The Solar Decision Book shows you how to calculate the heat losses from your structure. The method used is easy to understand. First, you will calculate the heat losses through walls, windows, and doors. Then, you will calculate the heat losses through ceilings and floors. You will add the air change loss (infiltration), and you will total these loss figures in terms of Btu per hour per °F. This method allows for recalculating the heat losses, no matter where the structure is located.

As a last step then, you can calculate the total monthly or yearly heat losses. You will use degree-day data for the particular area in which the structure is located. These loss figures would identify your monthly or annual heating requirements.

WALLS, WINDOWS, DOORS. Use the sample form, *Wall Heat Loss Calculations.* This form will help you calculate the transmission losses through *one* wall. Each wall in the structure should be studied separately. The loss calculations will help identify those walls needing special treatments for energy conservation. The form allows notation of the wall direction. Usually, you will make calculations for each of four exterior walls. More calculations may be required depending on the irregularity of the structure. Perform the calculations as follows:

1. Note the direction (N-E-S-W) of the wall.

2. Calculate the *net* wall area. This is the total wall area minus any windows or doors.

   NOTE: The form allows for entries on three types of above-grade sidewalls. A typical sidewall might include a portion of the concrete foundation, a block or brick section, and a standard-construction section.

3. Determine the number and type of windows in the wall, and calculate the total area for each type.

   EXAMPLE: There are four windows, each 3' wide by 4' high. The area of one window would be 12 square feet (12=3x4). The total area for the four windows would be 48 square feet (48=4 windows x 12 ft²).

4. Determine the number and type of doors in the wall, and calculate the total area for each type.

5. Calculate the area for any below-grade wall sections.

6. Using the *Heat Transmission* table, enter the appropriate U-factors for the various types of construction.

7. Calculate the heat losses through the above-grade wall sections, the windows, the doors, and the below-grade wall sections.

   NOTE: Heat loss equals Area times U-factor.

8. Add up the total heat losses through the particular wall, then perform the same calculations for other walls in the structure.

WALL HEAT LOSS CALCULATIONS

WALL IDENTIFICATION:			
Portion	Area, Sq. Ft.	U-Factor	Heat Loss, Btu/hr/°F
Above-Grade Sidewall A. Type_____ B. Type_____ C. Type_____			
Windows No. A. Single Glazed _____ B. Thermopane _____ C. Storm Window _____			
Doors A. 3/4" Wood _____ B. 1 5/8" Wood _____ C. 1 5/8" with Storm _____ D. Other _____			
Below-Grade Sidewall A. Type_____ B. Type_____			
		TOTAL:	_____

CEILINGS AND FLOORS. Use the sample form, *Ceiling & Floor Heat Loss Calculations.* This form will help you calculate heat losses through various types of ceilings and floors in your structure. You will use the same procedures as those for calculating wall heat losses. Make sure you enter the correct U-factors. Depending on the location of the ceiling or floor, the U-factor can change.

For concrete slab floors, the floor area is not used. Instead, the length of the slab perimeter must be calculated and then multiplied by the U-factor.

CEILING AND FLOOR HEAT LOSS CALCULATIONS

Portion	Area, Sq. Ft.	U-Factor	Heat Loss, Btu/hr/°F
Attic Ceiling			
First-Floor Ceiling			
First Floor			
Basement Floor			
On-Grade Slab (Edge)	(use lineal ft.)		

INFILTRATION. Infiltration losses are calculated by multiplying the volume of air in the structure by 0.018 Btu/cu ft/°F. This is then modified by the estimated number of air changes per hour. For average new construction, this would be one air change per hour. For a building which is constructed to limit air change, use 0.7 air change per hour. For an older building with poor-fitting windows and weather-stripping, use 2.0 air changes per hour. For easy reference...

Construction	Air Change/hr
Average	1.0
Tight	0.7
Old	2.0

TOTAL HEAT LOSS. Enter your calculated heat loss figures in the table, *Total Heat Losses — All Sources.* Some variation is possible because average U-factors are used in the calculations. However, the variations should cancel each other, and the total should provide you with an accurate heat-loss number for the structure.

TOTAL HEAT LOSS

HEAT LOSS SOURCE	HEAT LOSS, Btu/hr/°F
Transmission Losses	
North Wall	
South Wall	
East Wall	
West Wall	
Ceilings and Floors	
Infiltration Losses	
TOTAL:	

Heating Requirements

Your heating requirements can be calculated by using the table, *Heating Requirements*. By using the monthly degree-days, the heat required per month can be obtained. By using the annual degree-days, the heat required per year can be obtained.

To calculate the maximum heat needed to maintain the building temperature, use the following:

(65°F - design temp.) x (Btu/hr/°F) = Max heat per hour.

The design temperature is defined as the lowest outside temperature at which you may have to heat the building to 65°F. An additional 5°F, which is needed to bring the structure to a comfortable 70°F, is supplied by the heat generated in the building.

HEATING REQUIREMENTS

MONTH	DEGREE DAYS	X	24 HOURS	X	BTU/hr/°F	=	BTU/MONTH
January	_____		24		_____		_____
February	_____		24		_____		_____
March	_____		24		_____		_____
April	_____		24		_____		_____
May	_____		24		_____		_____
June	_____		24		_____		_____
July	_____		24		_____		_____
August	_____		24		_____		_____
September	_____		24		_____		_____
October	_____		24		_____		_____
November	_____		24		_____		_____
December	_____		24		_____		_____
ANNUAL	_____		24		_____		_____ Btu/Year

Evaluating An Energy Conservation Investment

1. Type of investment: _____

   _____

2. Cost of investment .... $ _____

3. Btu heat loss without investment .... _____ Btu/hr/°F

4. Btu heat loss with investment (recalculate structural change) .... _____ Btu/hr/°F

5. Energy (Btu) saved by investing (#3-#4) .... _____ Btu/hr/°F

6. Degree days in an average heating season .... _____ °Days

   NOTE: This value can be obtained by calling your local utility,
         oil supplier, or weather bureau.

7. Cost of fuel per million Btu .... $ _____

   NOTE: This value is found in Figure 1.13 in Decision 1.

8. First-year dollar savings by reducing heat losses .... $ _____

   NOTE: (Btu Saved) x 24 hrs x Degree days x ($/MM Btu)

9. Savings over 10 years, assuming 12-percent fuel-cost inflation ....

Year	1st Year Savings	X	Inflation Factor	=	Annual Savings In Year
1	_____	x	1	=	$ _____
2	_____	x	1.12	=	_____
3	_____	x	1.25	=	_____
4	_____	x	1.40	=	_____
5	_____	x	1.57	=	_____
6	_____	x	1.76	=	_____
7	_____	x	1.97	=	_____
8	_____	x	2.21	=	_____
9	_____	x	2.48	=	_____
10	_____	x	2.77	=	_____
					$ _____

10. Anticipated life of investment .... _____ Years

11. Savings over investment life .... $ _____

12. Return on investment .... _____ Percent

   NOTE: $\dfrac{\text{Total Savings x 100}}{\text{Cost}} = \%$ R.O.I.

Solar System Sizing Charts

A solar system sizing chart plots the percent of the total heat load carried by the solar system versus square feet of solar collector. Such a graph is shown below. This graph was drawn using data from the solar system sizing tables which are in this appendix.

The principle behind the solar system sizing charts is very simple. The design of the system, the size of the heat load, and the geographical location are assumed as constants. When this is done, the square feet of collector to produce a given amount of heat (%F) can be calculated.

These calculations can be made for a number of points and the points can be connected into a smooth curve. This makes a graph from which the collector area required for any desired percent of solar heat may quickly be found.

Refer to the typical solar system sizing chart for Indianapolis, Indiana. Assume that the heat load on the system is 300 Btu/hr/°F. Also, suppose that you want to build a system providing 65-percent solar heat. Read from 65-percent F to the 300 Btu/hr/°F load line (dotted line A). Then read down to the horizontal axis (dotted line B). This shows that 290 square feet of collector are required to provide 65-percent of the total heating load. If the heat load was 900 Btu/hr/°F, then 1000 square feet would be required.

Now refer to the sizing chart for Richmond, Virginia. In this location, a solar system can provide 65-percent of a 300 Btu/hr/°F load using slightly less than 200 square feet of collector. For a load of 900 Btu/hr/°F, 530 square feet of collector are needed to provide 65-percent of the load.

The differences are caused by weather variations. The temperatures are different and the days of sunshine are different. For this reason, a different sizing chart is needed for each geographical location.

A different chart is also needed for each different system design. The efficiencies of the system and its performance are a function of: the collectors, the heat exchangers, and the heat-delivery terminal temperature. Also, the collector siting must be considered. If the collector is changed in angle and/or pointed in any direction other than due solar south, the collection will change.

These variations may seem to present a bewildering array of alternatives that would preclude any meaningful design using a single graph. However, such is not the case.

Throughout The Solar Decision Book, you have been making decisions on the choice of equipment, siting, sizing, and design. If the design principles and selection criteria which were outlined in Decisions 9 through 19 are followed, the sizing charts in this appendix will be accurate.

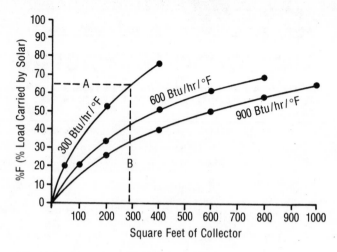

A typical solar system sizing chart for Indianapolis, Indiana.

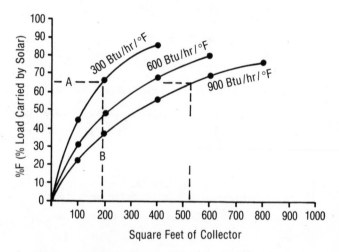

A typical solar system sizing chart for Richmond, Virginia.

Choosing The Solar Collector

Decision 10 discussed solar collectors. In that decision you learned that different collectors had different collection efficiencies. Your choice of a collector will have a major impact on the solar system sizing chart. A change from double-glazed collectors to single-glazed collectors requires a different sizing chart. This is also the case if you change from a nonselective absorber coating to a selective absorber coating.

In the charts shown in this appendix, the author has chosen to use a double-glazed, selective-surface collector which has a high efficiency enclosure with low losses. This is the most efficient collector currently available. As such, the charts in this appendix reflect the highest collection efficiency available. The average performance, as measured by ASHRAE 93-77, of collectors from five major manufacturers was used to build the sizing charts.

Before you can use these charts, make sure that the collectors you select have equivalent performance to those used here. Otherwise, the charts will not be accurate.

Solar System Sizing Chart Details

Solar system sizing data for 96 different geographical locations around North America are detailed on the following pages. This data is given in tabular form for water-heating systems and for water plus space-heating systems.

The data for water heating has the heat loads expressed in gallons of hot water required per day. The water plus space-heating data assumes 80 gallons of hot water per day plus an hourly space heating load.

The tables were compiled by computer simulation. The University of Wisconsin Solar Laboratories' F-Chart program was used.

A double-glazed, selective surface flat plate collector was used which had a $F_R \tau\alpha$ = 0.75 and a $F_R U_L$ = 0.67 Counterflow heat exchangers, with an effectiveness of 90-percent, were used in both the collector loop and the heat-delivery loop. The storage tank was designed to hold 1.75 gallons of water per square foot of collector.

The systems used were faced due south. In the space-heating data, the collectors were set at an angle of latitude plus 15°. For the water-heating systems, the collectors were at an angle equal to the latitude.

Hot water was assumed to be set at 140°F with the entrance water at 55°F.

In the space-heating system charts, computer runs were made for 300, 600, and 900 Btu/hr/°F loads plus 80 gallons of hot water. In the water-heating systems, loads of 60-, 80-, and 120-gallons/day were tabulated.

The F-Chart computer program will not show the added fraction of heat provided by a solar-assisted heat pump. Therefore, the space-heating system discussed in Decision 18 will outperform that used for the sizing charts. This provides a very comfortable margin of performance over chart design. The amount of added performance cannot be generalized because it contains too many variables.

Four- to five-percent variation in any one of the above variables will not appreciably affect performance. Care must be taken however, not to lower all the variables. A significant drop in performance would then be seen.

Use of F-Chart Generated Data

The computer-generated performance data is a powerful tool which will accurately predict the general performance range of a solar system in an average year. The data should be used to size systems. *The data should not be used to guarantee performance.* Weather, sunshine, and equipment operation are variables. As such, so is the system's performance.

Drawing An F-Chart From The Data Tables

To develop a solar system sizing graph for any given geographical area, proceed as follows:

1. Use graph paper or draw a grid such as that shown in the sizing chart for Birmingham, Alabama.
2. Draw a vertical and horizontal axis equal in length (10 divisions by 10 divisions).

3. Label the vertical axis as *"Percent Heat Load Carried by Solar"*
4. Label the horizontal axis as *"Square Feet of Solar Collector"*
5. Turn to the desired geographical sizing table.
6. Pick one heat load and plot the points shown.

Example: For Birmingham, Alabama, 900 Btu/hr/°F data would be plotted at 29/100, 45/200, 64/400, & 77/600. A smooth line would then be drawn from 0/0 through these points. The size of the "square feet of collector" scale can be expanded or contracted, as necessary, to accommodate the data in the tables. Space-heating data and water-heating data should not be combined on the same graph. A different-sized horizontal axis is generally required for the two different sets of data.

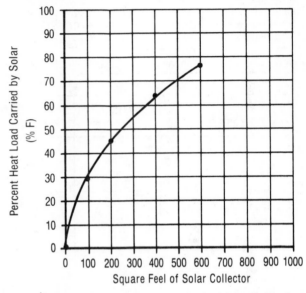

A sample sizing chart that shows a 900 Btu/hr/°F load in Birmingham, Alabama.

Sizing System Charts By Zones

The solar system sizing charts in this appendix have been split into five separate zones:

Zone 1	Zone 2	Zone 4
Connecticut	Alabama	Arkansas
Delaware	Florida	Oklahoma
District of Columbia	Georgia	Texas
Indiana	Louisiana	**Zone 5**
Kentucky	Mississippi	Alberta
Maine	North Carolina	Arizona
Maryland	South Carolina	British Columbia
Massachusetts	Tennessee	California
Michigan	**Zone 3**	Colorado
New Brunswick	Illinois	Idaho
New Hampshire	Iowa	Montana
New Jersey	Kansas	Nevada
New York	Manitoba	New Mexico
Ohio	Minnesota	Oregon
Ontario	Missouri	Saskatchewan
Pennsylvania	Nebraska	Utah
Quebec	North Dakota	Washington
Rhode Island	South Dakota	Wyoming
Vermont	Wisconsin	
Virginia		
West Virginia		

SYSTEM SIZING CHARTS

ZONE 1: Northeast United States and Canada

%F VERSUS SQUARE FEET OF COLLECTOR

States	Cities	Latitude	Degree Days	States	Cities	Latitude	Degree Days
Connecticut	Hartford	41.56	6350	New York	Binghamton	42.13	7285
Delaware	—	—	—	New York	New York	40.46	4811
Distr. of Columbia	Washington	38.51	4224	New York	Rochester	43.07	6719
Indiana	Indianapolis	39.44	5577	Ohio	Cleveland	41.24	6154
Indiana	Fort Wayne	41.00	6209	Ohio	Columbus	40.00	5660
Kentucky	Lexington	38.02	4729	Ontario	Toronto	43.40	6827
Maine	Caribou	46.52	9767	Pennsylvania	Philadelphia	39.53	4865
Maine	Portland	43.39	7311	Pennsylvania	Pittsburgh	40.30	5278
Maryland	—	—	—	Pennsylvania	State College	40.48	6132
Massachusetts	Boston	42.22	5634	Quebec	Montreal	45.30	8203
Michigan	Detroit	42.14	6419	Rhode Island	—	—	—
Michigan	Lansing	42.47	6904	Vermont	—	—	—
Michigan	Sault Ste. Marie	46.28	9048	Virginia	Richmond	37.50	3939
New Brunswick	Moncton	46.07	8727	West Virginia	Parkersburg	39.16	4817
New Hampshire	—	—	—				
New Jersey	Atlantic City	39.27	4693				
New York	Albany	42.40	6888				

STATE/CITY	TYPE OF SYSTEM	BTU/HR/°F OR GAL./DAY	%F AT COLLECTOR SQ. FT. SHOWN								
			10	25	50	100	200	400	600	800	1000
Connecticut Hartford (6350 Degree Days)	Heating & Hot Water	300 BTU			18	33	53	76			
		600 BTU				21	35	55	69	79	
		900 BTU					26	43	55	66	73
	Hot Water	60 GAL			65	90					
		80 GAL			53	83	96				
		120 GAL			38	65	90	99			
Dist. of Columbia Washington (4224 Degree Days)	Heating & Hot Water	300 BTU			22	39	59	80			
		600 BTU				26	41	61	73		
		900 BTU					31	49	61		
	Hot Water	60 GAL			64	89	98				
		80 GAL			52	81	95				
		120 GAL			38	64	89	78			
Indiana Indianapolis (5577 Degree Days)	Heating & Hot Water	300 BTU			19	33	50	69	80		
		600 BTU				21	33	51	62	70	
		900 BTU					25	40	50	58	65
	Hot Water	60 GAL			63	86	96				
		80 GAL			51	79	92				
		120 GAL			37	63	86	96			
Fort Wayne (6209 Degree Days)	Heating & Hot Water	300 BTU				33	51	71			
		600 BTU					34	51	63	72	
		900 BTU					25	40	51	60	67
	Hot Water	60 GAL			66	88	97				
		80 GAL			54	82	93				
		120 GAL			39	66	88	97			
Kentucky Lexington (4729 Degree Days)	Heating & Hot Water	300 BTU			26	44	63	83			
		600 BTU				29	44	64	76		
		900 BTU					34	52	64	73	
	Hot Water	60 GAL			76	93					
		80 GAL			63	89	97				
		120 GAL			46	76	93				

STATE/CITY	TYPE OF SYSTEM	BTU/HR/°F OR GAL./DAY	%F AT COLLECTOR SQ. FT. SHOWN						
			50	100	200	400	600	800	1000
Maine Caribou (9767 Degree Days)	Heating & Hot Water	300 BTU 600 BTU 900 BTU		24	42 26	64 44 33	78 57 45	66 54	74 61
	Hot Water	60 GAL 80 GAL 120 GAL	60 49 36	85 77 60	97 92 85	97			
Portland (7311 Degree Days)	Heating & Hot Water	300 BTU 600 BTU 900 BTU	18	32 20	52 34 26	76 55 43	69 55	65	73
	Hot Water	60 GAL 80 GAL 120 GAL	67 55 40	91 84 67	95 91	99			
Massachusetts Boston (5634 Degree Days)	Heating & Hot Water	300 BTU 600 BTU 900 BTU	17	30 19	48 32 24	69 50 39	81 62 50	71 59	66
	Hot Water	60 GAL 80 GAL 120 GAL	58 47 33	84 74 58	96 91 84	96			
Michigan Detroit (6419 Degree Days)	Heating & Hot Water	300 BTU 600 BTU 900 BTU	17	29	46 30	65 47 36	76 58 47	66 55	72 61
	Hot Water	60 GAL 80 GAL 120 GAL	61 50 36	84 77 61	95 90 84	95			
Lansing (6904 Degree Days)	Heating & Hot Water	300 BTU 600 BTU 900 BTU	16	28 17	45 29	64 46 35	76 57 46	66 54	72 61
	Hot Water	60 GAL 80 GAL 120 GAL	60 49 36	83 76 60	95 90 83	95			
Sault Ste. Marie (9048 Degree Days)	Heating & Hot Water	300 BTU 600 BTU 900 BTU		26	44 28 21	65 46 35	77 58 46	67 55	74 62
	Hot Water	60 GAL 80 GAL 120 GAL	61 50 37	84 77 61	95 91 84	95			
New Brunswick (Canada) Moncton (8727 Degree Days)	Heating & Hot Water	300 BTU 600 BTU 900 BTU		21	37 23	57 39 30	68 50 39	76 58 47	65 53
	Hot Water	60 GAL 80 GAL 120 GAL	52 42 30	77 67 52	93 86 77	93			

ZONE 1: Northeast United States and Canada (Continued)

STATE/CITY	TYPE OF SYSTEM	BTU/HR/°F OR GAL./DAY	%F AT COLLECTOR SQ. FT. SHOWN								
			10	25	50	100	200	400	600	800	1000
New Jersey Atlantic City (4693 Degree Days)	Heating & Hot Water	300 BTU			24	42	63	85			
		600 BTU				27	44	65	79		
		900 BTU					33	53	66	76	
	Hot Water	60 GAL			70	93					
		80 GAL			57	87	97				
		120 GAL			42	70	93				
New York Albany (6888 Degree Days)	Heating & Hot Water	300 BTU				30	48	69	80		
		600 BTU					31	49	62	71	
		900 BTU					23	38	50	59	66
	Hot Water	60 GAL			62	86	96				
		80 GAL			51	78	93				
		120 GAL			37	62	86	96			
Binghamton (7285 Degree Days)	Heating & Hot Water	300 BTU				27	44	64	75		
		600 BTU					29	45	56	65	
		900 BTU					21	35	45	53	60
	Hot Water	60 GAL			60	83	95				
		80 GAL			48	76	90				
		120 GAL			35	60	83	95			
New York (4811 Degree Days)	Heating & Hot Water	300 BTU				31	48	68	78		
		600 BTU					32	49	61	69	75
		900 BTU					24	38	49	57	64
	Hot Water	60 GAL			54	81	93				
		80 GAL			44	71	89				
		120 GAL			31	54	81	93			
Rochester (6719 Degree Days)	Heating & Hot Water	300 BTU				29	47	67	78		
		600 BTU					31	47	59	68	74
		900 BTU					23	37	48	56	63
	Hot Water	60 GAL			62	85	96				
		80 GAL			51	78	91				
		120 GAL			37	62	85	96			
Ohio Cleveland (6154 Degree Days)	Heating & Hot Water	300 BTU				29	45	63	74		
		600 BTU				18	30	46	56	64	70
		900 BTU					23	36	46	53	59
	Hot Water	60 GAL			59	81	93				
		80 GAL			48	75	88				
		120 GAL			35	59	81	93			
Columbus (5660 Degree Days)	Heating & Hot Water	300 BTU				32	49	68	79		
		600 BTU				20	33	50	61	69	75
		900 BTU					25	39	50	58	64
	Hot Water	60 GAL			62	85	95				
		80 GAL			50	78	91				
		120 GAL			37	62	85	95			

STATE/CITY	TYPE OF SYSTEM	BTU/HR/°F OR GAL./DAY	%F AT COLLECTOR SQ. FT. SHOWN								
			10	25	50	100	200	400	600	800	1000
Ontario (Canada) Toronto (6827 Degree Days)	Heating & Hot Water	300 BTU				26	42	60	72		
		600 BTU					27	42	54	62	68
		900 BTU					20	33	43	50	57
	Hot Water	60 GAL			55	79	92				
		80 GAL			44	70	87				
		120 GAL			32	55	79	92			
Pennsylvania Philadelphia (4865 Degree Days)	Heating & Hot Water	300 BTU				22	38	59	80		
		600 BTU					25	40	61	74	
		900 BTU					18	31	48	61	71
	Hot Water	60 GAL			67	91					
		80 GAL			55	85	96				
		120 GAL			40	67	91	99			
Pittsburgh (5278 Degree Days)	Heating & Hot Water	300 BTU				20	36	55	75		
		600 BTU					23	37	56	68	77
		900 BTU					28	44	56	65	72
	Hot Water	60 GAL			66	89	98				
		80 GAL			53	82	94				
		120 GAL			39	66	89	98			
State College (6132 Degree Days)	Heating & Hot Water	300 BTU					29	46	65	76	
		600 BTU				18	30	47	58	67	73
		900 BTU					23	37	47	55	61
	Hot Water	60 GAL			59	83	94				
		80 GAL			48	75	90	100			
		120 GAL			34	59	83	94			
Quebec (Canada) Montreal (8203 Degree Days)	Heating & Hot Water	300 BTU					22	37	55	66	73
		600 BTU					24	38	48	56	62
		900 BTU						29	38	45	51
	Hot Water	60 GAL			54	77	90				
		80 GAL			43	69	85	99			
		120 GAL			31	54	77	90	99		
Virginia Richmond (3939 Degree Days)	Heating & Hot Water	300 BTU				26	44	66	86		
		600 BTU					30	47	67	80	
		900 BTU					22	36	55	68	77
	Hot Water	60 GAL			70	93					
		80 GAL			57	87	97				
		120 GAL			41	70	93				
West Virginia Parkersburg (4817 Degree Days)	Heating & Hot Water	300 BTU				20	34	52	71		
		600 BTU					22	35	52	64	73
		900 BTU					27	41	52	60	67
	Hot Water	60 GAL			61	85	95				
		80 GAL			50	78	91				
		120 GAL			36	61	85	95			

ZONE 2: Southeast United States

%F VERSUS SQUARE FEET OF COLLECTOR							
States	**Cities**	**Latitude**	**Degree Days**	**States**	**Cities**	**Latitude**	**Degree Days**
Alabama	Birmingham	33.34	2844	Mississippi	Jackson	32.19	2300
Florida	Jacksonville	30.25	1327	North Carolina	Cape Hatteras	35.16	2731
Florida	Miami	25.47	214	North Carolina	Greensboro	36.05	3825
Florida	Pensacola	30.28	1578	South Carolina	Charleston	32.54	2033
Florida	Tallahassee	30.26	1563	South Carolina	Greenville	34.54	3163
Florida	Tampa	27.58	718	Tennessee	Chattanooga	35.02	3505
Georgia	Atlanta	33.39	3095	Tennessee	Memphis	35.03	3227
Louisiana	New Orleans	29.59	1385	Tennessee	Nashville	36.07	3696

STATE/CITY	TYPE OF SYSTEM	BTU/HR/°F or GAL./DAY	%F AT COLLECTOR SQ. FT. SHOWN								
			10	25	50	100	200	400	600	800	1000
Alabama Birmingham 2844 Degree Days	Heating & Hot Water	300 BTU		17	32	54	74				
		600 BTU			22	38	56	76			
		900 BTU				29	45	64	77		
	Hot Water	60 GAL	19	44	73	94					
		80 GAL		34	60	89	98				
		120 GAL		24	44	73	94				
Florida Jacksonville 1327 Degree Days	Heating & Hot Water	300 BTU		24	44	72					
		600 BTU			34	58	80				
		900 BTU			28	48	69	90			
	Hot Water	60 GAL	20	45	76	98					
		80 GAL	15	35	62	93					
		120 GAL		25	45	76	98				
Miami 214 Degree Days	Heating & Hot Water	300 BTU	16	37	64	97					
		600 BTU		35	61	94					
		900 BTU		33	58	90					
	Hot Water	60 GAL	23	51	85						
		80 GAL	18	40	70						
		120 GAL		28	51	85					
Pensacola 1578 Degree Days	Heating & Hot Water	300 BTU		23	42	69	89				
		600 BTU			32	54	73	92			
		900 BTU			26	44	62	84	94		
	Hot Water	60 GAL	21	46	77	97					
		80 GAL	16	36	63	93					
		120 GAL		25	46	77	97				
Tallahassee 1563 Degree Days	Heating & Hot Water	300 BTU		25	45	74					
		600 BTU			34	58	81				
		900 BTU			28	48	69	90			
	Hot Water	60 GAL	22	48	80	99					
		80 GAL	16	38	66	97					
		120 GAL		26	48	80	99				

STATE/CITY	TYPE OF SYSTEM	BTU/HR/°F or GAL./DAY	10	25	50	100	200	400	600	800	1000
Florida Tampa 718 Degree Days	Heating & Hot Water	300 BTU		32	57	90					
		600 BTU		27	49	79	97				
		900 BTU		23	43	70	91				
	Hot Water	60 GAL	23	52	85						
		80 GAL	18	41	70	99					
		120 GAL		28	52	85					
Georgia Atlanta 3095 Degree Days	Heating & Hot Water	300 BTU			31	53	75				
		600 BTU			21	37	56	77			
		900 BTU				28	43	64	78		
	Hot Water	60 GAL	19	44	73						
		80 GAL		34	60	91					
		120 GAL		24	44	73					
Louisiana New Orleans 1385 Degree Days	Heating & Hot Water	300 BTU			36	61	84				
		600 BTU			28	48	69	88			
		900 BTU			22	39	59	79			
	Hot Water	60 GAL		38	65	93					
		80 GAL		29	53	83					
		120 GAL		38	65	93					
Mississippi Jackson 2300 Degree Days	Heating & Hot Water	300 BTU			34	58	78				
		600 BTU			24	42	60	81			
		900 BTU				33	49	69	82		
	Hot Water	60 GAL	19	44	73						
		80 GAL		34	60	90					
		120 GAL		24	44	73					
North Carolina Cap Hatteras 2731 Degree Days	Heating & Hot Water	300 BTU		21	38	63	85				
		600 BTU			26	45	66	88			
		900 BTU				35	54	76			
	Hot Water	60 GAL	23	51	83						
		80 GAL	18	40	69	96					
		120 GAL		28	51	83					
Greensboro 3825 Degree Days	Heating & Hot Water	300 BTU			27	47	69	89			
		600 BTU				31	49	71	84		
		900 BTU				24	38	58	71		
	Hot Water	60 GAL	19	43	72						
		80 GAL		33	59	89					
		120 GAL		23	43	72	94				
South Carolina Charleston 2033 Degree Days	Heating & Hot Water	300 BTU			38	64	86				
		600 BTU			28	47	68	90			
		900 BTU				38	56	79			
	Hot Water	60 GAL	20	46	76						
		80 GAL	15	36	62	93					
		120 GAL		25	46	76					

A-15

STATE/CITY	TYPE OF SYSTEM	BTU/HR/°F or GAL./DAY	%F AT COLLECTOR SQ. FT. SHOWN								
			10	25	50	100	200	400	600	800	1000
South Carolina Greenville 3163 Degree Days	Heating & Hot Water	300 BTU			31	53	75				
		600 BTU			21	37	56	77			
		900 BTU				28	44	64	78		
	Hot Water	60 GAL	20	45	75	96					
		80 GAL	15	35	62						
		120 GAL		25	45	75					
Tennessee Chattanooga 3505 Degree Days	Heating & Hot Water	300 BTU			28	47	68	87			
		600 BTU				32	49	69	82		
		900 BTU				24	38	57	70	79	
	Hot Water	60 GAL	19	42	71	93					
		80 GAL		33	58	87					
		120 GAL		23	42	71	93				
Memphis 3227 Degree Days	Heating & Hot Water	300 BTU			30	50	70	89			
		600 BTU				35	51	71	84		
		900 BTU				26	40	59	72	81	
	Hot Water	60 GAL	20	44	74	93					
		80 GAL		35	61	89					
		120 GAL		24	44	74	93				
Nashville 3696 Degree Days	Heating & Hot Water	300 BTU			25	43	62	81			
		600 BTU				29	44	63	75		
		900 BTU					35	51	63	71	
	Hot Water	60 GAL	18	40	68	90					
		80 GAL		32	56	84					
		120 GAL		22	40	68	90				

ZONE 3: Northern Midwest

%F VERSUS SQUARE FEET OF COLLECTOR

States	Cities	Latitude	Degree Days	States	Cities	Latitude	Degree Days
Illinois	Chicago	41.59	6127	Missouri	St. Louis	38.45	4750
Illinois	Peoria	40.40	6098	Missouri	Springfield	37.14	4570
Iowa	Des Moines	41.32	6710	Nebraska	Lincoln	40.51	5867
Kansas	Dodge City	37.46	5046	N. Dakota	Bismark	46.47	9044
Kansas	Wichita	37.39	4687	N. Dakota	Fargo	46.54	9271
Manitoba	Winnipeg	49.54	10679	S. Dakota	Rapid City	44.09	7345
Minnesota	Duluth	46.50	9756	Wisconsin	Green Bay	44.29	8098
Minnesota	Minneapolis	44.53	8159	Wisconsin	Milwaukee	42.57	7444
Missouri	Kansas City	39.17	5161				

STATE/CITY	TYPE OF SYSTEM	BTU/HR/°F OR GAL./DAY	%F AT COLLECTOR SQ. FT. SHOWN								
			10	25	50	100	200	400	600	800	1000
Illinois Chicago (6127 Degree Days)	Heating & Hot Water	300 BTU				33	51	72	84		
		600 BTU				20	34	52	65	74	
		900 BTU					25	40	52	61	69
	Hot Water	60 GAL			65	89					
		80 GAL			53	82					
		120 GAL			38	65	89				
Peoria (6098 Degree Days)	Heating & Hot Water	300 BTU				34	52	72	83		
		600 BTU				21	34	52	64	73	
		900 BTU					26	41	52	61	68
	Hot Water	60 GAL			67	89					
		80 GAL			55	83					
		120 GAL			40	67	89				
Iowa Des Moines (6170 Degree Days)	Heating & Hot Water	300 BTU				33	51	72	83		
		600 BTU				20	34	52	64	73	
		900 BTU					25	40	52	60	67
	Hot Water	60 GAL			68	90					
		80 GAL			56	84					
		120 GAL			41	68	90				
Kansas Dodge City (5046 Degree Days)	Heating & Hot Water	300 BTU				30	51	74			
		600 BTU				19	33	53	77		
		900 BTU				25	40	63	78		
	Hot Water	60 GAL			85						
		80 GAL			71						
		120 GAL			53	85					
Wichita (4687 Degree Days)	Heating & Hot Water	300 BTU				27	46	68	89		
		600 BTU					30	47	69	83	
		900 BTU					22	36	56	70	80
	Hot Water	60 GAL			77	96					
		80 GAL			64	92					
		120 GAL			47	77	96				

ZONE 3: Northern Midwest (Continued)

STATE/CITY	TYPE OF SYSTEM	BTU/HR/°F OR GAL./DAY	%F AT COLLECTOR SQ. FT. SHOWN								
			10	25	50	100	200	400	600	800	1000
Manitoba Winnipeg (10679 Degree Days)	Heating & Hot Water	300 BTU 600 BTU 900 BTU				25	42 26	65 44 33	78 57 44	67 54	74 61
	Hot Water	60 GAL 80 GAL 120 GAL			66 54 40	89 82 66	89				
Minnesota Duluth (9756 Degree Days)	Heating & Hot Water	300 BTU 600 BTU 900 BTU				24	41 26	63 43 33	75 55 43	65 52	72 59
	Hot Water	60 GAL 80 GAL 120 GAL		36 28	62 50 36	86 78 62	86				
Minneapolis (8159 Degree Days)	Heating & Hot Water	300 BTU 600 BTU 900 BTU				27	44 28	64 44 34	76 56 44	65 53	72 59
	Hot Water	60 GAL 80 GAL 120 GAL		37 29	62 51 37	87 79 62	87				
Missouri Kansas City (5161 Degree Days)	Heating & Hot Water	300 BTU 600 BTU 900 BTU			23	40 26	60 41 31	80 60 48	73 60	70	77
	Hot Water	60 GAL 80 GAL 120 GAL		43 34 23	72 59 43	93 87 72					
St. Louis (4750 Degree Days)	Heating & Hot Water	300 BTU 600 BTU 900 BTU				40 26	59 41 31	80 60 48	73 60	69	76
	Hot Water	60 GAL 80 GAL 120 GAL		41 32	69 57 41	91 86 69	91				
Springfield (4570 Degree Days)	Heating & Hot Water	300 BTU 600 BTU 900 BTU			34	51 38 31	69 52 43	87 70 59	81 70	78	
	Hot Water	60 GAL 80 GAL 120 GAL		49 40 31	76 64 49	95 91 76					
Nebraska Lincoln (5867 Degree Days)	Heating & Hot Water	300 BTU 600 BTU 900 BTU				38 24	59 40 30	81 60 48	74 61	71	78
	Hot Water	60 GAL 80 GAL 120 GAL		43 33	71 59 43	94 88 71	94				

A-18

STATE/CITY	TYPE OF SYSTEM	BTU/HR/°F OR GAL./DAY	%F AT COLLECTOR SQ. FT. SHOWN								
			10	25	50	100	200	400	600	800	1000
North Dakota Bismarck (9044 Degree Days)	Heating & Hot Water	300 BTU				31	51	73	86		
		600 BTU					32	52	65	75	
		900 BTU					24	40	52	62	69
	Hot Water	60 GAL		44	73	93					
		80 GAL		35	60	88					
		120 GAL		24	44	73					
Fargo (9271 Degree Days)	Heating & Hot Water	300 BTU				25	42	63	75		
		600 BTU					26	43	55	64	71
		900 BTU					19	33	43	51	58
	Hot Water	60 GAL		38	64	87					
		80 GAL		29	52	80					
		120 GAL		20	38	64	87				
South Dakota Rapid City (7345 Degree Days)	Heating & Hot Water	300 BTU				39	62	87			
		600 BTU				24	41	65	79		
		900 BTU					31	51	66	76	
	Hot Water	60 GAL		48	79	97					
		80 GAL		38	66	94					
		120 GAL		27	48	79	97				
Wisconsin Green Bay (8098 Degree Days)	Heating & Hot Water	300 BTU				26	43	64	76		
		600 BTU					28	44	56	65	72
		900 BTU					21	34	44	53	60
	Hot Water	60 GAL		36	61	85					
		80 GAL		28	49	77	92				
		120 GAL		19	36	61	85				
Milwaukee (7444 Degree Days)	Heating & Hot Water	300 BTU				29	46	67	79		
		600 BTU					30	47	60	68	75
		900 BTU						37	48	56	63
	Hot Water	60 GAL		38	64	87					
		80 GAL		29	52	80					
		120 GAL		20	38	64	87				

ZONE 4: Southern Midwest

%F VERSUS SQUARE FEET OF COLLECTOR							
States	**Cities**	**Latitude**	**Degree Days**	**States**	**Cities**	**Latitude**	**Degree Days**
Arkansas	Fort Smith	35.20	3336	Texas	Big Spring	32.15	2591
Arkansas	Little Rock	34.44	3219	Texas	Corpus Christi	27.46	930
Louisiana	Lake Charles	32.25	2184	Texas	El Paso	31.48	2700
Louisiana	Shreveport	30.13	1459	Texas	Fort Worth	32.50	2405
Oklahoma	Oklahoma City	35.24	3695	Texas	Houston	29.58	1434
Texas	Amarillo	35.14	4183	Texas	San Antonio	29.32	1546

STATE/CITY	TYPE OF SYSTEM	BTU/HR/°F OR GAL./DAY	%F AT COLLECTOR SQ. FT. SHOWN								
			10	25	50	100	200	400	600	800	1000
Arkansas Fort Smith (3336 Degree Days)	Heating & Hot Water	300 BTU			29	49	69	88			
		600 BTU				33	50	70	83		
		900 BTU					39	58	71	80	
	Hot Water	60 GAL	19	43	72						
		80 GAL		34	59	88					
		120 GAL		23	43	72					
Little Rock (3219 Degree Days)	Heating & Hot Water	300 BTU			29	50	69	88			
		600 BTU				34	51	71	83		
		900 BTU					40	58	71	81	
	Hot Water	60 GAL	19	43	72						
		80 GAL		34	59	88					
		120 GAL		23	43	72	93				
Louisiana Lake Charles (1459 Degree Days)	Heating & Hot Water	300 BTU		24	43	70					
		600 BTU			33	55	75				
		900 BTU				45	64	86			
	Hot Water	60 GAL	21	46	77	97					
		80 GAL		36	63	93					
		120 GAL		25	46	77	97				
Shreveport (2184 Degree Days)	Heating & Hot Water	300 BTU			35	59	79				
		600 BTU			25	43	61	82			
		900 BTU			19	34	50	70			
	Hot Water	60 GAL	19	44	73	94					
		80 GAL		34	60	90					
		120 GAL		24	44	73	94				
Oklahoma Oklahoma City (3695 Degree Days)	Heating & Hot Water	300 BTU			33	55	77				
		600 BTU			22	37	57	80			
		900 BTU				28	45	66	81		
	Hot Water	60 GAL	23	50	82						
		80 GAL		40	68	96					
		120 GAL		28	50	82					

STATE/CITY	TYPE OF SYSTEM	BTU/HR/°F OR GAL./DAY	%F AT COLLECTOR SQ. FT. SHOWN								
			10	25	50	100	200	400	600	800	1000
Texas Amarillo (4183 Degree Days)	Heating & Hot Water	300 BTU			34	58	82				
		600 BTU				39	60	85			
		900 BTU				29	47	71			
	Hot Water	60 GAL	25	55	88						
		80 GAL	19	44	74	98					
		120 GAL		31	55	88					
Big Spring (2591 Degree Days)	Heating & Hot Water	300 BTU			39	64	86				
		600 BTU			27	46	67	89			
		900 BTU				36	54	77			
	Hot Water	60 GAL	23	51	83						
		80 GAL		40	69	96					
		120 GAL		28	51	83					
Corpus Christi (930 Degree Days)	Heating & Hot Water	300 BTU		28	50	78	94				
		600 BTU		22	41	65	84				
		900 BTU			34	56	75	92			
	Hot Water	60 GAL	21	48	80						
		80 GAL		38	66	93					
		120 GAL		26	48	80					
El Paso (2700 Degree Days)	Heating & Hot Water	300 BTU		26	47	73	94				
		600 BTU			33	54	76				
		900 BTU			25	42	62	87			
	Hot Water	60 GAL	29	62	96						
		80 GAL	22	49	82						
		120 GAL		35	62	96					
Fort Worth (2405 Degree Days)	Heating & Hot Water	300 BTU		22	39	64	85				
		600 BTU			28	47	67	89			
		900 BTU			21	36	54	77			
	Hot Water	60 GAL	23	50	83						
		80 GAL	17	40	69	95					
		120 GAL		28	50	83					
Houston (1434 Degree Days)	Heating & Hot Water	300 BTU		23	43	69	88				
		600 BTU			33	54	73				
		900 BTU			26	45	62	83			
	Hot Water	60 GAL	20	46	77						
		80 GAL		36	63	92					
		120 GAL		25	46	77	96				
San Antonio (1546 Degree Days)	Heating & Hot Water	300 BTU		25	45	72					
		600 BTU			34	56	77				
		900 BTU			27	46	66				
	Hot Water	60 GAL	22	49	81						
		80 GAL	17	39	67	95					
		120 GAL		27	49	81					

ZONE 5: Far West

% F VERSUS SQUARE FEET OF COLLECTOR

States	Cities	Latitude	Degree Days	States	Cities	Latitude	Degree Days
Arizona	Phoenix	33.26	1552	Montana	Glasgow	48.13	8996
British Columbia	Vancouver	48.59	5515	Montana	Great Falls	47.29	7750
California	Fresno	36.46	2611	Nevada	Ely	39.17	7733
California	Inyokern	35.39	2370	Nevada	Las Vegas	36.05	2709
California	Sacramento	38.31	2843	Nevada	Reno	39.30	6022
California	San Diego	32.44	1507	New Mexico	Albuquerque	35.05	4292
California	San Francisco	37.47	3080	Oregon	Medford	42.23	4930
California	Santa Maria	34.54	2967	Oregon	Portland	45.36	4792
Colorado	Denver	39.45	6016	Utah	Salt Lake City	40.46	5983
Colorado	Grand Junction	39.07	5639	Washington	Seattle	47.27	4424
Idaho	Boise	43.34	5809	Washington	Spokane	47.40	6835
Idaho	Pocatello	42.55	7063	Wyoming	Lander	42.48	7870
Montana	Billings	45.48	7265	Wyoming	Laramie	41.18	8839

STATE/CITY	TYPE OF SYSTEM	BTU/HR/°F OR GAL./DAY	\%°F AT COLLECTOR SQ. FT. SHOWN								
			10	25	50	100	200	400	600	800	1000
Arizona Phoenix (1552 Degree Days)	Heating & Hot Water	300 BTU		32	56	83					
		600 BTU		24	43	67	88				
		900 BTU			35	55	77				
	Hot Water	60 GAL	28	61	95						
		80 GAL	22	49	82						
		120 GAL		34	61	95					
California Fresno (2611 Degree Days)	Heating & Hot Water	300 BTU			37	60	79				
		600 BTU			26	43	62	80			
		900 BTU				34	50	70	81		
	Hot Water	60 GAL	23	50	81						
		80 GAL		40	68	91					
		120 GAL		28	50	81					
Inyokern (2370 Degree Days)	Heating & Hot Water	300 BTU		32	58	80					
		600 BTU		22	40	61	84				
		900 BTU			31	49	71	92			
	Hot Water	60 GAL	33	70	98						
		80 GAL	25	56	91						
		120 GAL	17	40	70	98					
Sacramento (2843 Degree Days)	Heating & Hot Water	300 BTU			35	57	76				
		600 BTU			24	41	59	79			
		900 BTU				32	48	68	79		
	Hot Water	60 GAL	22	49	79	93					
		80 GAL		39	66	89					
		120 GAL		27	49	79	93				
San Diego (1507 Degree Days)	Heating & Hot Water	300 BTU		24	44	73	97				
		600 BTU			34	58	85				
		900 BTU			28	49	74	97			
	Hot Water	60 GAL	21	46	77						
		80 GAL		36	63	95					
		120 GAL		25	46	77					

STATE/CITY	TYPE OF SYSTEM	BTU/HR/°F OR GAL./DAY	10	25	50	100	200	400	600	800	1000
California (cont.) San Francisco (3080 Degree Days)	Heating & Hot Water	300 BTU			33	57	87				
		600 BTU				23	41	69	93		
		900 BTU					32	56	84		
	Hot Water	60 GAL	20	45	74						
		80 GAL		35	61	91					
		120 GAL		25	45	74	96				
Santa Maria (2967 Degree Days)	Heating & Hot Water	300 BTU		22	41	70	96				
		600 BTU			29	52	80				
		900 BTU			22	41	68	93			
	Hot Water	60 GAL	25	55	88						
		80 GAL	19	44	74	98					
		120 GAL		31	55	88					
Canada British Columbia Vancouver (5515 Degree Days)	Heating & Hot Water	300 BTU				23	38	55	65	71	
		600 BTU					26	41	50	57	62
		900 BTU					20	33		48	53
	Hot Water	60 GAL			44	66	82				
		80 GAL			36	58	75				
		120 GAL			25	44	66				
Colorado Denver (6016 Degree Days)	Heating & Hot Water	300 BTU				28	48	74			
		600 BTU					31	51	77		
		900 BTU						39	62	78	
	Hot Water	60 GAL	24	54	86						
		80 GAL	19	42	72	98					
		120 GAL		30	54	86					
Grand Junction (5639 Degree Days)	Heating & Hot Water	300 BTU				28	48	71			
		600 BTU					31	49	73		
		900 BTU					23	37	59	73	
	Hot Water	60 GAL	24	54	86						
		80 GAL	19	43	72						
		120 GAL		30	54	86					
Idaho Boise (5809 Degree Days)	Heating & Hot Water	300 BTU				39	59	79			
		600 BTU				25	41	61	72	81	
		900 BTU					31	49	61	69	76
	Hot Water	60 GAL	20	45	74						
		80 GAL		36	62	87					
		120 GAL		25	45	74	91				
Pocatello (7063 Degree Days)	Heating & Hot Water	300 BTU				38	59	82			
		600 BTU				24	40	62	75		
		900 BTU					30	49	62	72	79
	Hot Water	60 GAL	22	48	78						
		80 GAL		38	65	90					
		120 GAL		27	48	78					

ZONE 5: Far West (Continued)

STATE/CITY	TYPE OF SYSTEM	BTU/HR/°F OR GAL./DAY	% F AT COLLECTOR SQ. FT. SHOWN								
			10	25	50	100	200	400	600	800	1000
Montana Billings (7265 Degree Days)	Heating & Hot Water	300 BTU				36	57	81			
		600 BTU					38	59	74	83	
		900 BTU					28	46	60	70	78
	Hot Water	60 GAL	20	45	74	94					
		80 GAL		35	61	88					
		120 GAL		25	45	74	94				
Glasgow (8996 Degree Days)	Heating & Hot Water	300 BTU				33	54	78			
		600 BTU					35	56	70	80	
		900 BTU						44	56	67	74
	Hot Water	60 GAL	21	47	77	95					
		80 GAL		37	64	91					
		120 GAL		26	47	77	95				
Great Falls (7750 Degree Days)	Heating & Hot Water	300 BTU				34	55	79	90		
		600 BTU				21	36	57	72	81	
		900 BTU					27	45	58	68	76
	Hot Water	60 GAL	20	44	73	93					
		80 GAL		35	60	88					
		120 GAL		24	44	73	93				
Nevada Ely (7733 Degree Days)	Heating & Hot Water	300 BTU			24	44	69	93			
		600 BTU				27	47	73	87		
		900 BTU					35	58	74	84	
	Hot Water	60 GAL	25	55	87						
		80 GAL		44	74	97					
		120 GAL		31	55	87					
Las Vegas (2709 Degree Days)	Heating & Hot Water	300 BTU		26	46	72	92				
		600 BTU			32	52	74	95			
		900 BTU				41	61	85	95		
	Hot Water	60 GAL	28	61	95						
		80 GAL	22	49	81						
		120 GAL		34	61	95					
Reno (6022 Degree Days)	Heating & Hot Water	300 BTU				29	50	76			
		600 BTU					33	54	80		
		900 BTU					24	42	66	81	
	Hot Water	60 GAL	26	56	89						
		80 GAL	20	45	75	97					
		120 GAL		32	56	89					
New Mexico Albuquerque (4292 Degree Days)	Heating & Hot Water	300 BTU				37	61	85			
		600 BTU					41	64	89		
		900 BTU					31	50	75	90	
	Hot Water	60 GAL	28	61	95						
		80 GAL	22	49	81	99					
		120 GAL		34	61	95					

STATE/CITY	TYPE OF SYSTEM	BTU/HR/°F OR GAL./DAY	%F AT COLLECTOR SQ. FT. SHOWN								
			10	25	50	100	200	400	600	800	1000
Oregon Medford (4930 Degree Days)	Heating & Hot Water	300 BTU				38	57	74			
		600 BTU					40	58	69	75	
		900 BTU					31	47	59	66	71
	Hot Water	60 GAL		42	69	84					
		80 GAL		33	57	80	89				
		120 GAL		23	42	69	84	93			
Portland (4792 Degree Days)	Heating & Hot Water	300 BTU				30	48	67	77		
		600 BTU					33	51	62	69	75
		900 BTU						41	51	59	65
	Hot Water	60 GAL		30	52	76					
		80 GAL			42	68	84				
		120 GAL			30	52	76	90			
Utah Salt Lake City (5983 Degree Days)	Heating & Hot Water	300 BTU				38	59	80			
		600 BTU					40	60	73	81	
		900 BTU					30	48	61	70	77
	Hot Water	60 GAL		44	73	92					
		80 GAL		35	61	87					
		120 GAL		24	44	73	92				
Washington Seattle (4424 Degree Days)	Heating & Hot Water	300 BTU				32	50	67	75		
		600 BTU					36	52	62	69	73
		900 BTU						28	53	60	65
	Hot Water	60 GAL		31	54	75					
		80 GAL		24	43	68	82				
		120 GAL			31	54	75				
Spokane (6835 Degree Days)	Heating & Hot Water	300 BTU				33	51	71	81		
		600 BTU					34	53	65	73	79
		900 BTU						42	53	62	68
	Hot Water	60 GAL		41	67	85					
		80 GAL		32	56	81					
		120 GAL			41	67	85				
Wyoming Lander (7870 Degree Days)	Heating & Hot Water	300 BTU				24	43	68	92		
		600 BTU					26	45	71	86	
		900 BTU						34	56	72	82
	Hot Water	60 GAL	25	54	87						
		80 GAL		43	73	97					
		120 GAL		30	54	87					
Laramie (8839 Degree Days)	Heating & Hot Water	300 BTU				35	59	86			
		600 BTU					22	39	63	79	84
		900 BTU						29	49	64	75
	Hot Water	60 GAL	22	48	78						
		80 GAL		38	65	94					
		120 GAL		26	48	78					

APPENDIX D

Solar Window Projections

In Decision 9 of The Solar Decision Book, you learned that most of the sun's energy reaches your building through a "solar window" in the sky. This window outlines the sun's positions for various times of the year and for various times of the day. You also learned that this window can be drawn on a type of map called a Mercator's projection. This map unfolds the site details from the horizon to straight above and from north to north (360° around the site). With such a projection, you can plot any and all obstacles which might shield your collectors from the sun's rays.

Projection Details

The drawing below shows how the projection is put together. The various lines are labelled. The lower curve of the solar window represents the *winter solstice*, the point at which the sun is the lowest in the sky. The upper curve represents the *summer solstice*, the point at which the sun is the highest in the sky. The diagonal line at the left represents 3 PM solar time. The diagonal line at the right represents 9 AM solar time. Solar noon is at the center of the window.

The base line of the chart represents the horizon. And, the top line of the diagram represents the vertical (90° angle from the horizon, directly overhead). The figures on the vertical scales represent the degrees above horizontal while the base line figures represent the degrees away from solar south.

As can be seen in the illustration, the sun is at 45° east of south at an angle of 22° above the horizon on December 21 (the winter solstice) at 9 AM in the morning. At solar noon, the sun is due south at 38° above the horizon. At 3 PM, it is 45° west of south at 22° above the horizon. The projection also

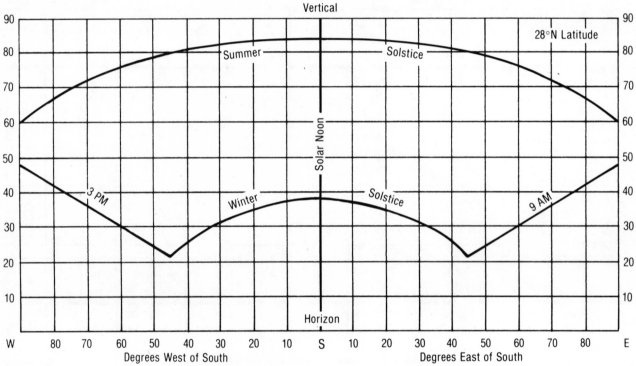

This appendix contains Mercator's projections of the solar window for eight different latitudes. The latitudes covered are 24°N, 28°N, 32°N, 36°N, 40°N, 44°N, 48°N, and 52°N. These basically cover most of North America. As would be expected, the solar window is smallest for the northernmost latitudes and the largest for the southernmost latitudes. In fact, at 24°N the solar window extends beyond the top of the projection. For such latitudes, the sun is overhead and even behind an observer during part of the summer.

These projections are for plotting solar shade. They are drawn so that they can be easily traced or reproduced in any convenient size. For latitudes which are different than those shown here, the solar windows can be drawn with reasonable accuracy by interpolation.

shows the sun's position at the summer solstice. And the sun's position at any other time during the year will lie between the solstices.

Solar shade can be easily plotted on the projection. You simply plot the height of the shade above the horizon at the various positions east and west of south. If the shade height rises above the sun tracing during the winter solstice, the shade will interfere with the solar window. Some sunlight will be lost. Overhangs, neighboring buildings, and other obstacles can also be easily plotted.

Plotting Solar Shade

A sextant or a surveyor's transit is excellent for plotting solar shade. However, if such instruments are not available, a homemade shade plotter can readily be substituted. The construction of such a simple device is shown below. To use this instrument, hold it level with your eye at the bridge of your nose. Then sight along the zero-angle-indicator nail to the horizon. Without moving the instrument, glance up at the obstruction and note where its top falls on the vertical stick.

Again, without moving the instrument, glance in the mirror and read the compass. The compass heading (corrected for local magnetic deviation) and the height of the obstruction can then be combined and plotted on the Mercator's projection. By moving across the horizon, all shading problems can be quickly plotted.

If desired, a small line level can be added to this shade plotter. It should be mounted parallel with the horizontal horizon sighting stick. It will provide an artificial horizon.

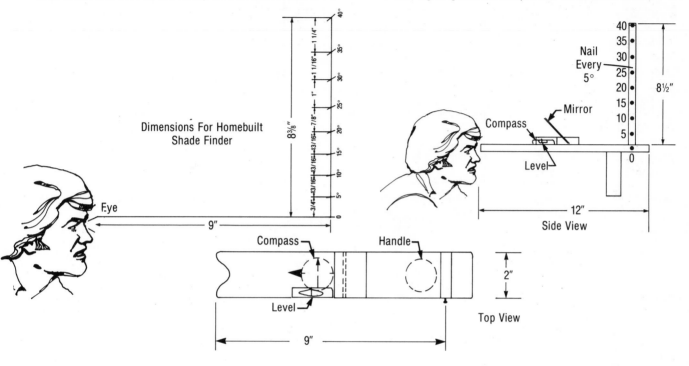

Dimensions For Homebuilt Shade Finder

Side View

Top View

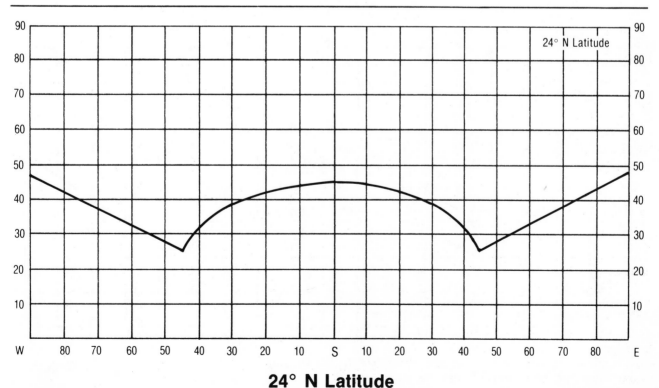

24° N Latitude

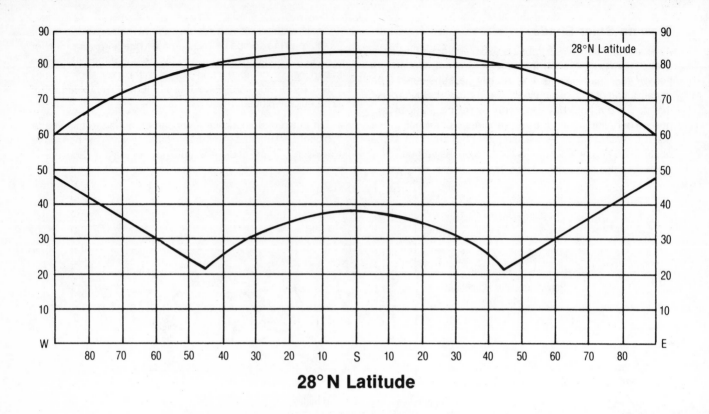

28° N Latitude

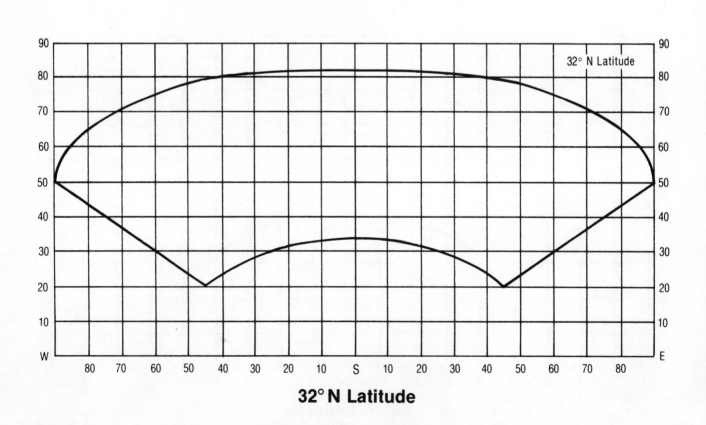

32° N Latitude

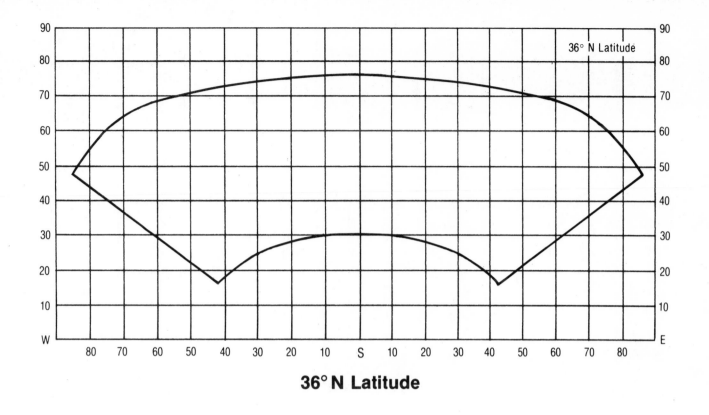

36° N Latitude

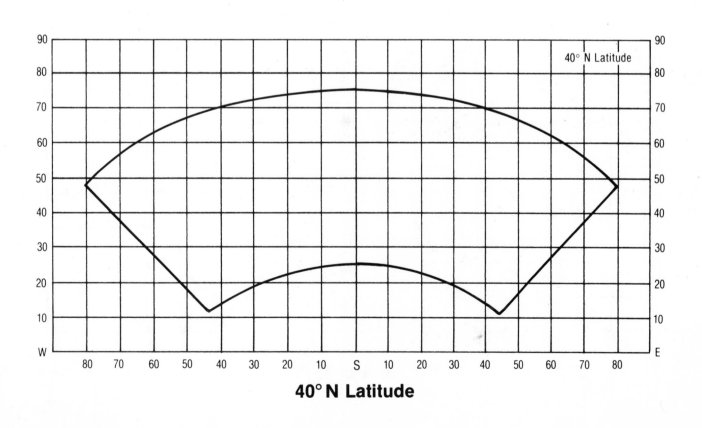

40° N Latitude

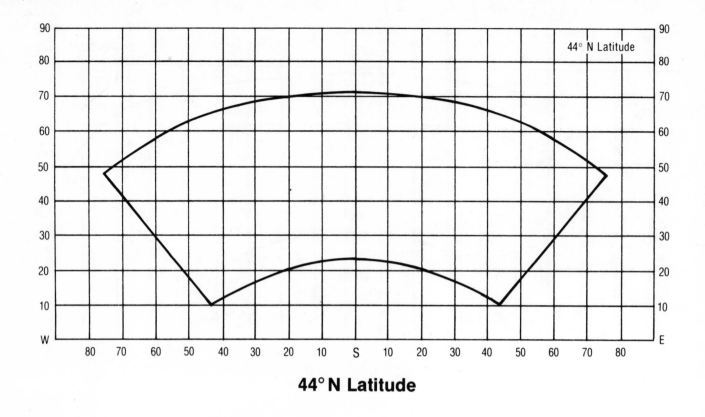

44° N Latitude

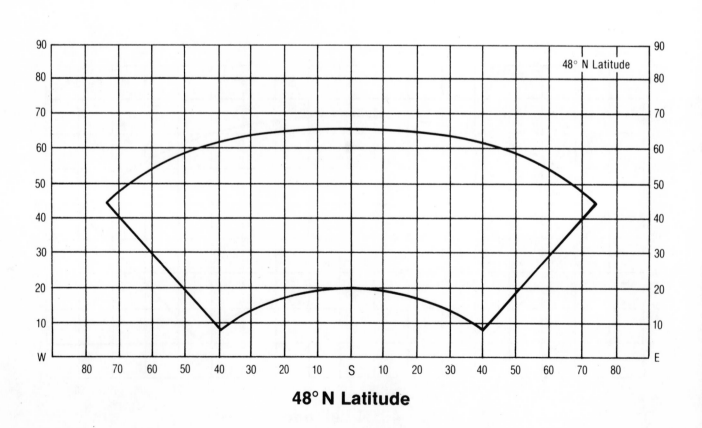

48° N Latitude

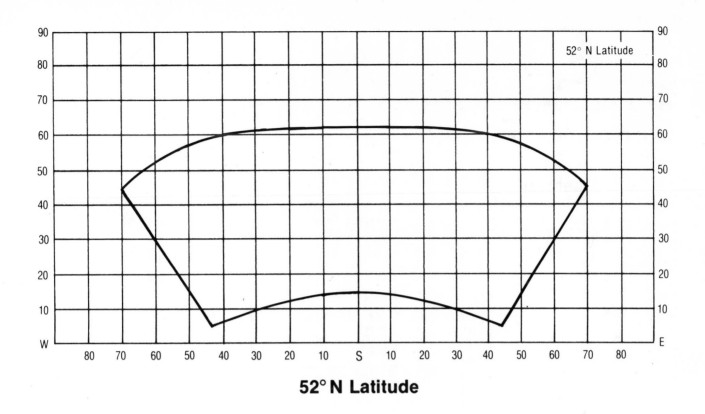

52° N Latitude

APPENDIX E

Conversion Factors

METRIC TO ENGLISH		
Metric Unit	**x Conversion Factor**	**= English Unit**
Meters	3.28	Feet
Meters	39.37	Inches
Centimeters	0.394	Inches
Grams	0.0022	Pounds
Kilograms	2.205	Pounds
Liters	0.2642	Gallons
Calories	0.004	Btu
Watts	3.413	Btu/hr
Watts/m^2	0.317	Btu/(hr) (ft^2)
Langleys	3.687	Btu/ft^2
Calories/(cm) (sec)	13.272	Btu/(hr) (ft^2)
Langleys/minute	221.2	Btu/(hr) (ft^2)
Calories/(hr) (cm^2) (°C)	2.048	Btu/(hr) (ft^2) (°F)
Degrees C	C = 5/9 (F-32)	Degrees F

UNIT TO UNIT

Unit	x Conversion Factor	= Unit
Kilowatt-hours	3413	Btu
Btu	2.93×10^4	Kilowatt-hours
Horsepower	2544	Btu/hour
Tons of Air Conditioning	12,000	Btu/hour
Cubic feet	7.48	Gallons
Gallons	0.134	Cubic feet
Cubic foot of water	62.37	Pounds @ 60°F
Cubic feet/second	448.83	Gallons/minute
Gallons/minute	0.0022	Cubic feet/second
Feet of water	0.434	Pounds/square inch
Feet of water	0.8827	Inches of mercury
Gallons of water	8.35	Pounds of water @ 60°F
Inches of mercury	0.491	Pounds/square inch
Pounds of water	0.1198	Gallons

ENGLISH TO METRIC

English Unit	x Conversion Factor	= Metric Unit
Feet	0.305	Meters
Inches	0.0254	Meters
Inches	2.54	Centimeters
Pounds	0.454	Kilograms
Pounds	454	Grams
Pounds/in^2	703.1	Kilograms/m^2
Gallons	3.79	Liters
Btu	252	Calories
Btu/hour	0.293	Watts
Btu/hour	293	Kilowatts
Btu/(hr) (ft^2)	3.154	Watts/m^2
Btu/(hr) (ft^2)	0.075	Calories/(cm) (sec)
Btu/(ft^2)	0.271	Langleys
Btu/(hr) (ft^2)	0.00452	Langleys/minute
Horsepower, U.S.	1.014	Horsepower, metric
Horsepower	745.7	Watts
Btu/(hr) (ft^2) (°F)	0.488	Calories/(hr) (cm^2) (°C)
Degrees F	$F = 9/5\ C + 32$	Degrees C

GLOSSARY

absorber — a coated panel in a collector that absorbs the solar radiation transmitted through the cover plate and converts it to heat energy.

absorber fluid — pipes or ducts that enable the heat-transfer medium to flow through the absorber panel and carry collected heat to storage.

absorber response time — the length of time the absorber panel takes to heat up or cool down.

absorptance — the ratio of solar energy absorbed by a surface to the radiation striking it. Energy not absorbed is transmitted or reflected.

absorptive coating — covers the absorber plate and improves its ability to absorb energy without reflecting it away.

absorptive index — measure of how much energy the surface will absorb.

active solar system — a system that has equipment to trap the sun's energy and mechanically move that energy to its point of intended use for water heating, space heating, and possibly space cooling. Usually has storage capabilities.

air-type collector — a collector that uses air as the heat-transfer medium.

angle of incidence — angle at which solar energy strikes a surface.

anode — electrically positive metal. Opposite of cathode.

appraisal value — the value a lending institution places on the investment. Not necessarily cost or market price.

ASHRAE — the American Society of Heating, Refrigerating, and Air Conditioning Engineers.

auxiliary heater — some type of conventional heating system, fossil fuel or electric, used to provide backup energy for water heating and/or space heating when the solar system cannot meet the energy demand.

azimuth — the angle between solar south and the direction in which the collectors are faced. Used in F-Chart calculations.

binary process (geothermal) — utilizes the liquid-dominated reservoir mixture by circulating the water or brine through a heat exchanger. A second fluid is heated for use in the turbine.

biomass — waste products such as paper, plastics, and agricultural residues from crops, waste sludges, and animal wastes.

British thermal unit (Btu) — the amount of heat required to raise the temperature of one pound (one pint) of water, one degree Fahrenheit.

building design load — the total heat loss that must be made up by the heating system under the severest winter conditions for the area.

building design temperature — the lowest temperature expected for the building's location. When subtracted from 65°F and multiplied by the heat loss, it can be used to calculate the building design load.

cathode — electrically negative metal. Opposite of anode.

ccf — 100 cubic feet. A common unit of measure for natural gas.

centrifugal pump — a type of pump which has blades that rotate and whirl the fluid around so that it acquires sufficient momentum to discharge from the pump body. The fluid is thrown outward by centrifugal force.

closed-loop system — no part of the system is vented to the atmosphere. The system liquid is recirculated.

coefficient of heat transmission — U-factor.

coil-in-tank heat exchanger — a finned coil in the bottom of a water tank. Most commonly used on solar-water heating systems.

collector — a device used to collect solar radiation (energy) and to convert it into usable heat.

collector efficiency — the performance of a collector, measured as a ratio of useful energy collected to the incident (available) energy striking the collector. Expressed in percent.

collector housing — prevents moisture, dirt, dust and air from entering the collector.

collector loop the part of the solar system that has solar collectors, a water preheater tank or storage tank, a heat exchanger, and the necessary piping, valves, pumps, and controls for collecting energy.

collector-rise factor (CRF) — the ratio of the temperature difference across the collector compared to the temperature difference between the collector inlet and the storage tank outlet.

collector tilt angle — the angle between the collector and a horizontal or level surface.

compound parabolic mirror collector — a concentrating collector that uses special mirrors to gather both direct and diffuse solar radiation without tracking the sun.

GLOSSARY (continued)

concentrating collector — a collector which uses reflective devices or optical lens arrangements to concentrate the sun's rays onto a small collector/absorber area. Usually has means for tracking sun.

conduction — heat movement through a solid mass.

Consumer Price Index (CPI) — used to predict the cost of all consumer goods. Measures the rate of inflation. A relative value of current costs to those in a given base year (i.e. 1967 = 100).

convection — heat movement in a moving body of air or liquid.

counterflow heat exchanger — a self-contained heat exchanger in which the two substances flow in opposite directions.

cover plate — transparent sheet of glass or plastic that is mounted above the absorber plate. Also called glazing.

crevice corrosion — associated with bad gasketing, poorly fitting joints, internal blockage, scale deposits from hard waters, and poor design.

degree day — a unit of measurement used in heat-loss calculations and solar-system sizing. Shows degrees difference between 65°F and the day's mean outdoor temperature. A 25 degree-day would have a mean temperature of 40°F. Two such days would add up to 50 degree-days.

density — weight per unit.

differential thermostat — measures the difference between the collector and the tank temperatures. Issues the appropriate instructions to the control system.

diffuse radiation — scattered, nonparallel energy rays from the sun. Makes the sky blue on clear days and gray on hazy days. Caused by dust, moisture, clouds.

direct process (geothermal) — utilizes the liquid-dominated reservoir mixture by separating the steam from the water or brine and using it in a turbine to produce mechanical work.

direct radiation — composed of parallel rays coming straight from the sun. Casts shadows on clear days.

drum or pillow rooftop heater — the simplest form of solar-water heating Water storage is on roof to collect energy.

electrolyte — a fluid solution, such as saltwater, which is capable of carrying an electrical current.

emissivity — measure of a surface's tendency to emit thermal radiation.

EPA — the Environmental Protection Agency. Sets and reviews guidelines for measures to protect the environment (air and water) from damage caused by industrial pollution.

erosion/corrosion — a type of corrosion caused by high-velocity liquid flow over a metal's protective coating.

expansion tank — takes up the overflow created when the heat-transfer fluid expands.

F-chart — computer simulation program that predicts the average performance of a solar system under average weather conditions. Used for sizing systems, thermal analysis, and cost-benefit analyses.

flash point — the temperature at which fluid vapors will flashover if an ignition source is present.

flat-plate collector — converts the sun's radiation into heat on a flat surface within a simple box. Does not use reflecting surfaces, lens arrangements.

flux — for collectors, the intensity of heat flow; for soldering, a substance used to clean the pipe surfaces and to promote a good bond.

fossil fuels — energy sources such as oil, natural gas, and coal. Formed by decayed vegetation under tons of soil and rock millions of years ago.

fuel ignition temperature — the lowest temperature at which a fuel will ignite.

galvanic corrosion — caused by an electrochemical reaction between two or more different metals in a system.

galvanic series — metals ranked from electrically positive to electrically negative. Measures relative "corrodability" of each metal when used in a multimetal system.

getter — a column or cartridge containing an active metal which will be sacrificed to protect some other metal in the system against galvanic corrosion.

head — for pumping considerations, the vertical rise to the highest point in the system. Does not include the horizontal run to that point. Head losses are important for determining flow rates and pump size.

headers — main passages through which the heat-transfer medium enters into or exits from the collector. Also called manifolds.

heat capacity — amount of heat that can be stored in the material to raise the temperature 1°F. Found by multiplying specific heat by density.

heat-delivery loop — the part of the system that takes energy from storage and uses it for space heating. Includes auxiliary heater.

heat exchanger — a device which transfers heat from one substance to another substance without mixing the two.

heat-exchanger effectiveness — the ratio of the actual rate of heat transfer to the theoretical maximum rate of heat transfer in an infinitely large heat exchanger.

heat-loss principles — describe heat energy movement from a space or object to another space or object.

heat pump — a device which uses a compressible refrigerant to tranfer heat from one source to another, cooling the first and heating the second. Can be liquid-to-air or air-to-air. Can provide heat in winter, cool air in summer by switching mode.

heat-transfer medium — air or liquid that is heated used to transmit energy to its point of use.

GLOSSARY (continued)

heat transmission — the rate of which heat is conducted through a solid.

hourly design load — hourly heat loss multiplied by 65°F minus the building design temperature.

hysteresis setting — factory adjustment of the control system. Refers to a time-delay circuit, which prevents the pump from being cycled on or off, following a pump turn-off or turn-on event.

inhibitors — additives to storage water to prevent algae and corrosion.

input sensors — located in the collector loop and heat-delivery system. They provide instructions to the control system, by measuring temperatures.

insolation — the total amount of solar radiation striking a collector cover plate. Includes direct, diffuse, and reflected radiation.

isogonic chart — shows magnetic compass deviations from true north.

kwh — kilowatt-hours. Equals 1000 watt hours. Electricity is sold in kwh.

linear concentrating collector — collects solar radiation by reflecting the energy off a large curved mirror to a receiver that contains a heat-transfer liquid.

linear-trough, fresnel lens collector — solar radiation passing through the lens is bent to strike a small absorber plate at the bottom of a trough, which contains a heat-transfer liquid.

liquid-dominated reservoir — a geothermal resource site that contains a mixture of hot water (or brine) and steam.

LNG — liquid natural gas. Gas is liquefied by extremely cold temperatures.

liquid-type collector — a collector that uses a liquid as the heat-transfer medium.

log mean temperature difference — a complex mathematical function used to describe fluid temperatures in a heat exchanger.

Mercator's projection — map that has latitude and longitude drawn in straight lines. Used for plotting obstacles on the solar window which might block energy collection.

microprocessor — an electronic device with computer capabilities. Used in contols to compare the sensor data and issue instructions to the pump.

mixed-flow heat exchanger — a heat exchanger in which one substance sees the average temperature of the other substance. The two substances flow across each other. Also called cross-flow.

nonselective surface — an absorber-panel coating which absorbs most of the sunlight hitting it but emits a high level of thermal radiation. Typically, a flat-black paint.

ocean thermal power — electricity is produced by using the difference in water temperature.

ocean tidal power — electricity produced by using the rise and fall of ocean tides.

oil shale — oil-bearing rock. It can be mined and cooked to drive the oil out.

OPEC — The Organization of Petroleum Exporting Countries. Regulates base prices of worldwide oil supply.

open-loop system — some part of the system is vented to the atmosphere, or the system contains fresh or changeable water.

passive system — a solar system which has no mechanical means to move or regulate the release of collected energy.

payback period — the amount of time (years) needed for a building owner to recover the system investment in fuel-cost savings.

phase-changing materials — able to change from solid to liquid and back to solid. Certain salts and paraffins being studied for use in solar storage.

pitting corrosion — caused by metal ions leaving localized areas causing a pitted surface or uneven corrosion.

pump staging — a method of placing two or more pumps together to increase flow or overcome head losses. Series-staged pumps are placed in the same line. Parallel-staged pumps are placed in two separate lines, feeding a common line.

quad — quadrillion Btu. Convenient for making energy statements.

radiation — heat movement from a warm surface.

reflected radiation — solar energy sent to the collectors from adjacent surfaces.

refractive index — measure of how much a surface will bend energy beams as they pass through the material.

retrofitting — the installation of a solar energy system on an existing building.

risers — flow passages (pipes or channels) that distribute heat-transfer fluid across the absorber panel in a collector.

R-value — the tested insulation value which is used to calculate the U-factor. "R" is the resistance to heat flow.

selective surface — an absorber-panel coating which absorbs most of the sunlight hitting it and emits very little thermal radiation. Metal oxides that are selective to certain energy wavelengths are commonly used.

solar radiation — the sun's energy that comes to earth in the form of direct, diffuse, and reflected rays.

GLOSSARY (continued)

solar storage — a water tank or rock-pebble bed that absorbs collected solar energy and holds it until needed.

solar window — an outline of an area in the sky through which a maximum amount of direct solar radiation reaches the collectors during a year. Described by summer solstice, winter solstice, and 9 AM to 3 PM solar time.

specific heat — number of Btu required to raise the temperature of one pound of the material one-degree Fahrenheit.

stagnation — a condition in a system that results when the heat-transfer fluid does not flow. Common in summertime.

storage-type water heater — functions as both a solar energy collector and a warm-water storage unit. A drum or pillow rooftop heater is an example.

storage water — nonpotable water, unsuitable for drinking. Usually de-mineralized and treated with corrosion and fungi inhibitors.

sun path diagram — a circular drawing of the sky that shows the sun's position at various times of the year. Used to draw the solar window.

Syncrude — synthetic crude oil.

SNG — synthetic natural gas made by coal gasification or biomass conversion.

System CLP — cost, life and performance of a solar system. Used to measure the relative value of the system. Can be expressed as dollars per Btu collected.

tar sands — oil-bearing sand.

Tennessee Valley Authority (TVA) — controls 48 fully developed dam sites in the Tennessee river basin. The world's largest single producer of electrical power.

tertiary oil recovery — used to recover oil that remains after primary and secondary methods.

thermal mass — a building's ability to soak up and retain energy. High-thermal-mass materials change temperature very slowly.

thermal radiation — heat energy emitted by a warm surface.

thermistor — sensing device that changes its electrical resistance according to temperature. Used in the control system to generate input data on collector and storage tank temperatures.

thermostat — temperature-sensing device.

thermosyphon loop — a natural convection loop in a solar collector. Water in the collector is heated by the sun, becomes lighter, and flows into a storage drum.

threshold setting — factory adjustment of the control system. Refers to the size of the temperature difference between the pump turn-on and turn-off temperatures.

transmittance — the ratio of solar energy passed through a surface to the radiation striking it. Energy not transmitted is absorbed or reflected.

U-factor — the number of Btu which pass through one square foot of solid in one hour if there is a one degree (F) difference between the two sides. Used to express heat transmission. The reciprocal of "R" ($U = 1/R$).

vapor-dominated reservoir — a geothermal resource site that contains super-heated steam.

wavelength — the distance between the start and finish of an energy pulse.

Wholesale Price Index (WPI) — used to predict the selling price of various energy sources to utilities and fuel outlets. A relative value of a current price to a price in a given base year (i.e. 1967 = 100).

INDEX

BIOGRAPHICAL NOTES

THE AUTHOR

Richard H. Montgomery is a Senior Market Specialist at Dow Corning Corporation, Midland, Michigan. A native of Ayer, Massachusetts, he attended the Lowell Technological Institute where he received a B.S. degree in Engineering in 1952. Following two years in the Army, Dick joined Dow Corning, the world's leading manufacturer and marketer of silicone materials for industrial, commercial, and medical uses. His task: find new markets for silicones. Except for a brief period during which he worked in his family's construction business, Dick "has been tangled up in finding new market opportunities for silicones ever since." He has concentrated on silicones for textile, paper, electrical/electronic, chemical, and heat-transfer applications. Most recently, Dick has spearheaded Dow Corning's successful marketing efforts in two important areas. The first involved the commercialization of a silicone liquid to replace PCB-containing askarels for cooling and insulating power transformers. This book wraps up his involvement in the second: silicone heat-transfer fluids for solar energy systems. The need for such a publication became apparent as Dick spoke to and worked with companies as well as individuals throughout the newborn solar industry. He sums up his career thus far as one which "keeps me busy."

THE EDITOR

Jim Budnick is a writer and Vice President at Bradford-LaRiviere, Inc., in Saginaw, Michigan. Born and raised in Grand Rapids, Michigan, he received a B.S. degree in Electrical Engineering from Michigan Technological University in 1967. Jim began writing while being trained as a sales engineer for a manufacturer of electric-utility equipment. Then, with a move to a major advertising agency, he chose writing as a career. His agency assignment: Dow Corning and its silicones. After "packing 10 years' worth of experience into two years," he left the agency to start a writing group in the art and photographic studios of Bradford-LaRiviere. He is now one of four owners in the corporation which has become a leading Michigan supplier of industrial training programs and promotional materials. In addition to serving as "editor and cheerleader" on The Solar Decision Book, Jim is currently working on three books of his own. These will be published by John Wiley and Sons in its Automotive Mechanics series.

ORDERING INFORMATION

Copies of The Solar Decision Book can be ordered for $10.00 each. Please complete the order blank, and enclose a check or money order for the number of books desired. Send your order to: ➜ Dow Corning Corporation
THE SOLAR DECISION BOOK
Department 2268
Midland, Michigan 48640

The Solar Decision Book is distributed to the trade by Dow Corning Corporation. Please send requests for wholesale book orders to: ➜ Mr. Richard Hoover
Dow Corning Corporation
CO-2314
Midland, Michigan 48640

THE SOLAR DECISION BOOK

Enclosed is a check or money order for $_____. Please send_____copies of **The Solar Decision Book** to:

Name: _____

Address: _____

City: _____ State: _____ Zip: _____

THE SOLAR DECISION BOOK

Enclosed is a check or money order for $_____. Please send_____copies of **The Solar Decision Book** to:

Name: _____

Address: _____

City: _____ State: _____ Zip: _____

THE SOLAR DECISION BOOK

Enclosed is a check or money order for $_____. Please send_____copies of **The Solar Decision Book** to:

Name: _____

Address: _____

City: _____ State: _____ Zip: _____